Aging in Rural Canada:

An Annotated Bibliography, 1985 - 2005

Laurel A. Strain, PhD
Director
Alberta Centre on Aging
Professor
Department of Sociology
University of Alberta

Bonnie M. Dobbs, PhD
Director of Research
Division of Care of the Elderly
Associate Professor
Department of Family Medicine
University of Alberta

With assistance from
Deanna Wanless, MA
Christine N. Vandenberghe, MEd
Kristina Babich, BA
and Paul Lali

Alberta Centre on Aging
University of Alberta
Edmonton, Alberta, Canada

This publication may be reproduced in whole or in part, and/or stored in a retrieval system with the following citation:

Strain, L. A. & Dobbs, B. M. (2007). *Aging in Rural Canada: An Annotated Bibliography, 1985-2005*. Edmonton, AB: Alberta Centre on Aging, University of Alberta.

Design and formatting: Alberta Centre on Aging, University of Alberta

Published by: Alberta Centre on Aging, University of Alberta

The Alberta Centre on Aging is an interdisciplinary research and education centre with a mission to promote cutting-edge research, education, and service in aging, through interdisciplinary collaboration and through partnerships with stakeholders. For further information, contact:

Alberta Centre on Aging
University of Alberta
305 Campus Tower
8625 - 112 Street
Edmonton, AB T6G 1K8
Phone: (780) 492-3207
Fax: (780) 492-3190
E-mail: aging@ualberta.ca

ISBN: 978-1-55195-157-7

ACKNOWLEDGEMENTS

This bibliography was a labour-intensive activity made possible by the invaluable research and administrative assistance provided by Deanna Wanless, Christine Vandenberghe, Kristina Babich, and Paul Lali. Their commitment and contributions are gratefully acknowledged. Colleagues across the country willingly provided information about their own research and the work of their colleagues and students. Their contributions were critical in ensuring that the bibliography was as comprehensive as possible. The document delivery service at the University of Alberta is to be commended for dealing with our numerous requests in a timely manner. The preparation of the bibliography was supported by a New Emerging Team (NET) grant funded by CIHR's Institute of Aging and the Rural and Northern Health Research Initiative (HAS-63179) (PI: Laurel Strain).

Despite our efforts to make this a comprehensive bibliography, items worthy of consideration will no doubt have been overlooked. We apologize for these inadvertent omissions. Individuals aware of articles that should be considered for future editions are asked to contact the Alberta Centre on Aging, 305 Campus Tower, University of Alberta, Edmonton, Alberta, T6G 1K8; Tel: 780-492-3207; E-mail: aging@ualberta.ca

TABLE OF CONTENTS

INDEX OF TABLES

INDEX OF FIGURES

AGING IN RURAL CANADA:
AN ANNOTATED BIBLIOGRAPHY, 1985-2005

INTRODUCTION

The rural environment is an important context for the study of aging. Rural areas are diverse and frequently have higher concentrations of older residents than urban communities. The study of rural aging presents valuable opportunities to better understand this segment of the elderly population. However, the existing research literature on aging in rural environments is widely scattered and often difficult to locate.

Aging in Rural Canada: An Annotated Bibliography, 1985 – 2005 is a comprehensive bibliographic listing, drawing together Canadian material on rural aging from a wide variety of sources. Published academic articles and the 'grey' literature have been reviewed. Each entry was selected for its concern, in whole or in part, with rural aging. Interest is on contemporary rural aging rather than historical reports.

It is important to note that 'rural' may be defined in many ways. Our intent was to be as inclusive as possible. In some publications, specific definitions of rural were provided. Sometimes the only definition was the author's indication that the setting was rural. In other instances, reference was made to small towns/communities or remote communities, and although the authors may not have specifically identified the community as rural, sufficient information on population size, population density, distance from services, and/or some other feature of the community lead to the inclusion of the publication in the bibliography.

In instances where there was a rural-urban comparison, emphasis was placed on the results pertaining to rural aging. It should be noted that the rural content was the main focus in some entries while in others, it provided a context but was not the primary area of interest. As the emphasis here is on rural aging, the included annotations focus on that aspect of the research, even for entries that have an urban component.

The bibliography begins with a brief discussion of the methodology and selected characteristics of the entries. The annotations are then presented alphabetically by topic area. Both an author index and a geographic index that indicates the province/region of study have been provided.

METHODOLOGY

The compilation of *Aging in Rural Canada: An Annotated Bibliography, 1985-2005* was a multi-step, labour-intensive process. Online searches and selected hand searches were conducted and key authors were contacted. Articles were reviewed for potential inclusion in a systematic manner. References identified from the included articles were examined for inclusion. The articles were reviewed independently by two reviewers. One researcher wrote the abstracts in the format developed for the bibliography, and another researcher reviewed these abstracts to ensure accuracy and consistency. In this section, the methodology is briefly outlined; additional information is available upon request.

Online Searches

Online searches were conducted initially in Academic Search Premier, Ageline, Agricola, Cumulative Index to Nursing and Allied Health Literature (CINAHL), Educational Resources Information Centre (ERIC), HealthSTAR, Web of Science, MEDLINE, the Physiotherapy Evidence Database (PEDro), and PsycINFO. Attention was then turned to the ProQuest Dissertations and Theses Database, Anthropology Plus, Gender Studies Database, Humanities Abstracts, Historical Abstracts, Sociological Abstracts, Geography, Canadian Business and Current Affairs, Canadian Periodicals Index (CPI.Q), Journal Storage (JSTOR), Contemporary Women's Issues, Sociology: A SAGE Full-text Collection, SocINDEX, and Scopus. Databases were searched using the following keywords (* denotes exploded terms):

Rural	Aging	Canada
non-metropolitan	older adult	Prince Edward Island
village	older	New Brunswick
town	old	Newfoundland
small town	in old age	Nova Scotia
agricultur*	aging	Quebec
agricultural	elder*	Ontario
farm*	geriatric*	Manitoba
non-urban	senior*	Saskatchewan
rural*	nursing home*	Northwest Territories
rural health	long term care	Yukon
rural hospitals	long-term care	Nunavut
rural health services	frail elderly	Alberta
rural population	health services for the aged	British Columbia
	aged	Canad*

Each article identified in the database searches was assigned a Rural Aging in Canada (RAC) number. An article identified in multiple databases was assigned only one RAC number although a record was made of its listing in other databases.

Two reviewers independently reviewed abstracts from the database searches to determine if the articles fit the criteria for inclusion in the bibliography. For some articles, a review of the abstract was sufficient to determine if there was content related to rural aging in Canada. More often, the abstract provided insufficient detail on geographical location and the full document was retrieved and reviewed. A standardized inclusion/exclusion sheet was completed independently by the reviewers who subsequently met to arrive at a consensus regarding the status of each article (see Appendix 1). Articles were excluded based on hierarchical criteria (Figure 1).

Figure 1. Exclusion Criteria for Bibliography

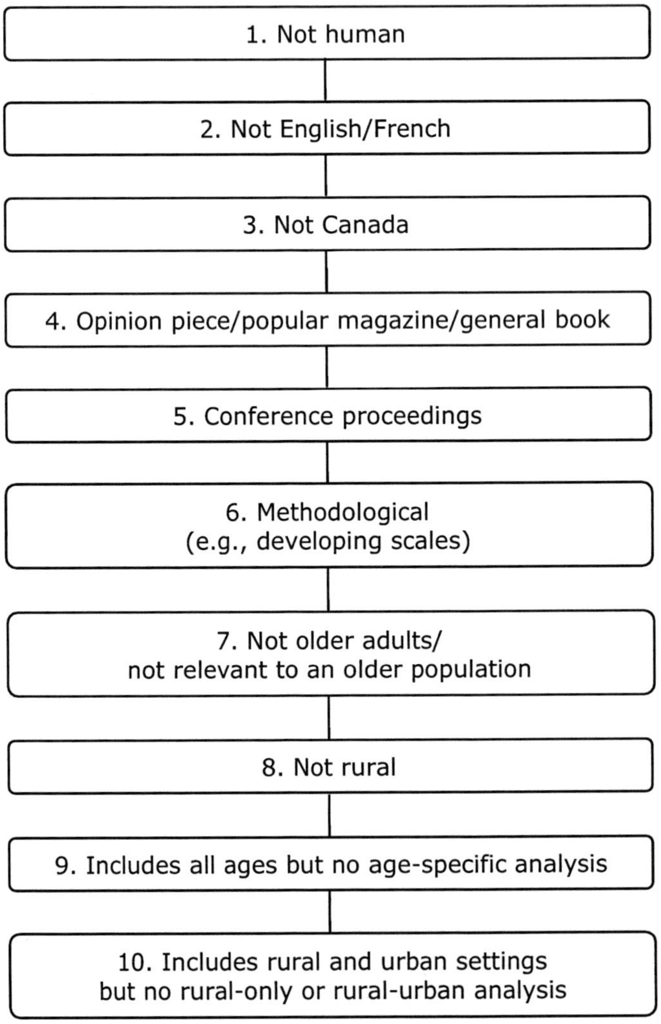

```
┌─────────────────────────────────────────────────┐
│ 1. Not human                                     │
└─────────────────────────────────────────────────┘
                         │
┌─────────────────────────────────────────────────┐
│ 2. Not English/French                            │
└─────────────────────────────────────────────────┘
                         │
┌─────────────────────────────────────────────────┐
│ 3. Not Canada                                    │
└─────────────────────────────────────────────────┘
                         │
┌─────────────────────────────────────────────────┐
│ 4. Opinion piece/popular magazine/general book   │
└─────────────────────────────────────────────────┘
                         │
┌─────────────────────────────────────────────────┐
│ 5. Conference proceedings                        │
└─────────────────────────────────────────────────┘
                         │
┌─────────────────────────────────────────────────┐
│ 6. Methodological                                │
│    (e.g., developing scales)                     │
└─────────────────────────────────────────────────┘
                         │
┌─────────────────────────────────────────────────┐
│ 7. Not older adults/                             │
│    not relevant to an older population           │
└─────────────────────────────────────────────────┘
                         │
┌─────────────────────────────────────────────────┐
│ 8. Not rural                                     │
└─────────────────────────────────────────────────┘
                         │
┌─────────────────────────────────────────────────┐
│ 9. Includes all ages but no age-specific analysis│
└─────────────────────────────────────────────────┘
                         │
┌─────────────────────────────────────────────────┐
│ 10. Includes rural and urban settings            │
│     but no rural-only or rural-urban analysis    │
└─────────────────────────────────────────────────┘
```

Hand Searches

In addition to online searches, a number of hand searches were undertaken. The reference lists of all included articles were reviewed. Each article with possible rural content was considered and articles not already identified through the online searches were retrieved. Both reviewers assessed each article from these hand searches in light of the exclusion criteria. The reference list of each retained article also was reviewed for potential inclusions.

Edited books whose chapters were identified during the online search were retrieved and reviewed to identify other relevant chapters that did not emerge through the online searches. Chapters that had a rural aging component were added and their reference lists were reviewed for potential inclusions.

A manual search of the *Canadian Journal on Aging*, Volumes 2 - 24 (1985 - 2005) was conducted independently by two reviewers and a manual search of the *Canadian Journal of Rural Medicine*, Volumes 1 – 10 was undertaken by one reviewer. This approach was deemed necessary as some articles that the reviewers knew had rural aging content did not appear in the database searches. Articles were identified and reviewed for possible inclusion. The reference lists of the articles deemed to meet the criteria for the bibliography also were reviewed for potential inclusions.

Twenty key authors with research expertise in aging in rural Canada and whose articles were included in the bibliography were identified (based on the included articles at that point in time). Each author's university website, if available, was reviewed for recent publications or a recent curriculum vitae, and any potential publications were reviewed. Seventeen individuals were contacted and provided with a list of their publications already included in the bibliography. They were asked to identify any other publications (journal articles, books, chapters, reports, etc.) and student's theses or dissertations that may be eligible. The publications were reviewed using the established inclusion/exclusion criteria and the reference lists of the included publications were examined. Three authors were not contacted directly but author-specific searches were made in Academic Search Premier, Ageline, Agricola, CINAHL, ERIC, HealthSTAR, MEDLINE, PEDro, and PsychINFO.

All editions of the *Rural and Small Town Bulletin*, a Statistics Canada publication, were reviewed to identify new articles. Finally, some articles were identified through other sources such as newsletters or alerts from colleagues who were aware of the preparation of the bibliography.

Number of Articles/Abstracts Reviewed and Included

The number of articles/abstracts reviewed and subsequently included from the various sources are summarized in Table 1. A total of 3,010 articles were reviewed for possible inclusion. Of these, 391 (13%) met the inclusion criteria. The 'hit rate' varied greatly by source. The relatively low hit rate for database searches reflects the challenge of limiting the key words while casting a sufficiently wide net. Almost one-half (49%) of the entries in the bibliography were identified through database searches. The remainder of the entries were found through a review of the references of included articles, hand searches of the two Canadian journals, contacts with key authors, and other sources.

Table 1. Summary of Search Outcomes

Source	Total	Excludes	Includes	Hit rate*	Final makeup (n=391)
Database searches	1461	1268	193	13.2%	49.4%
References of includes**	651	550	101	15.5%	25.8%
1st round	(474)	(403)	(71)	(15.0%)	(18.2%)
2nd round	(139)	(114)	(25)	(18.0%)	(6.4%)
3rd round	(38)	(33)	(5)	(13.2%)	(1.3%)
Chapter(s) of edited book(s) identified from database searches or references of includes	40	27	13	32.5%	3.3%
Additional sources (colleagues, newsletters, etc.)	29	4	25	86.2%	6.4%
References of additional sources	19	16	3	15.8%	0.8%
Hand searches of *Canadian Journal on Aging* and *Canadian Journal of Rural Medicine****	717	694	23	3.2%	5.9%
References of included articles from hand searches	36	26	10	27.8%	2.6%
Key authors	37	18	19	51.4%	4.9%
References of included articles from key authors	20	16	4	20.0%	1.0%
Total	3010	2619	391	13.0%	100.0%

*   Hit rate = number of articles included divided by number of articles reviewed.
**   1st round refers to the reference lists of the 193 includes from the initial data base search; 2nd round refers to the reference lists of 71 includes identified in the previous review of reference lists; and 3rd round refers to the reference lists of the 25 includes identified in the 2nd round.
***   The number of includes from hand searches refers to the number of articles identified through the hand search that did not emerge in either the database searches or the review of reference lists of included articles.

CHARACTERISTICS OF THE BIBLIOGRAPHIC ENTRIES

The characteristics of the entries are described below in terms of format, number of entries per year, topic areas, rural-only versus rural-urban focus, definitions/descriptions of rural, and geographical area.

Format of Bibliographic Entries

The 391 entries in the annotated bibliography were published in various formats. These included:

- journal articles (n=267, 68.3%),
- reports (n=71, 18.2%),
- books/book chapters (n=27, 6.9%), and
- dissertations/theses (n=26, 6.6%).

Number of Bibliographic Entries per Year

The number of entries per year varied somewhat (Figure 2), although the general pattern reveals an increase over time. It is difficult to ascertain whether this increase reflects an actual increase in the publication of aging-related rural research or the increased likelihood of identifying articles due to the availability of electronic databases.

Figure 2. Number of Bibliographic Entries by Year

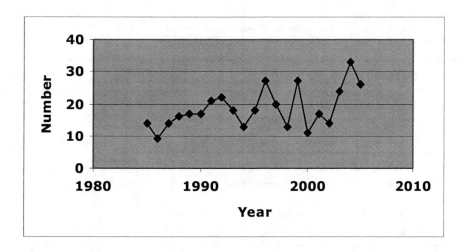

Topic Areas Covered by Bibliographic Entries

Using an iterative process, the 391 bibliographic entries were grouped into 18 topic areas, ranging from abuse to transportation/driving (Table 2). The largest percentage of articles was found under *Health and Social Services* (26%), followed by *Functional/Physical Health* (11%), *Epidemiology* (11%), and *Community Support/Amenities* (10%). Other topics each accounted for less than 10% of the entries. Where appropriate, topics have been divided into sub-topics (see Appendix 1 for information regarding entries for each sub-topic).

Table 2. Topic Areas Covered by Bibliographic Entries

Topic	Bibliographic entries	
	n	%
Abuse	4	1.0%
Community Amenities/Support	39	10.0%
Demographics/Migration	24	6.1%
Economics	2	0.5%
Education/Leisure	18	4.6%
Epidemiology	41	10.5%
Farm Transfers/Work	8	2.0%
Functional/Physical Health	44	11.3%
Health and Social Services	100	25.6%
Health Promotion/Screening	10	2.6%
Informal Care/Support	28	7.2%
Injuries	30	7.7%
Medications/Immunization	18	4.6%
Methods/Conceptual Issues	4	1.0%
Mortality	5	1.3%
Quality of Life/Life Satisfaction	6	1.5%
Transportation/Driving	9	2.3%
Multiple (Authored Book)	1	0.3%
Total	391	100.1%

Over time, there have been increases in the number of entries in some topic areas, decreases in others, and relative consistency in still others. Overall, the most dramatic increase has been in the number of entries in the *Health and Social Services* category. For the period 1985 – 1989, there were 11 entries in this category compared to 47 for the period 2000 – 2005. Table 3 shows the ranking of the top topic areas based on the number of entries across four time periods.

Table 3. Top Five Topic Areas Based on Number of Bibliographic Entries by Years

Topic	Rank ordering			
	1985-89	1990-94	1995-99	2000-05
Community Amenities/Support	1	2	---	3*
Health and Social Services	2	1	1	1
Functional/Physical Health	3*	3	3	3*
Demographics/Migration	3*	5*	---	---
Informal Care/Support	5	---	5	---
Epidemiology	---	4	4	2
Education/Leisure	---	5*	---	---
Injuries	---	---	2	---
Medications/Immunizations	---	---	---	3*

*   Tie
---   Not in the top 5

Of the 391 bibliographic entries, 380 entries can be considered as empirical studies. The remaining 11 entries are more conceptually-based.

Rural-Only versus Rural-Urban Focus of Bibliographic Entries

Entries in this bibliography may focus on rural settings only or may have a rural-urban comparison. Overall, 58% of the 380 empirically-based entries had a rural-only focus while 42% had rural-urban coverage. Among the entries studying both rural and urban locations, 10% considered a rural-urban continuum while 90% employed a simple dichotomy of rural versus urban.

Definitions/Descriptions of Rural Used in Bibliographic Entries

One of the challenges facing researchers and consumers of rural research is the varying definitions of rural. The definition used to select bibliographic entries was broad and not restricted to a specific population size or density, distance from services, etc.

Notwithstanding the broadness of the definition used here, the November 2001 edition of Statistics Canada's *Rural and Small Town Canada Analysis Bulletin* provides an informative discussion of the definitions of rural. DuPlessis and colleagues[1] write (pp. 5-6):

> *For national level analysis in Canada, at least six alternative definitions of "rural" are available:*
>
> - ***Census rural*** *refers to individuals living in the countryside outside centres of 1,000 or more population;*
> - ***Rural and small town*** *refers to individuals in towns or municipalities outside the commuting zone of larger urban centres (with 10,000 or more population). These individuals may be disaggregated into zones according to the degree of influence of a larger urban centre (called census metropolitan area and census agglomeration influenced zones (MIZ));*
> - ***OECD (Organization of Economic Co-operation and Development) rural communities*** *refers to individuals in communities with less than 150 persons per square kilometre. This includes the individuals living in the countryside, towns and small cities (inside and outside the commuting zone of larger urban centres);*
> - ***OECD predominantly rural regions*** *refers to individuals living in census divisions with more than 50 percent of the population living in OECD rural communities. This includes all census divisions without a major city;*
> - ***Beale non-metropolitan regions*** *refers to individuals living outside metropolitan regions with urban centres of 50,000 or more population;*
> - ***Rural postal codes*** *refers to individuals with a "0" as the second character in their postal code. These individuals live in areas where there are no letter carriers (i.e. residents go to a post office or corner postal box to pick up their mail). (Note: Our discussion relates specifically to the situation existing at the time of the enumeration of the 1996 Census of Population. Since that time, Canada Post has changed all the rural postal codes in New Brunswick and most of the rural postal codes in Quebec).*

These authors argue that the question being addressed in the study should determine the most appropriate definition to use. As a starting point or benchmark, their recommendation is use of the *rural and small town* definition.

---

[1] DuPlessis, V., Beshiri, R., & Bollman, R.D. (2001). Definitions of rural. *Rural and Small Town Canada Analysis Bulletins, 3*(3). Statistics Canada Catalogue No. 21-006-XIE.

The standard definitions outlined above were used in only 8% of the 380 empirically-based bibliographic entries (Table 4). The limited use of these standard definitions reflects, in part, the local nature of some studies. As well, in some entries, the study may have been based on one of these definitions but this was not explicit in the documentation.

Table 4. Standard Definitions of Rural Used in Bibliographic Entries

Definition	Bibliographic entries	
	n	%
No standard definition	351	92.4%
Census rural	18	4.7%
Rural and small town	7	1.8%
Rural postal codes	4	1.1%
Total*	380	100.0%

* Eleven articles were conceptually-based and were excluded from this analysis.

Population size of the study location was reported in 45% of the 380 empirically-based bibliographic entries (Table 5). For 16% of the entries, the size was 10,000 or larger. In some instances, the population being reported referred to the region or geographical area which may encompass a number of smaller communities and/or farms.

Table 5. Population Size of Study Location

Population size	Bibliographic entries	
	n	%
Not specified	207	54.5%
<1,000	22	5.8%
>1,000 and <10,000	89	23.4%
>10,000	32	8.4%
Other*	30	7.9%
Total**	380	100.0%

* Other includes entries where incomplete information on population size was presented. For example, the population of a particular ethnic group was reported but the population size of the entire community was not.

** Eleven articles were conceptually based and were excluded from this analysis.

Geographical Area of Study in Bibliographic Entries

The geographical area of study varied across the entries (Table 6). Over one-quarter of the entries (27%) examined communities/towns/villages and 21% covered health regions/units or catchment areas for health services.

Table 6. Geographical Area of Study Identified in Bibliographic Entries

	Area	
	n	%
Community/town/village	103	27.1%
Municipality/county/township	31	8.2%
Community/town/village and municipality/county/township	11	2.9%
Census divisions	8	2.1%
Health region/unit/catchment area	81	21.3%
First Nations reservation	7	1.8%
Farms	37	9.7%
Farms and communities	4	1.1%
Non-metropolitan area	1	0.3%
Geographical area of province	13	3.4%
Province(s)	59	15.5%
Canada (national-level information only)	25	6.6%
Total*	380	100.0%

* Eleven articles were conceptually based and were excluded from this analysis.

While communities/towns/villages and health regions/units/catchment areas often were identified as the areas of study, specific place names were provided less frequently (details available upon request). Indeed, only 20% of the entries included the specific names of the communities/towns/villages under study. Provinces were more frequently identified (42%), providing the reader with general, albeit limited information on the rural setting.

The number of entries according to province where the study was undertaken is illustrated in Table 7. Ontario was represented the most (accounting for 26% of the entries), followed by Manitoba (16%). Some studies were conducted in more than one province but not the entire country; these were categorized according to the geographical region of study. Only 14% of the studies were national in scope.

Table 7. Province or Region of Bibliographic Entries

Province or region	Bibliographic entries	
	N	%
Alberta	37	9.5%
British Columbia	22	5.6%
Manitoba	63	16.1%
New Brunswick	3	0.8%
Newfoundland and Labrador	11	2.8%
Northwest Territories	7	1.8%
Nova Scotia	8	2.0%
Ontario	101	25.8%
Quebec	22	5.6%
Saskatchewan	33	8.4%
Atlantic Canada	10	2.6%
Central Canada	1	0.3%
Northern Canada	7	1.8%
Western Canada	8	2.0%
Canada (National)	56	14.3%
Not specified	2	0.5%
Total	391	99.9%

Overall, an examination of the characteristics of the entries reveals the complexity and diversity in the study of rural aging. Extensive and multi-faceted search techniques are required to identify articles with a rural aging component. Various definitions of rural need to be employed. The geographical area covered may range from a single, small community to all 'rural' areas of the country. It is with these challenges in mind that attention now turns to the bibliographic entries.

ANNOTATIONS

The remainder of this bibliography provides the complete citation and an annotation for each bibliographic entry. Each annotation has been specifically written with a rural emphasis and includes:

- Author(s), year, title, journal
- Objectives
- Methods
- Definition of rural
- Results related to rural aging
- Conclusions

The annotations are presented by topic and sub-topics, if appropriate. In each topic area, the annotations are organized alphabetically by author, and, if necessary, by title.

ABUSE

Bond, J. B., Jr., Cuddy, R., Dixon, G. L., Duncan, K. A., & Smith, D. L. (1999). The financial abuse of mentally incompetent older adults: A Canadian study. *Journal of Elder Abuse & Neglect, 11*(4), 23-38.

OBJECTIVES: To explore the incidence of suspected financial abuse, to identify characteristics of mentally incompetent older adults most at risk, and to identify indicators of financial abuse, among clientele of the Province of Manitoba's Office of Public Trustee.

METHODS: Data were from the client administrative files from the Office of Public Trustee of Manitoba for the period April 1, 1995 to March 31, 1996. Of the 354 files opened on mentally incompetent individuals aged 60+, 76 were cases of suspected financial abuse. A comparison group of 76 non-financial abuse cases was randomly selected. Information was gathered on age, gender, marital status, place of birth, geographic region of residence, type of residence prior to and at the time of the Order of Supervision, property ownership, household members, monthly income, money in bank accounts, and whether the individual had living children. The sample consisted of 55 males and 97 females; ages ranged from 60 to 101.

DEFINITION OF RURAL: Winnipeg/non-Winnipeg comparisons were made. Winnipeg is the major urban centre in the province; non-Winnipeg was all areas outside of Winnipeg.

RESULTS RELATED TO RURAL AGING: The majority of abuse cases (71%) were reported from Winnipeg. However, 47 of the 102 Winnipeg cases (46%) were categorized as suspected financial abuse, compared to 24 of the 41 non-Winnipeg cases (59%).

CONCLUSIONS: Financial abuse is a problem for mentally incompetent older adults whose cases are managed by the Public Trustee in Manitoba. The authors speculate that the large majority of cases being found in urban versus rural settings may reflect the role of social networks in rural areas.

Brozowski, K., & Hall, D. R. (2003). Elder abuse in a risk society. *Geriatrics Today,* *6*(3), 167-172.

OBJECTIVES: To identify the prevalence of risk factors associated with elder abuse in Canada and to explore an elder abuse model based on interpersonal risk theory.

METHODS: Data were from Statistics Canada's 1999 Canadian General Social Survey that involved a national probability sample of 25,876 respondents. This analysis focused on a subset of 2,070 women and 1,302 men aged 65+. Their mean age was 72.7 years; 23% resided in a rural area. A summary variable was created by Statistics Canada that measured emotional or financial abuse by a child or caregiver or current partner or ex-partner.

DEFINITION OF RURAL: No definition of rural was provided.

RESULTS RELATED TO RURAL AGING: Seven percent of the respondents were identified as dealing with issues of elder abuse. Rural older residents had an increased likelihood of emotional or financial abuse from a partner/ex-partner, child, or caregiver than their urban counterparts, when controlling for demographic characteristics, socioeconomic status, social and cultural background, and health status. In addition to rural residence, men, separated individuals, respondents who had a prior marriage or cohabitation partner, and respondents with sleeping problems or health-related activity limitations had a significantly higher risk of emotional or financial abuse.

CONCLUSIONS: The complexity of the risk factors for elder abuse was evident in these analyses. The authors call for research on specific forms of elder abuse and the associated risk factors.

Harbison, J., Coughlan, S., Karabanow, J., & VanderPlaat, M. (2004). Offering the help that's needed: Responses to the mistreatment and neglect of older people in a rural Canadian context. *Rural Social Work, 9*(2), 147-157.

OBJECTIVES: To explore locally occurring, indigenous responses to the mistreatment, neglect, and self-neglect of older people in rural communities of an eastern Canadian province.

METHODS: Using a grounded theory approach, this qualitative study involved document review, 55 interviews, and 5 focus groups about what help is offered, by whom, and how various helpers relate to one another while providing assistance. Interview respondents were identified through a snowball technique, and included governmental and non-governmental health/social service professionals and volunteers, individuals involved in policing and transition-house work, faith leaders, members of seniors organizations, and lay individuals. Focus group participants were providing direct assistance to abused older adults.

DEFINITION OF RURAL: The authors acknowledge the challenge of defining rural and provide a description of their rural setting in terms of population distribution, geography and occupation, wealth and income, and accessibility of health and social services.

RESULTS RELATED TO RURAL AGING: Professionals and lay people engaged in service delivery were informed about the limitations of the legislation and understood that it mandated responses in only a small number of situations. Both professionals and lay helpers were concerned about respecting older people's rights and wishes and demonstrated caring, creativity, and collaboration with others in their efforts to assist. One of the chief barriers appeared to be access to scarce resources and to help that was acceptable to older abused individuals. Themes discussed included contextual limitations in providing help, best interests versus rights, offering help that's needed, threats to flexibility and creativity, and situations when attempts to help fail.

CONCLUSIONS: The authors conclude that in order to meet older people's needs, as opposed to simply managing risk, and to prevent their social exclusion, both resources and support for collaborative and innovative ways of helping are required.

See also Harbison, J., Coughlan, S., Karabanow, J., & VanderPlaat, M. (2005).

Harbison, J., Coughlan, S., Karabanow, J., & VanderPlaat, M. (2005). A clash of cultures: Rural values and service delivery to mistreated and neglected older people in eastern Canada. *Practice, 17*(4), 229-246.

OBJECTIVES: To explore the challenges that cultural norms, such as the high value that older generations place on their privacy and family integrity, and on their ability to cope and remain in charge of their lives, pose for formal and informal helpers providing assistance to mistreated and neglected older adults in rural eastern Canada.

METHODS: Using a grounded theory approach, this qualitative study used snowball sampling to recruit adult protection workers, community nurses and social workers, physicians, other health professionals, police and lay police services, faith leaders, senior volunteers, community volunteers, and women's shelter workers. Interviews were conducted with 45 participants (n = 27 in District 1 and n = 18 in District 2). Focus groups (n = 2 in District 1 and n = 3 in District 2) and feedback groups (n = 2 in District 1 and n = 2 in District 2) also were held.

DEFINITION OF RURAL: The rural areas were selected to represent a range of economic and social circumstances. Two health services delivery districts of comparable geographic size were chosen. However, one district had a greater number of concentrated areas of population with 80,000 people as compared to 33,000 in the other. Differences in occupation, wealth, and ethnicity were noted.

RESULTS RELATED TO RURAL AGING: Responses across services delivery districts, geographic communities, professional disciplines, and among lay people were very consistent. Themes included: expressions of rural values, respect for older people's rights and wishes, mandates and roles in helping, the decision to report, the evolving role of the adult protection worker, collaborative teamwork, alternative service delivery, and threats to the sustainability and continuing growth of creativity in service delivery. Important values included keeping matters of abuse within the family, and acknowledging older people's need for independence and the right to remain in their own homes. The efforts of formal and informal helpers to accommodate older people's cultural norms, and to respond to what they want were described as frequently successful. However, this help was perceived to be continually under threat from the centralization and rationalization of service delivery, as well as an increasing focus on the potential for litigation resulting from harm to clients or helpers.

CONCLUSIONS: The authors argue that their exploratory study raises important questions about attempts to respond to older people in situations of mistreatment and neglect. Issues for further consideration and implications of these findings for practice are discussed.

See also Harbison, J., Coughlan, S., Karabanow, J., & VanderPlaat, M. (2004).

COMMUNITY AMENITIES/SUPPORT

Housing/Neighbourhood Amenities

Break, H. (1985). *Impact study of the Sandy Cove Acres retirement community on existing home care/support services in Innisfil Township.* **Master's thesis, University of Guelph, Guelph, ON.**

OBJECTIVES: To determine the potential impact of retirement communities on municipal-level home care/support services, to provide baseline information on resident characteristics, and to provide a case study that could be used by rural municipalities planning to accommodate a retirement community, drawing on a case study in the province of Ontario.

METHODS: This case study was conducted in Sandy Cove Acres, a retirement community located in Innisfil Township in Simcoe County. A review of current homecare/support services available to older adults was undertaken based on information from the Simcoe Health Unit, the Ministry of Community and Social Services, and the Ministry of Health. In-person interviews using a structured questionnaire that focused on demographic and socioeconomic characteristics, previous place of residence, health status, use of support services, level of satisfaction with support services, and perceived need for new/improved services were completed. The sample consisted of 68 Sandy Cove residents (35 males, 33 females); 19% were aged < 65, 57% were aged 65 - 74, and 24% were 75+. Five were employed; 34% lived alone while 62% lived with their spouse.

DEFINITION OF RURAL: The Census definition of rural as territory lying outside urban areas which are areas having a population concentration of ≥ 1,000 and a population density of ≥ 400 per square kilometre was discussed. However, Sandy Cove Acres had 1,643 residents at the time of the study.

RESULTS RELATED TO RURAL AGING: Residents were most likely to have moved from an urban area to this retirement community. Most were involved in social activities, either inside or outside of Sandy Cove Acres. Help with minor household repairs and with yard work was in greatest demand. Awareness of available services varied from 95% being aware of bus services to 19% being aware of prescription delivery service.

CONCLUSIONS: Several questions regarding access to home care/support services, service characteristics, transportation assistance, housing type, and lifestyle offered by retirement communities were raised. While acknowledging the small scale nature of this study, recommendation regarding service delivery and future research are presented.

Canadian Mortgage and Housing Corporation. (2003). Housing needs of low income people living in rural areas: The implications for seniors. *Research Highlights, July 2003*, 1-6. Socio-Economic Series 03-012. Ottawa, ON: Canadian Mortgage and Housing Corporation.

OBJECTIVES: To profile the housing situations (type, tenure, needs, opportunities, and barriers) in rural households in Canada.

METHODS: The project involved a review of literature on rural housing, an analysis of Census and Statistics Canada data from 1996, and 12 case studies that included a review of local documents and key informant interviews.

DEFINITION OF RURAL: Statistics Canada's definition of rural and small town as the population living outside the commuting zones of urban centres with a population of 10,000+ was used.

RESULTS RELATED TO RURAL AGING: A typology of rural communities was presented, including growing communities, stable or slow growth communities, declining communities, bedroom communities, retirement communities, and northern communities. Access to housing and services, and affordability varied across these different types of communities. Examples of the ways in which rural communities are responding to the aging of the population and older adults' housing needs were discussed in terms of land and land assembly, financial incentives, conversion of non-residential buildings to residential use, zoning, and non-profit organizations.

CONCLUSIONS: While the housing situation in rural areas presents some challenges for older adults, rural communities offer some distinct advantages. Limitations including the small amount of literature on rural housing in Canada are noted.

Corbett, R. (1990). Coming of age: A profile of the elderly in Atlantic Canada. *Plan Canada, 30*(4), 13-25.

OBJECTIVES: To examine the characteristics of older adults living in rural and small town Atlantic Canada.

METHODS: Data were from a 1986 - 1987 rural residential survey that included questions on locational preference, feelings about community, housing type, tenure, financing, and acquisition. Of the 1,840 returned questionnaires, 261 were from individuals aged 65+. This group had an average age of 72 years; only 1% was aged 80+.

DEFINITION OF RURAL: Urban areas with populations > 20,000 were excluded.

RESULTS RELATED TO RURAL AGING: The older respondents were generally satisfied with their place of residence. Average length of residence was 47 years. Having been born in the community and being close to family/friends were the most important factors for location. Travel distances of > 1 mile to obtain required goods and services were common, including a distance of > 5 miles for hospital care for approximately half of the respondents. Not owning or having access to a private vehicle was reported by 25% of the respondents, with a higher proportion of females not having access compared to their male counterparts. In terms of housing, 87% lived in single-family dwellings, with 90% owning their homes. Major problem areas were limited retail variety, recreational facilities, housing choices, and access to services.

CONCLUSIONS: The authors outline a number of policy and planning issues such as the challenge of service provision in rural areas, the need for careful marketing to the older segment of the population, and housing and transportation needs.

Dunnett, B. C. (1991). *Housing and support services for the elderly in small communities: The potential for the Abbeyfield model in rural Ontario.* **Master's thesis, University of Guelph, Guelph, ON.**

OBJECTIVES: To assess the potential for a specific small-scale supportive seniors' housing model (the Abbeyfield House) in small towns and villages in the southern portion of the province of Ontario. The Abbeyfield model is an example of small-scale, service-enriched housing which fits in the continuum between totally independent living and institutionalization.

METHODS: Community-level information on demographic characteristics, housing, and support services was reviewed. Key informant interviews were conducted in 1990 with housing and support service representatives (n = 14), other local government officials (n = 6), and senior citizen representatives (n = 10).

DEFINITION OF RURAL: Communities were selected based on urban proximity, population size, and population aging experiences (net elderly migration and aging in place). The communities and their 1986 populations were Hanover (6,415), Durham (2,520), Markdale (1,230), Fergus (6,275), Mount Forest (3,590), and Erin (2,320).

RESULTS RELATED TO RURAL AGING: The more remote rural communities generally had higher proportions of residents aged 65+ and aged 80+, higher elderly dependency ratios, and sex ratios that indicated a predominance of females. Housing options varied across the communities, with more options tending to be available in the more urban-proximate and larger communities. A lack of social support services such as family/caregiver relief, security and surveillance, and information referral/counseling was evident in the more remote communities. All key informants saw a need for a variety of additional housing options for older people in their communities and many identified service needs. Informants from urban-proximate communities were more familiar with the Abbeyfield model although it was those from more remote communities that more often identified the model as filling a gap in housing within their community. Urban-proximate key informants were more likely to identify housing options they would prefer over an Abbeyfield House.

CONCLUSIONS: This thesis highlights the variation among rural communities and the need to consider various options to fill housing and service gaps. Suggestions for future research are provided.

See also Hallman, B. C., & Joseph, A. E. (1997). Note that Dunnett, B. C. now publishes as Hallman, B. C.

Gutman, G. M., & Hodge, G. (1990). *Housing and support service needs and preferences of rural seniors from three regions in Canada.* **Vancouver, B.C.: Gerontology Research Centre, Simon Fraser University.**

OBJECTIVES: To field test a Seniors' Survey designed to assist rural communities in determining accommodation and support service needs of older adults in three different regions of Canada.

METHODS: The Seniors' Survey was completed by 417 individuals aged 65+ in 10 small communities in three regions (Central Kootenay Regional District, BC; Wellington and Perth Counties, ON; Kings County, NS) between May and September 1988. Surveys were distributed at a community meeting with seniors. Topics addressed included sociodemographic and functional characteristics, current housing and living arrangements, housing costs, need for home repairs, knowledge and use of federal and provincial housing assistance programs, housing preferences, support service needs and future housing plans.

DEFINITION OF RURAL: All communities had 1986 populations of < 10,000: Nelson, BC (8,113); New Denver, BC (596); Riondel, BC (310); Silverton, BC (233); Erin, ON (2,320); Listowel, ON (5,107); Morefield, ON (700); Canning, NS (796); Kentville, NS (5,208); and Scott's Bay, NS (296). The proportion of residents aged 65+ ranged from 5% to 52%.

RESULTS RELATED TO RURAL AGING: This descriptive report covered six broad categories, including housing needs, knowledge and use of federal housing assistance programs, housing preferences, support service needs, transportation needs, and future housing plans and preferences. More than 80% of the respondents reported having no difficulty in meeting their shelter costs. Few had used federal programs to improve their living conditions and there was a low level of awareness of such programs. Between one-third and one-half of the homeowners expressed an interest in sheltered housing, congregate housing, or purchasing a retirement home unit. Fewer were interested in garden apartments, buying a smaller single family dwelling/mobile home, or moving into co-op housing or an Abbeyfield House. Homesharing was the most popular option for aging in place with revenue. Support services were needed for indoor/outdoor house maintenance such as heavy cleaning, snow removal, home repairs, or yard work, and for transportation. Few respondents had immediate plans to move but would prefer to remain in the same community or region if a move was needed. Regional findings were presented although no tests of significance were included.

CONCLUSIONS: The authors call for more information on the rural elderly that takes into account variations across rural communities.

Hallman, B. C., & Joseph, A. E. (1997). Housing the rural elderly: A place for Abbeyfield? *Journal of Housing for the Elderly, 12*(1/2), 83-103.

OBJECTIVES: To assess the potential of the Abbeyfield model of small congregate housing to meet the needs of the rural elderly in the southern portion of the province of Ontario. The Abbeyfield model of housing emphasizes family-like accommodation for single elderly people with an emphasis on lifestyle as much as shelter.

METHODS: Using a case study approach in six rural, southern Ontario communities, baseline data on the local availability of age-segregated housing were collected and interviews were conducted with 30 key informants in 1990. Key informants included municipal officers, elderly opinion leaders, and managers/providers.

DEFINITION OF RURAL: The communities were selected based on population size (1,000 - 2,499; 2,500 - 4,999; and 5,000 - 9,999) and urban proximity. Population sizes ranged from 1,370 to 7,940.

RESULTS RELATED TO RURAL AGING: Communities with a population < 5,000 offered extremely limited housing options to their older residents. The exception was institutionalization that often was the only option for many older adults in these communities, particularly for those with low income. In general, as the community size increased, so did the availability of housing supply/residential choice. Nearly all the key informants indicated that their community needed additional age-segregated housing. Managers/service providers identified a gap in supportive living options for older adults with limited assistance. Positive and negative comments about the Abbeyfield model were obtained. Key informants in smaller communities tended to rate the potential of the Abbeyfield model higher than those in larger communities. Most believed it would be 'somewhat difficult' to set up an Abbeyfield House in their communities. Managers/service providers tended to be the most skeptical about the Abbeyfield model, with availability of financial support for the development and operation of the residence a major concern.

CONCLUSIONS: Rural older adults face limited housing options, reflecting the difficulty of supplying a variety of housing forms to a small and limited market. The Abbeyfield model is viewed as having the greatest potential in the smaller, more remote communities where there are a small number of older adults who are in need of supportive housing and are interested in moving.

See also Dunnett, B. C. (1991).

Halseth, G., Hanlon, N., Pow, V., & Clasby, R. (2004). *"Looking to the future, now":* *Mackenzie and area seniors needs project final report.* **Prince George, BC: Geography Program, University of Northern British Columbia.**

OBJECTIVES: To examine housing and support service needs for older residents in the District of Mackenzie and surrounding area in the province of British Columbia.

METHODS: This project was undertaken in Summer 2004 and included a review of Census population data, key informant interviews, focus groups, and household surveys. As reported in the methodology report, 1,840 surveys were distributed and 381 were completed and returned (response rate 20.7%). The age distribution was 21% aged 55 - 64 and 10% aged 65+. The final report focused on the survey results relating to housing; transportation; community participation and local services; physical environment; family, friends, and care networks; retirement and retirement planning; and pensions.

DEFINITION OF RURAL: In 2001, the population of McKenzie was 5,206 with 2.3% of the population aged 65+.

RESULTS RELATED TO RURAL AGING: The main advantages of retiring in Mackenzie were seen to be the 'benefits of a small community' and having family and friends in town. Most residents reported a high level of social support from family and friends. The majority was active in, and satisfied with, the various social clubs and recreational activities in the town. Concerns were expressed regarding the limited availability of health services and the lack of suitable housing to meet the needs of an aging population. Nearly 90% of the respondents indicated that current housing does not meet the needs of older residents and seniors. A seniors' housing complex was suggested by many respondents. Other suggestions included a new seniors' activity centre, more attention to the clearance of ice on sidewalks, and a local-regional shuttle service to facilitate access to needed services. Age differences were described in some sections but no data were presented making it difficult to systematically identify the extent to which different age groups had similar views.

CONCLUSIONS: The authors argue that the increases in the seniors population in Mackenzie bring specific challenges around the provision of housing and support services. Both advantages and concerns of living/retiring in Mackenzie were identified.

Note: Additional information on this study (Executive Summary, Final Report, Background Literature Report, Methodology Report, Population Background and Trends Report, and Seniors' Housing and Support Services Database Compendium) is available at the following website under the heading Mackenzie and Area Seniors' Needs Overview: http://web.unbc.ca/geography/faculty/greg/print_research.shtml#SeniorsNeeds

Hodge, G. (1987). Assisted housing for Ontario's rural elderly: Shortfalls in product and location. *Canadian Journal on Aging, 6*(2), 141-154.

OBJECTIVES: To assess the quality of publicly assisted housing for older adults in the eastern portion of the province of Ontario.

METHODS: In 1983, a survey of senior citizen apartment projects in nine small eastern Ontario towns was conducted. Data collection included an appraisal of five of nine areas in the Physical and Architectural Features Checklist (PAF), including physical amenities, social-recreational aids, safety features, prosthetic aids, and orientational aids. Walking distances to community services were measured. Tenants (n = 124; 55% of total) were interviewed regarding their preferences.

DEFINITION OF RURAL: Nine specific towns were identified; all had populations of < 10,000.

RESULTS RELATED TO RURAL AGING: Only two housing projects had > 50% of the physical and architectural features considered desirable for shelter care facilities for older adults. Projects were more likely to have social and recreational aids and least likely to have orientational aids. Residents reported that they most frequently used a grocery store, the post office, and a variety store. The median walking distance to frequently used resources was 546 metres, with a range from 342 to 1048 metres.

CONCLUSIONS: The author discusses the shortfalls in the product and location, and the perversity in the process where there are building designs and construction programs subject to governmental approval but inadequacy in design and location.

Hodge, G., McKay, L., Beeckmans, P., & Intergovernmental Committee on Urban and Regional Research. (1993). *Canada's aging rural population: The role and response of local government.* **Toronto, ON: Intergovernmental Committee on Urban and Regional Research.**

OBJECTIVES: To assess the impact of rural population aging on the provision of services to individuals aged 65+ by local governments in rural regions of Canada.

METHODS: In 1992, 209 rural municipalities with populations < 10,000 were surveyed. Responses were received from 183 municipalities (88%). Questions focused on 31 support services and facilities for seniors, demographic trends, and the impact of an aging population. Five categories of services were examined: (1) health care (family physicians, nursing home/intermediate care, extended care hospital, acute care hospital, home care nursing service, adult day care centre, palliative care, special care [Alzheimer's], and medical equipment loan service); (2) housing (senior's apartments [public], retirement housing [private], congregate housing/lodge, supportive housing, and home sharing match-up); (3) home support (homemaker service, handyman service, meals-on-wheels, emergency response system, seniors' counseling, hospice service, support group[s], and information and referral service); (4) social/recreational (seniors' activity centre, wellness program, and community centre programs for seniors); and (5) transportation (regular community bus service, taxi, bus for handicapped, and volunteer drivers). The questionnaire was included in the report.

DEFINITION OF RURAL: Rural municipalities were those municipalities with a 1991 population of < 10,000, and in rural areas. It is important to note that the study focused on those parts of rural areas covered by municipal units. As a result, the southern rural portions of the prairie provinces (Manitoba, Saskatchewan, and Alberta), Ontario, Quebec, and Prince Edward Island were almost fully covered. In rural British Columbia, Newfoundland, New Brunswick, and Nova Scotia, about half of the rural population lives in areas that have no municipal organization and thus no local government unit responds to seniors' needs.

RESULTS RELATED TO RURAL AGING: Only 8 of the 31 basic supports were found in at least 50% of the rural municipalities. The most common were homemaker services (78%), family physicians (74%), seniors' public housing (73%), home care nursing (72%), seniors' activity centre (64%), bus for the handicapped (57%), nursing home/intermediate care centre (57%), and meals-on-wheels (53%). The lowest were regular community bus service (15%), special care units (12%), wheels-to-meals (9%), supportive housing (2%), and home sharing match-up (0%). Communities with a population < 500 tended to have only four basic supports while those of 5,000+ residents were more likely to have 20+ of these services. Transportation options were very limited. Only 15% of the municipalities reported problems with the number of seniors; these related to the broad categories of having difficulties in providing additional services and feeling pressure on existing services and infrastructure. More frequent was the view that there were benefits from their presence such as a willingness to participate in/volunteer for community activities, acting as a source of historical/cultural background, and providing experience/expertise for community endeavours.

CONCLUSIONS: The authors conclude that seniors in rural Canada have not only fewer support services available to them but usually no choice when services do exist. Overall population growth, the proportion of seniors in the population, and the extent of the local tax base may affect the supportiveness of the local environment. While not solely responsible for managing the needs of an aging population, small rural municipalities may play a role in lobbying the province for services and facilities, encouraging and assisting local groups to develop seniors' services, providing local infrastructure to make community environments more amenable to seniors, and planning supportive land-use arrangements.

Joseph, A. E., & Hollett, R. G. (1992). When I'm 65: The retirement housing preferences of the rural elderly. *Canadian Journal of Regional Science, 25*(1), 1-19.

OBJECTIVES: To identify salient features of residential and locational preferences of country and village/town residents in the province of Ontario.

METHODS: This case study focuses on individuals aged 55 to 64. A random sample was drawn from the school support lists derived through municipal enumeration. A total of 61 residents (39 from Nichol; 22 from Arthur) were interviewed in person. Questions focused on present and past housing, retirement housing attributes (price, tenure, housing/service options, dwelling size, location), and socioeconomic characteristics.

DEFINITION OF RURAL: Two communities, Nichol Township (1986 population 3,591) and the Village of Arthur (1986 population 1,842) were selected to represent rural dispersed and rural nucleated settlements, respectively. Both are in the County of Wellington located approximately 100 kilometres west of Toronto.

RESULTS RELATED TO RURAL AGING: The preferred 'package' of attributes was an owned conventional, two-bedroom home, located in a small rural community, and priced at $125,000. The two-bedroom home represented a down-sizing for most respondents. Location emerged as the attribute most readily traded off. The only significant difference in attributes between respondents of Nichol Township and the Village of Arthur residents was with regard to location. Residents in both communities placed higher utility on options corresponding with their present location. Overall, respondents had a negative view of retirement communities, considering them primarily a 'dependent' housing option.

CONCLUSIONS: While recognizing the limitations of their sample, the authors conclude that many older adults consider the setting of housing as well as its tenure, size, and price characteristics as simultaneously important. They call for more research that integrates locational and residential dimensions of retirement housing choice.

Kuntz, M. E. (1989). Planned retirement communities in the rural-urban fringe: An elderly housing alternative. In K. M. Cossey (Ed.), *Rural environments and the elderly: Impact, contributions and needs fulfillment* (pp. 45-71). Sackville, NB: Rural and Small Town Research and Studies Programme, Department of Geography, Mount Allison University.

OBJECTIVES: To identify characteristics of individuals who purchase housing in retirement communities, reasons for a move, and level of satisfaction with the environment in the province of Ontario.

METHODS: Personal interviews were conducted with a random sample of 225 households in seven retirement communities. The communities were selected based on the age of development, the number of housing units, dwelling type, dwelling cost, and location (relative to major urban centres, in-town vs. out-of-town, and tourist vs. non-tourist).

DEFINITION OF RURAL: The retirement communities were located in Stroud, Strathroy, Stayner, Bobcaygen, Grand Bend, Sutton, and Newcastle; these communities were classified as rural/semi-rural in close proximity to large urban centres.

RESULTS RELATED TO RURAL AGING: The majority of residents of these retirement communities were in two-person households comprised of married couples with no children living at home. They tended to have relatively high levels of education and were more likely to have had professional, managerial, and administrative positions than Ontario seniors as a whole. Almost 40% spent up to six months each year away from their retirement community residence. The majority originated from an urban centre of 30,000+ and almost 40% had moved from within an 80 kilometre radius. The three most important reasons for a move were a desire to move away from city living, a need/desire to move away from inappropriate housing, and economic considerations. The majority of the residents were satisfied with the retirement community. The most liked features were social and psychological attributes such as friendly people, neighbours, lifestyle, and a safe/secure environment.

CONCLUSIONS: The author calls for further research on advantages and disadvantages of locating retirement communities within the rural-urban fringe.

McIlravey, G. P. (1985). *Sources of satisfaction in a rural nonfarm residential environment: An empirical example.* **Master's thesis, University of Guelph, Guelph, ON.**

OBJECTIVES: To investigate rural non-farm residents' degree of satisfaction with various aspects of their residential environments in a southern portion of the province of Ontario.

METHODS: Data were from a sample of 120 non-farm residents of Puslinch Township. Non-farm residences were identified on the basis of maps compiled by airphotos, followed by field survey verification and revisions. Every sixth house along each concession sideroad and county road within the township and around its boundaries was sampled. Six dimensions of the rural non-farm residential environment and their related attributes were examined, including physical aspects of the dwelling unit, accessibility, the surrounding physical environment, the surrounding social environment, financial considerations, and municipal service considerations. Respondents rated the importance of the residential environment, satisfaction in the context of their present residential situation, and overall satisfaction with their entire residential environment. Importance and satisfaction scores were combined multiplicatively, resulting in weighted satisfaction scores on each dimension and attribute. Of the 120 respondents, 14% were aged 56 - 65 and 12% were > 65. Seventy-six percent of the sample was female.

DEFINITION OF RURAL: Puslinch Township (1981 population 4,544) is located in the southeast portion of Wellington County in southern Ontario, adjacent to the City of Guelph, and within commuting distance of major urban centres such as Toronto, Hamilton, and Kitchener-Waterloo.

RESULTS RELATED TO RURAL AGING: Physical aspects of the dwelling unit and financial considerations emerged as the most important dimensions when evaluating any residence. However, the surrounding physical environment and physical aspects of the dwelling unit were rated highest in terms of satisfaction with present residential situation. Significant differences in the residential evaluations were evident according to age and income level. The 56+ age group had significantly higher satisfaction ratings on the physical aspects of the dwelling unit than the < 36 age group, and on both accessibility and municipal service considerations than either the < 36 or the 36 - 55 age groups. In terms of importance, significant age differences were evident only on accessibility, with the older age group rating this higher than the 36 - 55 age group. Time/distance for shopping tended to be more important and times from schools less important to the 56+ age group.

CONCLUSIONS: The research highlights the complexity of residential evaluation and points to the importance of differences according to age and income level. The author discusses the implications for both research and planning for residential growth.

Nicolson, B. A. (1987). *Housing for rural small town seniors: The decision to stay living independently.* **Master's thesis, University of Guelph, Guelph, ON.**

OBJECTIVES: To explore living arrangements of rural small town seniors and to examine the relationship between social, health, environmental, and economic factors which influence their decision to stay living independently in a small rural town in the province of Ontario.

METHODS: A 'decision to stay' framework was constructed by adapting a decision to move theory and drawing on literature on decision-making and satisfaction. A small town in Bruce County, Ontario was used as a case study. A list of 283 older adults aged 65+ and living in independent situations was compiled from the assessment rolls and school support lists, with further discussion with the director of the local senior centre and public health officials. A random sample of 90 respondents was drawn. In-person interviews were conducted, with questions focusing on residential history, current housing and community characteristics, and personal characteristics.

DEFINITION OF RURAL: The Town of Chelsey in Bruce County is a small rural town with an agricultural hinterland (1985 population 1,845).

RESULTS RELATED TO RURAL AGING: The residential unit emerged as the most important contributor to overall satisfaction, followed by health services, access to family and friends, access to shopping, and access to social and recreational activities. Seven factors that discriminated between high and low satisfaction with the residential environment were health, percent of income spent on housing, the number of times older adults see their family, satisfaction with safety, type of housing, availability of housing alternatives, and service use. Respondents were characterized as voluntary and involuntary stayers. A sense of community emerged as an important reason for staying in the community.

CONCLUSIONS: The level of satisfaction is associated with residential, social, economic, and community factors. Recommendations for rural communities, policy-makers, and further research are provided.

Zimmer, Z., & Chappell, N. (1997). Rural-urban differences in seniors' neighbourhood preferences. *Journal of Housing for the Elderly, 12*(1/2), 105-124.

OBJECTIVES: To identify neighbourhood amenities preferences of rural and urban older adults in the province of Manitoba.

METHODS: This quantitative study involved a two-stage sampling approach. Purposive sampling was used to select eight rural Manitoba communities, based on distance to Winnipeg, the proportion of older adults in the community, and having/not having a Provincial Department of Health office. Within each community, a random sample of individuals aged 65+ was selected, stratified by age and gender. In-person interviews were conducted with 1,406 older adults (50% in Winnipeg and 50% in the rural communities).

DEFINITION OF RURAL: The rural communities ranged in size from 2,000 to 10,000 residents. Winnipeg was the only urban community.

RESULTS RELATED TO RURAL AGING: Having a medical centre, friends and relatives, a food store, and a pharmacy nearby were all reported as very important amenities by at least 50% of the rural older adults. Less than 20% indicated that having a senior centre, a library, or a park nearby were very important. Compared to their urban counterparts, rural older adults were more likely to view social interaction amenities (defined as having other seniors, friends/relatives, or a senior centre nearby) as very important. This difference remained when controlling for other factors such as gender, income, and health symptoms. Regression analyses revealed no rural-urban differences for the life enrichment or the necessity indices.

CONCLUSIONS: The authors suggest that social interaction has a more instrumental role for rural older adults. They argue that older adults need to be consulted about their views on the important amenities to have in their own neighbourhoods.

Supportive Communities

Bienvenue, R. M., & Havens, B. (1986). **Structural inequalities, informal networks: A comparison of native and non-native elderly.** *Canadian Journal on Aging, 5*(4), 241-248.

OBJECTIVES: To compare the standard of living and the availability of informal networks of rural native and non-native older adults in the province of Manitoba.

METHODS: Data were obtained from the 1971 Aging in Manitoba Study conducted by the Manitoba Department of Health and Social Development. An area probability sample of individuals aged 65+ was drawn. The sample for these analyses was restricted to 110 natives and 2,410 non-natives living in rural areas. Information on housing conditions, health care services, and the role of the family as a social support system was collected through in-person interviews.

DEFINITION OF RURAL: Rural was defined as living on a Canadian reservation (natives) or on farms/small towns (non-natives). Manitoba had no urban reservations at the time of the study.

RESULTS RELATED TO RURAL AGING: Compared to non-natives, the native respondents were more likely to live in substandard housing such as a lack of modern bathroom facilities and a lack of sufficient heat. Natives were more likely to report no regular doctor (34%), inadequate dental care (35%), and the need for eyeglasses/eye care (37%) compared to non-natives (11% for each service). They tended to live in larger households, have greater contact with relatives, and receive more assistance from the informal network but little assistance from organized agencies. No breakdowns by age, gender, or other characteristics were presented.

CONCLUSIONS: The authors conclude that their results confirm the disadvantaged status of the native population. They call for further research, including a focus on structural conditions and choice.

Chappell, N. L., & Horne, J. (1987). *Housing and supportive services for elderly persons in Manitoba.* **Ottawa, ON: Canada Mortgage and Housing Corporation.**

OBJECTIVES: To compare elderly persons living in their own homes in the community, in elderly persons' housing where support services were provided externally (EPH[NS]), in elderly persons' housing where support services were provided within (EPH[S]), and in senior citizens' housing where support services were provided internally as part of a multi-level care facility (MLC); to assess the funneling hypothesis; and, to compare costs in different settings, in the province of Manitoba.

METHODS: Data were from interviews conducted with older adults who were identified through a cluster random sample technique and from administrative databases on home care service use, medical claims, and in-patient hospital claims. Of the 599 older adults in the study, 299 resided outside Winnipeg.

DEFINITION OF RURAL: Winnipeg/non-Winnipeg comparisons were made. Winnipeg is the major urban centre in the province; non-Winnipeg was defined as all areas outside of Winnipeg.

RESULTS RELATED TO RURAL AGING: The report provided detailed information to address the questions of interest. Of relevance here are the findings related to Winnipeg/non-Winnipeg differences. Examples of such differences included that older adults outside Winnipeg were more likely to feel someone was close by in the event of an emergency, more likely to feel their residences were secure, and more likely to perceive that medical care was available. They tended to report greater interaction with friends but less interaction with neighbours than their Winnipeg counterparts. There were no Winnipeg/non-Winnipeg differences in the likelihood of receiving home care services or homemaking assistance once other factors were taken into account. Seniors who resided outside Winnipeg were more likely to be hospitalized than those in Winnipeg across all four residential settings, reflecting in part the relative abundance of hospitals in rural Manitoba. While medical services per user were lower in the non-Winnipeg respondents, the cost per user did not vary. Higher costs for MLC residents were concentrated in rural facilities.

CONCLUSIONS: The authors discuss their findings in terms of the implications for policies related to the provision of housing and supportive services to the elderly. The rural-specific implications relate to the greater likelihood of rural older adults to be hospitalized and the importance of the availability of alternatives to hospitalization.

Davenport, J., Rathwell, T. A., & Rosenberg, M. W. (2005). Service provision for seniors: Challenges for communities in Atlantic Canada. *Longwoods Review, 3*(3), 9-16.

OBJECTIVES: To identify challenges facing communities in Atlantic Canada in meeting the service needs of older adults.

METHODS: This article focuses on the Atlantic Canada component of a larger study entitled *Aging Across Canada: Comparing Service-Rich and Service-Poor Communities.* Data were from in-depth interviews conducted with 31 key informants (service providers from local governments, development authorities, healthcare institutions, and voluntary organizations) in four communities in Spring and Summer 2003.

DEFINITION OF RURAL: A cluster analysis identified 10 distinct clusters of communities ranging from major metropolitan centres to northern rural communities. Summerside, Prince Edward Island and Sydney, Nova Scotia were classified as semi-rural communities with low income, high social deprivation, and below average community health. Moncton, New Brunswick was classified as a semi-rural community with average income, low social deprivation, and good community health. St. Johns, Newfoundland was considered a medium-size city with average income, social deprivation, and community health.

RESULTS RELATED TO RURAL AGING: The challenges facing the four communities were similar although there were some specific challenges in the rural settings. The issues are discussed under four categories, namely broad systemic challenges, lack of housing and care options, lack of integration and coordination of services, and disparities between rural and urban geographies. Specific challenges for rural communities included rural hospital services having been reduced or eliminated, no easy access to 24/7 emergency services and pharmacies, recruitment/retention of health practitioners in rural areas, and access to good transportation. At the same time, residents of rural communities were considered to be 'close-knit' and to rely on each other more than those in urban environments.

CONCLUSIONS: The authors conclude that the challenges in Atlantic Canada are similar to those found in communities across Canada. They call on service providers to determine how to balance increasing pressure from population aging with decreasing resources, without comprising the quality of services for older adults.

Dobbs, B., Swindle, J., Keating, N., Eales, J., & Keefe, J. (2004). *Caring contexts of rural seniors: Phase II - technical report.* **Edmonton, AB: University of Alberta. Retrieved from:** <u>http://www.hecol.ualberta.ca/RAPP/documents/Phase%202%20technical%2 0report%20FINAL.pdf</u>

OBJECTIVES: To examine the social and service environments, and to assess the contribution of the social and physical environments to views of rural communities as good places to grow old, among rural seniors in Canada.

METHODS: Data were from the Caring Contexts for Rural Seniors project. The Royal Canadian Legion membership database was used for sampling; there were 36,013 individuals who resided in rural communities and were aged 65+. Telephone numbers were not available in the membership database so electronic matching of names and addresses with the Canadian Telephone Directories was completed for a stratified random sub-sample. Quota sampling was done based on age (50% aged 65 - 74; 50% aged 75+) and gender (50% male, 50% females). Telephone surveys were conducted between March and May 2004 with 1,322 individuals aged 65+ who resided in Royal Canadian Legion member households in rural communities across Canada. Wartime service was reported by 57% of the males and 6% of the females. The survey instrument was developed in part based on existing surveys.

DEFINITION OF RURAL: Rural respondents were identified, based on rural postal codes (second digit of postal code = 0).

RESULTS RELATED TO RURAL AGING: The vast majority of respondents (92%) reported having social networks ranging in size from 5 to 19, with a median of 10. The composition was diverse, with 90% having social networks of both males and females of all ages and kin relationships living either in the same community or at a distance from them. Support networks tended to be smaller (median = 3) and less diverse, with 12% of respondents having no support networks and 30% having two or fewer members. Some seniors reported a lack of services in their communities such as physicians (31%), pharmacists (31%), and dentists (44%), while 66% lived in communities without hospitals. However, 78% were fairly or very satisfied with the adequacy of stores (78%) within their community. Knowing where to go for services and having old friends were rated as the most important characteristics of making their community a good place to grow old. Women rated social aspects as more important than men did. Younger seniors rated physical aspects of their communities, such as the physical landscape, affordability, and cleanliness, more highly than the older age group. Overall, 73% of respondents rated their communities as very good places to grow old.

CONCLUSIONS: The authors conclude that rural seniors generally are quite accepting of their communities. They argue that the 'good places/bad places' dichotomy is an oversimplification as rural seniors differ considerably in their access to social support and in available services. They outline implications for Veteran Affairs Canada policy and practice.

Note: For the study's background/rationale, see Keating, N., Chapman, S. A., Eales, J., Keefe, J., & Dobbs, B. (2004). Caring contexts of rural seniors: Background and rationale for the program of research. Edmonton, AB: University of Alberta. Retrieved from: <u>http://www.hecol.ualberta.ca/RAPP/documents/Rural%20Seniors%20Overview%20Repor t%20FINAL.pdf</u>

Everitt, J. C. (1994). A tale of two towns: The geography of aging in southern Manitoba. *Small Town, 24*(5), 4-11.

OBJECTIVES: To examine population aging in two small communities in the province of Manitoba.

METHODS: In-person interviews were conducted with "approximately 200" older adults in each community (exact sample size was not provided nor was the age-cutoff).

DEFINITION OF RURAL: Portage la Prairie is a city of a population of 13,108 and is located on the Trans-Canada highway between Winnipeg (population 600,000) and Brandon (38,000). It had a population decline of 0.1% over the five years prior to the study. Killarney has a population of 2,163 and "lies off the beaten track" (p. 8). Its population declined 6.7% from 1986 to 1991. The percentage of residents aged 65+ was 16.1% for Portage la Prairie and 26.5% for Killarney in 1986.

RESULTS RELATED TO RURAL AGING: Killarney's older population was more culturally uniform and its residents had lived in the community for a significantly longer time than those in Portage la Prairie. Residents of Killarney had a higher level of overall social contacts and were engaged in more participatory activities such as church activities, informal social activities, music, art, theatre, and other community events (summary statements were provided; data were not presented).

CONCLUSIONS: The author argues that this study shows the diversity within and between rural environments. He calls for research to further examine this diversity and to provide information for planning purposes.

GermAnn, K., Smith, N., & Littlejohns, L. B. (2000). A healthy communities initiative in rural Alberta: Building rural capacity for health. In J. C. Montgomery & A. D. Kitchenham (Eds.), *Issues Affecting Rural Communities (II): Proceedings of the Rural Communities and Identities in the Global Millennium International Conference* (pp. 54-60). Nanaimo, BC: Malaspina Univ. College. Retrieved from: http://www.eric.ed.gov/ERICDocs/data/ericdocs2sql/content_storage_01/00 00019b/80/17/2e/91.pdf

OBJECTIVES: To describe the Healthy Communities Initiative (HCI), a community development model that involved the creation of a widely shared vision of a healthier community, in the central portion of the province of Alberta.

METHODS: Case studies of four rural communities in the David Thompson Health Region (DTHR) were presented. The HCI involved the assessment of community needs and selection of priority areas for action through the development of community-level indicators.

DEFINITION OF RURAL: The DTHR is a rural health region serving approximately 190,000 individuals. The authors considered Red Deer (population 60,000, and accounting for one-third of the region's population) as urban. The remaining two-thirds of the population resided in a rural area, reflective of their experience that "villages, towns, and rural areas have a way of life that distinguishes them from centres whose population is 20-, 30-, 50,000 or more" (p. 54). The four rural communities were Caroline (population approximately 2,500), Elnora (population of town only – 250; town and surrounding area - 16,000), Lacombe (population approximately 8,000), and Sylvan Lake (population approximately 5,100 with influx in the summer).

RESULTS RELATED TO RURAL AGING: Four health-related issues emerged consistently: need for youth development, preservation of the natural environment, maintaining a strong sense of community in the face of changing social dynamics, and access to health services. With regards to rural older adults, accessibility of health care services and the lack of long term care beds for this segment of the population were identified in Elnora. Similarly, in Lacombe, the need to increase access to all levels of care and services to older adults to ensure aging in place emerged as a priority action area; however, a review of resources suggested that many already existed.

CONCLUSIONS: The authors discuss lessons learned about integrating community capacity building and a healthy communities initiative.

Gfellner, B. M., & Everitt, J. C. (1997). *The qualitative experience of seniors' independence: The Brandon and Westman region results.* **(Working Paper No. 5). Brandon, MB: Departments of Psychology and Geography, Brandon University.**

OBJECTIVES: To clarify interview questions used in the Determinants of Seniors' Independence (DSI) research program, to attempt to understand the discrepancy between national and local survey responses, and to identify other pertinent areas that were not addressed in the survey instrument, among older adults living in Brandon and the Westman region of the province of Manitoba.

METHODS: A series of six focus groups were conducted in Westman (two in Brandon and four in small towns) between June 26 and July 10, 1997. The number of focus group participants ranged from 6 to 8, with a total of 42. Individuals were randomly selected from the roster of seniors who completed the DSI survey the previous summer and had indicated an interest in participating in a subsequent focus group. Topics covered were: transportation; assistance with activities of daily living; caregiving; expectations of the circumstances that would lead seniors to require greater assistance to live independently in the community, what the assistance would be, and how and from whom they would prefer to receive such assistance; perceptions of the most critical areas of need for seniors in the community; discrepancies in seniors' ratings of their health and activity limitations; medication use; and attitudes toward and use of alternative medicine and therapies.

DEFINITION OF RURAL: The small towns were Neepawa (1991 population 3,258; 30.7% aged 65+), Virden (1991 population 2,894; 28.3% aged 65+), Killarney (1991 population 2,163; 30.5% aged 65+), and Carberry (1991 population 1,481; 26.0% aged 65+). Brandon had a 1991 population of 38,567, with 15.5% of its population aged 65+.

RESULTS RELATED TO RURAL AGING: More potential problems were perceived to exist for rural older adults as they had fewer resources than those in the city. The problems related to transportation options, physicians and medical services, availability and costs of elderly persons' housing (EPH), a greater number of older EPH complexes in need of repairs and upgrading, difficulties selling one's home, readily available sources of information, and resources for decision-making. On the positive side, it was thought to be easier for rural seniors to manage because what they have is perceived as more readily accessible as a result of proximity and better channels of communication. The 'neighbourliness' of small communities was viewed as allowing people to attend more to one another.

CONCLUSIONS: A number of themes emerged in each of the focus group sessions with regard to service accessibility, availability, and barriers to maintaining an independent lifestyle in the community.

Note: Also available are three working papers: Everitt, J. C., & Gfellner, B. M. (1996). Determining seniors' independence: A participatory workshop (Working Paper No. 2); Everitt, J. C., & Gfellner, B. M. (1998). Determining seniors' independence: A profile of Brandon and the Westman region. (Working Paper No. 3); and Everitt, J. C., & Gfellner, B. M. (1997). Determining seniors' independence: A participatory workshop. (Working Paper No. 4).

Hodge, G. (1991). The economic impact of retirees on smaller communities: Concepts and findings from three Canadian studies. *Research on Aging, 13*(1), 39-54.

OBJECTIVES: To understand the various economic inputs and outputs in a community from a retirement population in the province of British Columbia.

METHODS: This analysis draws on earlier studies of the economic impact of retirees on three communities carried out in 1987, 1988, and 1989.

DEFINITION OF RURAL: Reference was made to small communities comprised of a larger centre and its surrounding rural area containing smaller villages. Three communities were examined: City of Powell River and rural areas within 25 miles (1986 population – 18,350), Port Hardy and smaller communities within 40 miles (1986 population – 10,580), and Salmon Arm and smaller communities within 35 miles (1986 population – 23,755). The percentages of the 1986 population 65+ were 12.9%, 2.1%, and 16.1%, respectively.

RESULTS RELATED TO RURAL AGING: The article begins with a discussion of a model to study economic impacts of retirees on small communities. Five kinds of data were identified as required to analyze retirees' economic impacts: demographic characteristics (number, age, gender, martial status) of retirees for some recent base data; annual personal household incomes of retirees; annual household expenditures for retirees; annual expenditures on behalf of retirees by agencies providing retirement support services; and, recent mobility tendencies of retirees. In the three smaller communities, retirees were found to bring a substantial amount of their income into a community directly and income from others on their behalf. However, the economic impacts varied by community, depending on changes in other sectors of the location population.

CONCLUSIONS: The author concludes that retirees are an economic blessing for a smaller community. Different scenarios of changes in the local population were discussed.

Note: This article was an extension of Hodge, G. (1989). Retirees in the local economy: Blessing or blight? In: K. Cossey (Ed.), Rural environments and the elderly: Impact, contributions and needs fulfillment (pp. 1-15). Sackville, NB: Rural and Small Town Research and Studies Programme, Department of Geography, Mount Allison University.

Joseph, A. E., & Cloutier-Fisher, D. (2005). Ageing in rural communities: Vulnerable people in vulnerable places. In G. J. Andrews & D. R. Phillips (Eds.), *Ageing in place: Perspectives, policy and practice* (pp. 133-146). London: Routledge Studies in Human Geography.

OBJECTIVES: To draw attention to the 'situated meaning' of rural change as it relates to the experience of growing old in rural communities. Case studies from a town in the province of Ontario are discussed.

METHODS: This book chapter included a review of literature related to the general features of rural populations and rural communities that promote vulnerability, rural places as contexts in which people grow old, and the impact of change in rural service delivery on the ability to remain in one's own home. In the section on the impact of change in rural service delivery, Canadian case studies were presented.

DEFINITION OF RURAL: The focus was on specific places that construct themselves as rural. Case studies from the Canadian town of Minto were provided. The population of Minto was not provided.

RESULTS RELATED TO RURAL AGING: Different and distinct vulnerabilities associated with aging and with living in rural communities were described as creating a kind of 'double jeopardy' for elderly people living in rural communities. Long and short cycles of change in the rural context were identified. The vulnerability of frail and disabled older persons to restructuring of health services was highlighted, drawing on 'stories' of eight elderly people who combined poor health with difficult personal circumstances.

CONCLUSIONS: The authors argue for the continued relevance of rural as an analytical category in the study of aging and call for an emphasis on the importance of place in determining the experience of rural aging.

Joseph, A. E., & Fuller, A. M. (1988). *Aging in rural communities: Interrelated issues in housing, services and transportation* (Paper No. 87/3). Guelph, ON: University of Guelph, Gerontology Research Centre.

OBJECTIVES: To explore the implications of population aging in rural communities for housing, services, and transportation, with an emphasis on the province of Ontario.

METHODS: Data were from Grey County and the Quality-of-Life Survey sponsored by the Gerontology Research Centre at the University of Guelph.

DEFINITION OF RURAL: Comparisons were made between rural communities found in three types of regions: urban core (census divisions of which a portion was within the boundaries of a 1971 census agglomeration [CA] or census metropolitan area [CMA] of ≥ 50,000), rural hinterland (census divisions beyond urban core areas in 1971 but which exhibited relatively continuous surface settlement and multi-directional surface transportation), and remote hinterland. Distinctions also were made between townships, villages, towns, and cities.

RESULTS RELATED TO RURAL AGING: This position paper was divided into five sections: (1) the special characteristics of the aging process in different rural regions of Ontario; (2) a synthesis of knowledge of the various links between population aging and housing, services, and transportation; (3) the use of survey data to expand on questions raised in sections 1 and 2; (4) a proposed two-tier conceptual framework for consideration of trends in housing, services, and transportation issues; and (5) the elaboration of policy directions, and proposal and research directions.

CONCLUSIONS: The authors argue that there is heterogeneity in both the population of rural older adults and in the structure of Ontario's rural communities, and that diversity is a key element in considering policy options/strategies for service provision to older adults in rural areas. A number of policy and research implications are presented.

See also Joseph, A. E., & Fuller, A. M. (1991).

Joseph, A. E., & Fuller, A. M. (1991). Towards an integrative perspective on the housing, services and transportation implications of rural aging. *Canadian Journal on Aging, 10*(2), 127-148.

OBJECTIVES: To examine the implications of population aging in rural communities for housing, services, and transportation, with an emphasis on the province of Ontario.

METHODS: This is a review article that assesses the adequacy of knowledge about links between housing, services, and transportation issues in light of population aging.

DEFINITION OF RURAL: No specific definition of rural was provided. Three features of the rural environment were discussed, including the heterogeneity of rural older adults, the lack of attention to the dynamics of rural life for older adults, and the highly integrated nature of rural communities.

RESULTS RELATED TO RURAL AGING: The authors concluded that the knowledge base on housing, services, and transportation for rural older adults is limited and fragmented. A modeling framework was presented that integrates housing setting, service support, and transportation.

CONCLUSIONS: Policy proposals and suggestions for research conclude the article. The need to consider the diversity of local communities, the dynamics of rural life, and the integrated nature of aging issues is highlighted.

See also Joseph, A. E., & Fuller, A. M. (1988).

Joseph, A. E., & Martin-Matthews, A. (1993). Growing old in aging communities. *Journal of Canadian Studies, 28*(1), 14-29.

OBJECTIVES: To provide a descriptive analysis of the experience of population aging in rural small towns in Canada.

METHODS: This review article drew primarily on existing Canadian literature. Section headings included the demography of the aging community, what are aging communities like, the characteristics of the rural elderly, the social world of the rural elderly, and the individual in the aging community.

DEFINITION OF RURAL: Rural included areas with < 1,000 population (Statistics Canada's definition of rural) and small urban places (1,000 - 4,999 population).

RESULTS RELATED TO RURAL AGING: In 1981, 21.9% of Canadians 65+ lived in rural areas. Rural small towns were home to more elderly residents than dispersed rural communities as well as larger towns and cities. Three factors were identified as key to discriminating small towns at the macro level: population size, proximity to urban areas, and the out-migration of younger populations or in-migration of older persons seeking better retirement locations. The inconsistent findings regarding social support patterns were noted. A general pattern regarding the availability of institutional facilities such as hospitals and nursing homes, and the lack of housing, health and home support services, and transportation was discussed. An examination of the ways in which 'personal troubles' become 'public issues' in rural small towns dealing with an aging population concluded the article.

CONCLUSIONS: The authors argue that aging rural communities in Canada will be caught, in the years ahead, between shifting public policy and the personal troubles of their older residents. The future experience of growing old in aging communities will be shaped by the rural small town's success at maintaining informal support networks, nurturing the voluntary sector, and retaining formal support services and institutions.

Note: This article also was published as a chapter in Marshall, V. W., & McPherson, B. D. (Eds.). (1994). Aging: Canadian perspectives. Peterborough, ON: Broadview Press.

Keating, N. C. (1992). Older rural Canadians. In D. A. Hay & G.S. Basran (Eds.), *Rural Sociology in Canada* (pp. 134-154). Toronto, ON: Oxford University Press.

OBJECTIVES: To address some of the stereotypes about being old in rural Canada by reviewing four facets of the lives of rural elders in Canada.

METHODS: This article reviews Canadian literature on rural seniors. Data from the 1981 and 1986 Censuses of Canada were presented where appropriate.

DEFINITION OF RURAL: Three aspects of rural were discussed where possible: occupation, population density, and ideology. Distinctions were made between urban, rural, farm, and non-farm when examining Census data.

RESULTS RELATED TO RURAL AGING: This book chapter was divided into four sections. Under Work and Retirement, labour force participation, retirement of employees, and retirement of the self-employed were examined. It was noted that there were insufficient data to inform on the importance of the rural environment in determining patterns of work and retirement. Under Independence, attention was given to control over the near environment and integration into the community. The knowledge of issues related to independence of rural elders was seen as very uneven. The Health section included a discussion of health status, health service utilization, and health service needs. The author concluded that knowledge of the variation in health status of rural seniors remains limited. Under Family, there was discussion of the household structure of rural seniors, family networks, family support, the marital relationship, the sibling relationship, and support as aid. The similarity of rural Canadian seniors' family structure and kinship interaction to those of urban seniors was noted.

CONCLUSIONS: The chapter highlights the heterogeneity of rural seniors. Several questions that need to be addressed were raised throughout the article. The author argues that the variety of experiences and living situations of rural seniors can only be expected to increase.

Keating, N., Keefe, J., & Dobbs, B. (2001). A good place to grow old? Rural communities and support to seniors. In R. Epp & D. Whitson (Eds.), *Writing off the rural West: Globalization, governments and the transformation of rural communities* (pp. 263-277). Edmonton, AB: University of Alberta Press.

OBJECTIVES: To consider whether rural communities in Canada are a good place to grow old.

METHODS: This book chapter draws primarily on Canadian literature to present a response to the question of whether rural communities are good places to grow old.

DEFINITION OF RURAL: Reference was made to a Statistics Canada definition of rural communities as those that have < 10,000 people and are not within daily commuting distance from a city.

RESULTS RELATED TO RURAL AGING: This book chapter was divided into three main sections: thinking broadly about health and the changes in the philosophy of health care, restructuring and the health of rural seniors, and policy challenges. Three issues that influence whether health restructuring threatens the health of rural seniors were identified, including how personal resources of rural seniors influence their ability to get access to products and services they need to maintain their health, whether erosion of family health services will make rural residence untenable for some seniors, and whether these barriers can be overcome through community support and strong informal support networks seen as part of the rural tradition. Policy challenges included the use of the broad definition of health as a basis for policy formation, support for informal caregivers, and customizing of solutions for a variety of rural settings.

CONCLUSIONS: The authors argue that rural communities in Canada could be good places to grow old, depending on policy responses to the needs of rural seniors.

Keefe, J., Fancey, P., Keating, N., Frederick, J., Eales, J., & Dobbs, B. (2004). *Caring contexts of rural seniors: Phase I - technical report.* **Edmonton, AB: University of Alberta. Retrieved from:**
http://www.hecol.ualberta.ca/RAPP/documents/Rural%20Seniors%20complete%20Technical%20report%20FINAL.pdf

OBJECTIVES: To determine characteristics that may be important in determining community supportiveness to rural seniors; to examine the relationship between characteristics of rural communities and their supportiveness to seniors; and to identify a set of characteristics that distinguishes rural communities that provide strong, moderate, and weak levels of support to seniors, across Canada.

METHODS: Data were from Statistics Canada's 2001 Census of the Population. The sample consisted of 2,759 rural census sub-divisions, considered here as rural communities. The measure of community supportiveness drew on responses to the question: *Last week (refers to Sunday, May 6 to Saturday, May 12, 2001), how many hours did this person spend providing unpaid care or assistance to one or more seniors? (Some examples include providing personal care to a senior family member, visiting seniors, talking with them on the telephone, and helping them with shopping, banking, or with taking medication).* Response categories were: < 5, 5 - 9, 10 - 19, and 20+ hours. Based on the proportion of the community that provided assistance to seniors, communities were divided according to the level of community supportiveness to seniors: weak (0% - 18%, n = 827); moderate (19% - 24%, n = 1,218); and strong (25% - 56%, n = 714). Physical locality (population size, land area, population density, distance from service centre, and region) and social aspects (age, gender, marital status, living arrangements, education, income, employment, long term residents, and unpaid work) were examined.

DEFINITION OF RURAL: Statistics Canada's Rural and Small Town (RST) definition was used to select census sub-divisions. The RST refers to towns or municipalities outside the commuting zone of larger urban centres (which have a population of ≥ 10,000).

RESULTS RELATED TO RURAL AGING: The range in supportiveness of communities was from < 1% to 56%. Population size, proportion of seniors, proportion of long-term residents, and average hours of unpaid housework provided to others emerged as key community characteristics for community supportiveness. Strong supportive communities appeared to benefit from having residents who had lived a longer time in the community, and to be smaller in size that potentially facilitate familiarity and increased interaction with one another. Weak communities were larger in population size and experienced more fluctuations in terms of migrants. However, this model cannot be applied consistently across regions and requires the addition of other characteristics specific to a region or regions of rural Canada.

CONCLUSIONS: The diversity of rural communities was readily apparent as were regional differences. The authors conclude that while their findings advance understanding of community supportiveness to seniors, there is more to be learned about what contributes to community supportiveness.

Note: For the study's background/rationale, see Keating, N., Chapman, S. A., Eales, J., Keefe, J., & Dobbs, B. (2004). Caring contexts of rural seniors: Background and rationale for the program of research. Edmonton, AB: University of Alberta. Retrieved from: http://www.hecol.ualberta.ca/RAPP/documents/Rural%20Seniors%20Overview%20Report%20FINAL.pdf

Li, P. S., & MacLean, B. D. (1989). Changes in the rural elderly population and their effects on the small town economy: The case of Saskatchewan, 1971-1986. *Rural Sociology, 54*(2), 213-226.

OBJECTIVES: To examine data for 304 small towns and villages in the province of Saskatchewan for the period 1971 to 1986, and to assess how population size affects change in the elderly population and how such change influences the diversity of local services and the volume of retail sales.

METHODS: The population data were from the Saskatchewan Hospital Services Plan (SHSP), a publicly funded medical care program that covers residents of the province. Population counts by age and gender were obtained for small towns and villages for 1971 to 1986. Information on the towns/villages in 1986 was gathered from the Saskatchewan Department of Tourism and Small Business in 1987. The focus was on the population of the town/village in 1971, the change in the population aged 65+ from 1971 to 1986, the proximity of each town/village to the nearest city (less than 50 kilometres or longer than 1 hour drive), average 10-year grain delivery of each town/village, diversity of services in each town/village, and volume of retail sales in 1986.

DEFINITION OF RURAL: The small towns had 1986 populations of 500 - 4,999 while the villages had populations < 500.

RESULTS RELATED TO RURAL AGING: The 65+ age group accounted for 7.6%, 7.7%, and 8.8% of the rural municipalities' populations in 1971, 1981, and 1986, respectively. The corresponding percentages for the small towns/villages were 15.9%, 20.2%, and 21.3%, respectively. The gains and losses in the elderly population in small towns were positively related to the relative population size of the towns. In turn, local retail sales and the functional diversity of towns were largely dependent upon change in the elderly population although the distance from a city and local economic conditions (e.g., agricultural prosperity) also affected services and retail sales. Population changes in other age groups produced a much weaker impact in the local economy.

CONCLUSIONS: The authors conclude that services and retail businesses in rural Saskatchewan are largely sustained by the elderly population. The authors speculate that declines in future cohorts of the elderly could lead to the demise of many small town economies.

MacKenzie, P. (2001). Aging people in aging places: Addressing the needs of older adults in rural Saskatchewan. *Rural Social Work, 6*(3), 74-83.

OBJECTIVES: To identify the challenges of growing older in an aging, rural community in the province of Saskatchewan and to make specific recommendations for improving services to rural elders.

METHODS: The review article was divided into the following sections: Introduction: the phenomenon of aging in place; theoretical perspectives on rurality and community; rural Saskatchewan: an example of aging in place in aging communities; the challenges of growing older in rural Saskatchewan; and recommendations for rural social work practice and rural communities. The author drew on her research examining the experiences of 18 senior women in several small communities in the province of Saskatchewan. No information was provided on recruitment, data collection process, or analysis approach.

DEFINITION OF RURAL: No definition of rural was provided; Canadian Census data were presented for the settlements of 1,000 to 4,999 population.

RESULTS RELATED TO RURAL AGING: The need to understand community was stressed. In rural Saskatchewan, agriculture has been the economic base of most communities. A connection to agriculture formed a commonality of experience shared by the majority of older, long-time residents, and provided a foundation for a rural identity. Drawing on the experiences of the women who were interviewed, the interweaving of 'belonging to a place' and a sense of personal identity was noted. The challenge of providing services in rural areas and transportation problems were discussed. Ten recommendations to improve services for seniors in rural areas were identified: provide financial or other incentives to physicians and allied-health professionals, introduce or expand the use of health technology in rural regions, create opportunities for nurse practitioners to provide significant preventive and maintenance health services, provide or increase funding for rural Adult Day Care programs, re-consider the closure and consolidation of nursing home beds in rural areas, develop a cost-shared or publicly funded transportation service, enhance caregiver support groups, expand the range of housing options in rural communities, address the issue of rural sustainability, and involve older people in making decisions.

CONCLUSIONS: The author argues that there is significant scope for social work practitioners to address the decline of rural infrastructure and to develop creative social programs that will respond to the needs of emerging populations such as elderly people who are aging in place.

MacLean, M. J. (1996). *Northern exposure and positive aging: Rural seniors assisted living study.* **Thunder Bay, ON: Northern Educational Centre for Aging and Health, Lakehead University.**

OBJECTIVES: To provide information for the District of Thunder Bay communities, the Thunder Bay District Health Council, and the Long-Term Care Office (Ontario Ministry of Health) which would enable them to plan for community-based support services for seniors in small communities in this area of the province of Ontario.

METHODS: The study was conducted in January and February 1996 in six communities in the District of Thunder Bay. The communities were selected through a purposive sampling process based on population, number of community health and social service resources, and distance from Thunder Bay. Surveys were completed by 460 older adults. Seniors (n = ~90) and services providers (n = ~40) participated in focus groups. Information was obtained on service needs, current service availability, seniors' service preferences, feasibility of implementing various service approaches, and potential implementation strategies.

DEFINITION OF RURAL: All communities had a 1991 population size of < 6,000 (Beardmore – 455; Geraldton – 2,635; Longlac – 2,075; Manitouwadge – 3,970; Marathon – 5,064; Nakina – 650). The percentages aged 65+ varied from 3% to 12% (Beardmore – 12%, Geraldton – 12%, Longlac – 4%, Manitouwadge – 3%, Marathon – 4%, Nakina – 6%). All communities were more than 200 kilometres from Thunder Bay.

RESULTS RELATED TO RURAL AGING: Findings for each community case study were presented. Nine themes were identified: (1) Seniors had lived in their communities for many years and felt that the advantages of living there greatly outweighed the disadvantages; (2) Seniors had made, and continued to make, significant contributions to their communities; (3) Seniors wanted to and planned to stay in their communities for the rest of their lives; (4) Seniors in small communities, like all seniors, needed formal and informal help in health, housing, and social services to stay in their own homes in their communities; (5) Priorities for services to help seniors stay in their own homes in small communities were similar but were sufficiently different to suggest locally-based initiatives to meet these priorities; (6) Seniors in small communities needed health, housing, and social services which were delivered in a flexible way to help them stay in their own homes and their communities; (7) Seniors were willing and able to contribute resources of time, energy, ideas, and money to meet the challenges of aging in small communities so they can remain in their homes and in their communities; (8) Service providers working with seniors in small communities had considerable experience in meeting challenges related to the health, housing, and social service priorities of keeping seniors in their own homes and communities; and (9) Service providers working with seniors in small communities were sometimes restricted in their health, housing, and social service interventions by policy guidelines that were not as relevant for small communities as they were for urban communities.

CONCLUSIONS: The author argues that health, housing, and social services in the District of Thunder Bay must be designed and delivered in ways that are sensitive to rural realities and experiences that influence seniors. The author calls for health, housing, and social service programs and guidelines that are more flexible for seniors in small communities in the District. Six specific recommendations are provided.

Martin Matthews, A. (1988). Aging in rural Canada. In E. Rathbone-McCuan & B. Havens (Eds.), *North American elders: United States and Canadian perspectives* (pp. 143-160). New York: Greenwood Press.

OBJECTIVES: To explore the situation of rural elderly Canadians.

METHODS: This book chapter integrates Canadian research on rural aging. Topics discussed included health status and use of health care delivery, social support networks, perceived quality of life, and transportation.

DEFINITION OF RURAL: Different definitions of rural were used in the literature reviewed. When Census data were examined, distinctions were made between urban ($\geq$ 1,000 population) and rural (farm and non-farm).

RESULTS RELATED TO RURAL AGING: In 1981, 22% of Canadians aged 65+ resided in rural areas, with significant regional variation. A perception that rural Canada responds relatively well to the needs of its elders at two extremes of the independence-dependence continuum was identified. The well elderly (those with a spouse and the ability to drive) were perceived to benefit from the emotionally supportive environment and express high levels of life satisfaction. Individuals in need of acute hospital services or long-term institutional care typically had these services available. For the middle group, rural life was seen as 'fraught with disadvantage'. Services may not be totally unavailable but they were frequently inaccessible.

CONCLUSIONS: The author calls for recognition of two important factors in policy development with respect to rural elders, namely the independent spirit of this group and the diversity of rural life.

Ministry of Municipal Affairs. (1987). *Planned retirement communities.* **Toronto, ON: Government of Ontario.**

OBJECTIVES: To investigate existing retirement communities in the province of Ontario and to initiate a discussion on the planning issues and concerns surrounding this type of housing development for older adults.

METHODS: An inventory of 15 planned retirement communities (defined as planned, low density, age-restricted developments offering extensive recreational services and constructed primarily by private capital as profit making ventures) was created. Seven communities were selected for indepth case studies. The case studies were presented in an appendix.

DEFINITION OF RURAL: No definition of rural was provided. Case studies were conducted in Stroud, Strathroy, Hawkestone, Stittsville, Bobcaygen, Newcastle, and a suburb of Hamilton.

RESULTS RELATED TO RURAL AGING: The inventory revealed that planned retirement communities tended to be in rural and recreational areas. There was wide variation in the type of developer involved, dwelling type, and price range. Planning considerations were identified, including: market identification; location; housing (number, type, and design of units); community services; tenure arrangements and land use controls; and, staging of construction.

CONCLUSIONS: In the conclusion, it is suggested that this initial examination has revealed few planning problems, and that both municipalities and residents are satisfied with the planned retirement communities. Several issues for future study are identified.

N. Barry Lyon Consultants Limited. (1991). *Residential satisfaction with retirement community living in Ontario.* **Ottawa, ON: Canada Mortgage and Housing Corporation.**

OBJECTIVES: To examine levels of importance and satisfaction with various aspects of the current residential environments among residents in five retirement communities in the province of Ontario.

METHODS: A stratified random sample of 50 residents per retirement community was targeted. As reported in the abstract, 219 residents were interviewed in person between June and July, 1989. Four broad dimensions of the residential environment were examined, including dwelling characteristics, location considerations, tenure options, and lifestyle considerations. Each dimension was comprised of a number of related residential attributes. Respondents were asked to rate each attribute in terms of its importance and their satisfaction. An administrator's questionnaire and a site/community evaluation also were completed.

DEFINITION OF RURAL: The communities were Tottenham, New Hamburg, Sarnia, Vineland, and Lancaster.

RESULTS RELATED TO RURAL AGING: Respondents were highly satisfied with their residential environments. Dwelling characteristics contributed the most to overall residential satisfaction, followed by lifestyle, location, and tenure options. A one-story dwelling was rated high on both importance and satisfaction. Being an adult community was important. Driving distances to various services and facilities were rated higher on both importance and significance than were walking distances. Most of the variation in residential evaluations was related to community of residence rather than housing type or tenure. Household income and respondent health were two of the most significant personal characteristics; age differences were not evident.

CONCLUSIONS: The authors suggest that their findings will improve understanding of buyer preferences and resident satisfaction.

Ontario Advisory Council on Senior Citizens. (1992). *Rural roots: Aging in small and rural communities in Ontario*. Toronto, ON: Ontario Advisory Council on Senior Citizens.

OBJECTIVES: To advance understanding of the needs and hopes of rural older adults in Ontario.

METHODS: This report was based on views of older adults and service providers expressed to the Ontario Advisory Council on Senior Citizens during a series of public meetings held in Ontario during 1990 and 1991. Public hearings with over 450 participants were held in the Counties of Haliburton, Bruce, Grey, and Hastings, and in the District of Kenora. A total of 31 written briefs were obtained. A request for written submissions appeared in the Summer 1990 issue of *Especially for Seniors* distributed to all seniors in Ontario.

DEFINITION OF RURAL: The description of rural was based on local views of a community's character and personality. In other words, it was dependent on the surroundings, and the attitudes and perceptions of the residents.

RESULTS RELATED TO RURAL AGING: Community profiles for Haliburton County, Grey County, Bruce County, and the District of Kenora were provided. Six areas of concern were identified, namely transportation, health care, income, housing, communications, and community services.

CONCLUSIONS: The Council argues that the needs of rural older adults continue to suffer from an historical pattern of public sector neglect and inattention. The report includes 29 recommendations. The need for separate attention directed to First Nation elders and to farm seniors is acknowledged.

Rosenberg, M. W., & Moore, E. G. (1990). The elderly, economic dependency, and local government revenues and expenditures. *Environment and Planning C: Government and Policy, 8,* **149-165.**

OBJECTIVES: To examine the relationships among the elderly population, its dependency on transfer payments, and local government service provision in the province of Ontario.

METHODS: A series of models were presented, drawing on 1986 data. The unit of analysis was census divisions (CD). Economic dependency was assessed by a ratio that measured the relative importance of transfer payments such as Old Age Security and the Guaranteed Annual Income supplement payments to employment income. Data on local government revenues and expenditures from 1981 to 1985 were from the Ontario Ministry of Municipal Affairs and Housing.

DEFINITION OF RURAL: No definition of rural was provided. Specific information for each of the 52 CDs was presented in a map format.

RESULTS RELATED TO RURAL AGING: Rural and northern CDs had significantly higher concentrations of older adults. The CDs with higher economic dependency ratios tended to be those with a high proportion of elderly residents. Geographical variation in per capita municipal spending on elderly residents was evident.

CONCLUSIONS: Rural CDS may have constrained revenue bases that make it difficult to shift resources, despite an increase in the aging population. Implications for various levels of government are discussed.

United Senior Citizens of Ontario. (1985). *Elderly residents in Ontario: Rural-urban differences.* **Toronto, ON: Ministry of Community and Social Services, Government of Ontario.**

OBJECTIVES: To examine rural-urban differences among older residents in the province of Ontario.

METHODS: Data were from the United Senior Citizens of Ontario (USCO) study conducted in 1982. A random sample of 846 individuals aged 65+ was interviewed in eight Ontario communities. A series of Tables provided the rural-urban breakdowns.

DEFINITION OF RURAL: Eight communities were included in the study and were categorized as rural (Cookstown/Athens/Bruce Mines – all with populations < 1,000), small-urban (Penetanguishene/Brockville), mid-sized urban (Sault Ste. Marie/Windsor), and Toronto (large urban).

RESULTS RELATED TO RURAL AGING: One-fifth of the respondents resided in rural communities. The rural residents were more likely than their urban counterparts to be men, to be married, to have less than nine years of formal education, to live in houses, and to own their residence. They reported a greater number of family contacts and a greater number of contacts with children; they did not differ from urban residents in the frequency of contacts by telephone or in person with family or friends. In terms of recreational activities, rural residents were more likely to garden, go for drives, and have family come to visit, and were less likely to attend theatre. Health status was generally similar for rural and urban residents although rural residents were the least likely to see medical specialists and to be hospitalized. Rural older adults were more likely to rely on friends and neighbours and were less likely to rely on family members for assistance than urban residents. Transportation modes differed, with rural residents more likely to drive themselves or to be driven by others to shopping, medical appointments, and social activities. The likelihood of the private automobile as the principle mode of transportation decreased as community size increased.

CONCLUSIONS: The authors argue that their findings dispel some of the preconceived assumptions about rural-urban differences among older adults. They call for consideration of community size in studies of elderly residents and in future planning endeavours.

VON Canada (1991). *The VON Canada P.E.P. Project: Promoting Elders Participation (Final Report).* **Ottawa, ON: VON Canada.**

OBJECTIVES: To undertake a pilot project to assist local communities in the identification of needs for community-based services and the development of community-based boards to take action on these needs.

METHODS: The Promoting Elders Participation Project (P.E.P) was undertaken by VON Canada and involved five case studies. In 1989, needs surveys were completed with older adults in the West Coast Region, Newfoundland (Corner Brook, n = 183; Deer Lake, n = 66; Summerside, n = 42); Kings County, Nova Scotia (Kentville, n = 44; Kingston, n = 69; Harbourville, n = 29); Rural Middlesex County, Ontario (Ailsa Craig, n = 70; Parkhill, n = 73; Delaware, n = 50; Strathroy, n = 90); Dundas County, Ontario (Winchester, n = 58; Mountain Township, n = 53; Iroquois, n = 52); and Hamilton-Wentworth, Ontario (Ancaster, n = 141; Jerseyville, n = 41; Binbrook, n = 46; Mount Hope, n = 31; Stoney Creek, n = 235). A "process evaluation" (see p. 74) was undertaken in 1990.

DEFINITION OF RURAL: No definition of rural was provided.

RESULTS RELATED TO RURAL AGING: Older adults frequently identified the need for assistance with heavy housework, snow shoveling, house cleaning, transportation, and grass/yard work. Less frequently identified was the need for small repairs, footcare, friendly visiting, information services, alert systems, wheels-to-meals, or health clinic/nurses although each was one of the top five home support needs within a particular community. The report provided detailed information for each community. Subsequent program design and development were influenced by the size of the target areas; existing community networks, volunteer organizations, and local resources; presence and role of home care; community support for the project; and interest and involvement of seniors in the P.E.P. The evaluation feedback identified positive benefits to both the communities and to the VON.

CONCLUSIONS: The report provides recommendations to Health and Welfare Canada and VON Canada, as well as community groups, planning bodies, and health and social organizations.

DEMOGRAPHICS/MIGRATION

National Demographics

The reader is advised to review Statistics Canada publications for rural-urban breakdowns. Selected examples are highlighted below.

Statistics Canada. (1986). *Profiles: Urban and rural areas, Canada, provinces and territories part 1* **(Cat. No. 94-129). Ottawa, ON: Minister of Supply and Services.**

Age-sex breakdowns for Canada's population in 1986 according to urban and rural areas were provided. Rural was sub-divided into rural farm and rural non-farm. Provincial data also were presented.

Statistics Canada. (1991). *Trends and highlights of Canadian agriculture and its people* **(Cat. No. 96-303SE and 96-303E). Ottawa, ON: Statistics Canada.**

This publication provided agricultural and socioeconomic profiles from the 1991 Census of Agriculture and the 1991 Census of Population. Across Canada, only 32% of farm operators were aged 55+ in 1991. Provincial percentages ranged from 26% in Newfoundland to 35% in Saskatchewan.

Statistics Canada (1993). *Profile of urban and rural areas – Part A: Canada, provinces and territories* **(Cat. No. 93-339). Ottawa, ON: Minister of Industry, Science and Technology.**

Age-sex breakdowns for Canada's population in 1991 according to urban and rural areas were provided. Rural was sub-divided into rural farm and rural non-farm. Provincial data also were presented.

Stone, L. O., & Fletcher, S. (1986). *Seniors boom: Dramatic increases in longevity and prospects for better health* **(1st ed.). Ottawa, ON: Statistics Canada.**

Chapter 2.5 of this government report focused on 1981 urban-rural age structure differences. Population pyramids for urban 100,000+ population, urban 30,000 - 100,000, urban < 30,000, rural non-farm, and rural farm areas were presented. The rural farm areas had 'unusually low' percentages of seniors; only 5.4% in 1981 were aged 65+. All the age pyramids showed a narrowing at the base, reflecting a decrease in the younger age groups relative to the older age groups. This trend was the least notable among the rural non-farm areas. The authors suggested that these urban-rural comparisons serve to highlight environments where service delivery to older people could be problematic.

Stone, L. O., & Frenken, H. (1988). *Canada's seniors: A dynamic force* **(Cat. No. 98-121). Ottawa, ON: Statistics Canada.**

Chapter 5 of this report provided information on the urban-rural residence of Canadians aged 65+ in 1986. Urban includes population sizes of 500,000+; 100,000 - 499,999; 30,000 - 99,999; 10,000 - 29,999; 5,000 - 9,999; 2,500 - 4,999; and 1,000 - 2,499. Rural was divided into farm and non-farm. Urban-rural comparisons of the percentage of the population aged 65+ and aged 75+ were presented for Canada and each of the provinces.

Provincial, Regional, and Local Demographics

The reader is advised to review Statistics Canada documents for demographic information at the provincial, regional, and local level. Various provincial, municipal, and local government departments and university-based centres also have prepared documents that include a rural-urban profile.

Dahms, F. (1996). The greying of south Georgian Bay. *Canadian Geographer, 40*(2), 148-163.

OBJECTIVES: To describe the 1991 geographical distribution of individuals aged 60+ in south Georgian Bay in the province of Ontario.

METHODS: Data for the 60+ population were provided by Statistics Canada for all census subdivisions in 1991 and for the origin of migration to these areas from 1986 to 1991.

DEFINITION OF RURAL: Statistics Canada's (1991) definition of urban and rural was used; urban referred to communities with a population of ≥ 1,000 while rural areas were all those outside urban places. Distinctions were made between rural non-farm (residing in rural areas and not members of households of farm operators) and rural farm (living in rural areas and members of households of farm operators living on their farms). Nucleated rural non-farm populations resided in named unincorporated places in rural areas in clusters of 5+ permanently occupied dwellings with at least 25 inhabitants. South Georgian Bay is less than two hours drive from metro Toronto. The economy is based on tourism, fishing, lumbering, apple growing, and manufacturing.

RESULTS RELATED TO RURAL AGING: The study area had 1991 concentrations of older adults that were higher than was found for the province or the country as a whole. Most residents resided in rural non-farm locations. In terms of migration, moving from outside the area was the most common although there was some internal migration.

CONCLUSIONS: The authors argue that the concentration of rural non-farm persons aged 60+ around Georgian Bay present both challenges and opportunities. The need for detailed studies in order to assist in planning is discussed.

Hodge, G. (1991). *Seniors in small town British Columbia: Demographic tendencies and trends, 1961 to 1986* (No. 91-04966). Vancouver, BC: Gerontology Research Centre, Simon Fraser University & Centre for Human Settlements, The University of British Columbia.

OBJECTIVES: To identify characteristics of small town older adults, the situation of living in small towns, and the impact on facility and service provision.

METHODS: Canada Census data on individuals aged 65+ were compiled for each British Columbia municipality for 1961, 1971, 1981, and 1986.

DEFINITION OF RURAL: The Canada Census provides two sets of data relevant to small communities. One divides communities by population size, with urban communities having a population of > 1,000 and meeting population density criteria. The second is comprised of incorporated municipalities.

RESULTS RELATED TO RURAL AGING: About one in four B.C. residents aged 65+ lived in rural settings, reflecting an increase of over 56% since 1961. Communities with a population < 1,000 had 12% of their population aged 65+ in 1986, with close to 40% of these individuals aged 75+. Among the 65+ in small towns, 68% were non-movers and 13% moved within the town from 1976 to 1981. Regional variations in some trends were evident. For example, in northern B.C., the smaller of the small communities tended to have larger concentrations of older adults. In the remote southern coastal communities, there was a much lower concentration of this age group.

CONCLUSIONS: The author concludes that the presence of older adults in small towns is increasing with the majority of the province's small towns projected to have elderly population concentrations of at least 20%. However, the overall number of older adults in each community is relatively small. Variations across the province need to be taken into account when considering service provision.

Meyer, B. (1992). Population, income and migration characteristics for urban/rural areas and farm/non-farm families in Saskatchewan. In R. D. Bollman (Ed.), *Rural and small town Canada* (pp. 301-318). Toronto, ON: Thompson Educational Publishing.

OBJECTIVES: To examine urban/rural and farm/non-farm differences in population, income, sources of income, and migration patterns in the province of Saskatchewan from 1982 to 1987.

METHODS: Data were from personal tax records from 1982 to 1987.

DEFINITION OF RURAL: A farm family was defined as a family in which one or both adult members of the family reported gross self-employment income from farming. The family unit was classified as urban or rural based on the postal code of the family mailing address; Canada Post assigns zero as the second digit of the postal code for rural areas.

RESULTS RELATED TO RURAL AGING: The age profile revealed that 11% of individuals in farm families were aged 65+ compared to 7% of non-farm families. Pension income (Canada Pension Plan [CPP], Old Age Security [OAS], and private pension income) represented 7% of the income for farm families and 8% for non-farm families. Such income was more likely to be reported for unattached farm women (26%) than their male counterparts (10%), consistent with the finding that 62% of unattached farm women were aged 65+ compared to 24% of the unattached farm males in that age group. The 1982 - 1987 migration rates for males and females aged 65+ in 1982 farm family units were 9.3% and 9.8%, respectively. These were the lowest rates for any age group.

CONCLUSIONS: Overall, there was a decline in the number of rural and farm families in Saskatchewan from 1982 to 1987. The increased role of self-employment income from sources other than farm income over the study period reflects the difficulties experienced by the agricultural sector in recent years. This trend has important implications for rural farm families in Saskatchewan.

Moore, E. G., Rosenberg, M. W., & Bekkering, M. (1989). *An atlas of the elderly population of the prairies*. Kingston, ON: Department of Geography, Queen's University.

OBJECTIVES: To examine the geographic distribution of the 65+ population in the prairie provinces of Manitoba, Saskatchewan, and Alberta from 1981 to 1986 and projections to 1996 and 2006.

METHODS: Data were from the 1981 and 1986 Censuses of Canada. Measures included the population aged 65+, population aged 80+, sex ratio of the population aged 65+, and the Old component of the Demographic Dependency Ratio (ODR). The projections were derived using cohort survival techniques. A series of charts provided pictorial representations of the geographical distribution.

DEFINITION OF RURAL: Comparisons were made between rural and urban census divisions.

RESULTS RELATED TO RURAL AGING: The rural census divisions of Manitoba and Saskatchewan had higher concentrations of the population aged 65+, particularly along the Saskatchewan-Manitoba border and along the Canada-United States border. Northern census divisions in all three provinces had few residents aged 65+. In the northern half of each province, elderly men outnumbered elderly females. This also was evident for several southern census divisions in Manitoba. In Saskatchewan and Alberta, the reverse was evident. The census divisions with the highest ODRs were found in Manitoba and Saskatchewan. The projections suggested that future geographic trends in the rural census divisions of Alberta will differ from those of Manitoba and Saskatchewan, in part related to the later out-migration of working age cohorts in rural Alberta.

CONCLUSIONS: The authors conclude that there will be a continuing depopulation of rural census divisions in the southern parts of these three provinces. Two challenges for provincial governments are identified. One pertains to the provision of services and facilities to an older population that is large relative to the working-age population but small and dispersed in absolute numbers in rural areas. The second is how to plan for services and facilities for a growing elderly population in major cities and resource communities that are most affected by the in- and out-migration of working age cohorts with the changing economy.

Pong, R. W., Salmoni, A., & Heard, S. (1999). Aging in a hurry: Changing population profile in Elliot Lake. In A. M. Mawhiney & J. Pitblado (Eds.), *Boom town blues: Elliot Lake, collapse and revival in a single-industry community* (pp. 204-218). Toronto, ON: Dundurn Press.

OBJECTIVES: To document demographic changes in Elliot Lake after the closure of uranium mining and to examine the characteristics of older adults who choose this community as a place to live in retirement. Elliot Lake is located in the northeastern area of the province of Ontario.

METHODS: Data were from the Elliot Lake Seniors' Needs Assessment conducted in 1994 and 1995. A telephone survey of 3,448 residents aged 50+ was completed by July 1995; useable mailed surveys were obtained from 480 residents in Summer 1995. Canada Census data also were used. Comparisons were made between old-timers (persons aged 50+ who have been living in Elliot Lake for 5+ years at the time of the survey) and newcomers.

DEFINITION OF RURAL: The population of Elliot Lake was 14,089 in 1991. The town converted itself from a natural-resource-based economy to a retirement community when the mine closure was announced in 1990.

RESULTS RELATED TO RURAL AGING: The number of persons aged 65+ in Elliot Lake increased from 475 in 1986 to 1,275 in 1991. The newcomers were considerably older than the old-timers; they also were less likely to be in the labour force and had lower annual household income. Old-timers had more relatives living in the community or sharing a household with others than newcomers. Marital status, level of education, and occupational backgrounds were similar.

CONCLUSIONS: The implications of the influx of older residents into Elliot Lake are highlighted, including the need for the provision and planning of services for this age group, the design of services that meet the needs of an older population with special characteristics and needs, and the longer-term plans of individuals and the community.

Rosenberg, M. W., Moore, E. G., & Ball, S. B. (1989). Components of change in the spatial distribution of the elderly population in Ontario, 1976-1986. *Canadian Geographer, 33*(3), 218-229.

OBJECTIVES: To examine the geographical structure of change in the distribution of the population aged 65+ between 1976 and 1986 in the province of Ontario.

METHODS: Data were from the 1976, 1981, and 1986 Censuses for Ontario. The components of change for the population were cohort survival and net migration.

DEFINITION OF RURAL: No definition of rural was provided. Distinctions were made between counties and townships.

RESULTS RELATED TO RURAL AGING: At the county level, counties with high growth in the 65+ population included a block of central rural counties (including Victoria, Peterborough, and Frontenac) and Niagara, all having significant appeal in retirement amenities. The highest relative concentrations of older adults were almost entirely in the rural areas. At the township level, with a focus on Frontenac, Lennox, and Addington in eastern Ontario, the uneven distribution of older adults throughout the region was evident. Some of the northern sections of these townships experienced a high growth rate, reflecting the winterizing of cottages to provide retirement homes.

CONCLUSIONS: The authors discuss issues at the county and local level. They argue that the decline of older adults in some areas and their concentration in others have implications for the vitality of communities, the vulnerability to policy changes at higher levels of government, and the ability to provide and sustain effective levels of service.

Weaver, D., & Nilson, R. (1991). *Older adults in Saskatchewan: A geographic perspective.* **Regina, SK: University of Regina Press.**

OBJECTIVES: To examine the spatial distribution of individuals aged 65+ in Saskatchewan and to explore the implications of the patterns.

METHODS: Data were from the 1988 Saskatchewan Hospital Services Plan. Information on Saskatoon and Regina were based on the 1986 Census of Canada. Maps and population pyramids were included.

DEFINITION OF RURAL: Five residential categories were used: cities (an urban centre with ≥ 5,000 population), towns (urban centres with between 500 and 5,000 population), villages (semi-urban centres with < 500 population), rural municipalities (blocks of rural land containing farms and unincorporated settlements), and Indian reservations (areas set aside federally for the residence of status Indians).

RESULTS RELATED TO RURAL AGING: In 1988, 13% of Saskatchewan's population was 65+. The proportion was higher than the provincial average in towns (21%) and villages (18%) and lower in the rural municipalities (10%) and on Indian reservations (3%).

CONCLUSIONS: The authors speculate that the rural towns and villages of southern Saskatchewan are indicative of what the province as a whole will be like in 40 years if present trends continue. As younger economically-active individuals leave due to the lack of job opportunities, the towns and villages face challenges in the provision of health care and other services and facilities for older adults.

Migration and Mobility

Bodig, M. G. (1986). *Residential migration and residential mobility of seniors living in Harriston, Ontario.* **Master's thesis, University of Guelph, Guelph, ON.**

OBECTIVES: To develop an understanding of the interrelationships between the types of residential moves made in retirement and personal sociodemographic circumstances and motivations of local movers, migrants, and stayers in a rural community in the province of Ontario.

METHODS: This thesis involved personal interviews with 88 individuals aged 65+ residing in Harriston, Ontario in 1985. The sample was stratified between migrants (43%), local movers (18%), and stayers (39%). Information was collected on the sequence of residential moves made in retirement, sociodemographic characteristics, and motivations for making residential moves in retirement.

DEFINITION OF RURAL: Harriston, a small town located in the north end of Wellington County in southern Ontario, had a 1981 population of 1,940. The 60+ age group accounted for 31% of the population.

RESULTS RELATED TO RURAL AGING: The majority of moves occurred in a relatively restricted local area. First moves by individuals living outside of town tended to occur early in retirement with a move into town and the purchase of a home. A second move occurred locally to tenant apartment living arrangements as housing needs changed by the death of a spouse, health problems, and difficulties in maintaining the home. Stayers were younger than either migrants or local movers. Local movers were more likely to be females, to be widowed or single, and to live alone than were the migrants or stayers. Health reasons and physical upkeep were the most important factors for moving.

CONCLUSIONS: The author argues that the growth of the elderly population in small towns raises concerns about the demand on housing, medical, and social services, and calls for the town to make Harriston an accommodating place for seniors to live, with an active participatory role by seniors and municipal affairs.

Bryant, C., & Joseph, A. E. (2001). Canada's rural population: Trends in space and implications in place. *Canadian Geographer, 45*(1), 132-137.

OBJECTIVES: To describe broad rural population trends, to address population aging and migration, to examine the intersection of economic, social, and political processes with demographic trends, and to reconsider 'diversity' and speculate about the future population geography of rural Canada.

METHODS: Recent trends in several Ontario and Quebec communities were included in the examination of migration and population aging.

DEFINITION OF RURAL: Statistics Canada's Rural and Small Town (RST) definition was used; rural included towns of 1,000 – 9,999 people as well as dispersed farm and non-farm populations.

RESULTS RELATED TO RURAL AGING: Contrasting examples of migration and population change for dispersed rural settlements, for nucleated settlements, and for rural resource hinterlands highlighted the socioeconomic and sociodemographic diversity of rural population structures in particular places.

CONCLUSIONS: Rural population change can be described by two major demographic processes, namely migration and population aging. The authors argue that significant challenges exist for rural communities.

Collins, D. C. (2002). *A longitudinal perspective of residential relocation among Manitoba seniors.* Master's thesis, University of Manitoba, Winnipeg, MB. Retrieved from:
http://proquest.umi.com/pqdweb?index=0&did=766551981&SrchMode=1&sid=1&Fmt=13&VInst=PROD&VType=PQD&RQT=309&VName=PQD&TS=1172605033&clientId=12301

OBJECTIVES: To examine relationships between seniors' characteristics and residential relocation (move vs. non-move) and to explore relocation characteristics of these moves in the province of Manitoba.

METHODS: This thesis drew on data collected in 1983, 1990, and 1996 for the Aging in Manitoba Study (AIM). Respondents were 1,799 urban and rural residents aged 65+ and living in the community in 1990. Factors considered (measured in 1983 and 1990 to predict 1996 moves) included demographic and physical health characteristics, functional and cognitive performance indicators, physical and social environment characteristics and, to a limited extent, economic factors. Thirty-eight percent of respondents resided in Winnipeg and 62% resided in non-Winnipeg areas.

DEFINITION OF RURAL: Winnipeg/non-Winnipeg comparisons were made. Winnipeg is the major urban centre in the province; non-Winnipeg was defined as all areas outside of Winnipeg.

RESULTS RELATED TO RURAL AGING: There was a 3:2 ratio between non-Winnipeg and Winnipeg residents in terms of movers. The reason for a move varied, with non-Winnipeg residents tending to move to be in a desired situation and Winnipeg residents moving in order to be independent or to move away from an undesirable situation. There was no significant Winnipeg/non-Winnipeg difference in the distances moved. Non-Winnipeg respondents were more likely to remain homeowners and less likely to be renters than their Winnipeg counterparts.

CONCLUSIONS: Policy and practice implications of the findings are placed in the context of seniors' housing and community support services. No rural-specific implications are discussed.

Dahms, F. A. (1987). *Population migration and the elderly: Ontario 1971-1981.* **Guelph, ON: Department of Geography, University of Guelph.**

OBJECTIVES: To examine migration within Ontario from 1971 to 1981, and specifically in 12 small settlements and four rural townships in the province of Ontario.

METHODS: This report began with a review of the literature, followed by a demographic analysis on migration within Ontario. Mobility/migration was examined for 1971 to 1976 and 1976 to 1981 for three age groups. Special tabulations from the 1976 Census of Canada were used to map the distribution of migrants to/from the 12 small settlements. Some of these numbers were too small for consideration of age group. Migration by rural township also was examined for 1976 to 1981, using special tabulations for the 1981 Census.

DEFINITION OF RURAL: The four rural townships and their 1971, 1976, and 1981 populations, respectively, were: Huron (1,585; 2,205; 2,685); Grey (1,900; 2,060; 1,975); Erin (4,355; 5,505; 5,945); and Puslinch (3,595; 4,370; 4,540). The 12 small settlements had 1971 populations < 1,000 (Lion's Head, 465; Mildmay, 960; Ripley, 445; Tiverton, 565; Bayfield, 500; Blyth, 815; Brussels, 910; Hensall, 970; Clifford, 555; Drayton, 750). The exception was Arthur with a population of 1,415.

RESULTS RELATED TO RURAL AGING: Between 1976 and 1986, the settlements gained almost twice as many migrants aged > 60 as they lost. From 1976 to 1981, almost 15% of the in-migrants to these places on average were aged > 60. All places received a significant number of elderly migrants from the cities. Short moves from rural areas to the closest incorporated places were evident, particularly among the > 60 age group.

CONCLUSIONS: These findings were consistent with trends reported in other countries. Retirees from cities appear to be attracted to smaller communities while some farmers often make a short move from the farm to the local market town. The issue of stress on local services is raised.

Dahms, F., & Hallman, B. (1991). Population change, economic activity and amenity landscapes at the outer edge of the urban fringe. In K. B. Beesley (Ed.), *Rural and urban fringe studies in Canada.* (pp. 67-90). York, ON: Geographical Monographs, Geography Department, York University-Atkinson College.

OBJECTIVES: To examine population change, migration, and commuting between 1971 and 1981 in the south Georgian Bay area in the province of Ontario.

METHODS: Data were from the 1981 and 1986 Censuses of Canada.

DEFINITION OF RURAL: The townships of Wasaga, Collingwood, Nottawasaga, and Sunnidale are located approximately 100 kilometres from the city of Toronto. Their combined 1981 population was 31,680, with 6,660 individuals aged 60+.

RESULTS RELATED TO RURAL AGING: Between 1981 and 1986, there was an 11% increase in the number of residents aged 60+. The largest single origin of migrants from outside the study area since 1981 was metropolitan Toronto. Changes in rural townships were smaller than those in the resort areas. Local movers tended to re-locate to local service centres while long-distance movers were more likely to head to resort areas.

CONCLUSIONS: The authors argue that the area offers major attractions such as beaches, hills, recreational facilities, and a rural atmosphere to affluent retirees. At the same time, they caution that overdevelopment may be detrimental to this type of migration.

Everitt, J., & Gfellner, B. (1996). Elderly mobility in a rural area: The example of southwest Manitoba. *Canadian Geographer, 40*(4), 338-351.

OBJECTIVES: To assess mobility decisions of older rural residents who had relocated within the last five years (movers) and to compare their quality of life with non-movers, in the province of Manitoba.

METHODS: Data from the Manitoba Health Services Commission were used to identify individuals aged 65+ in the Westman area of Manitoba who had moved over the past five years and a random sample of older adults in the region who had not moved. In-person interviews were conducted in Summer 1992, with 202 movers (131 females, 71 males) and 155 non-movers (88 females, 67 males). The focus was on social demographic indicators, social spaces, life satisfaction, and the relocation process.

DEFINITION OF RURAL: No definition of rural was provided. The Westman area was considered a rural region; historically, it has had the highest proportion of people 65+ in the province.

RESULTS RELATED TO RURAL AGING: The most important reason movers gave for their move was that it was part of their retirement plan. Other reasons included a desire to be closer to relatives and friends, and an inability to manage at their previous residence. Very poor health, being physically unable to maintain the home, having problems getting around, and the death of a spouse were identified as factors that might precipitate a further move. Forty percent of the movers perceived the moving process as a 'good event in their life', 38% perceived it as 'difficult', and only 1% saw it as 'very threatening'. The process of moving had positively affected the movers' perceived quality of life. Both groups held a pragmatic image of the future, but non-movers were more apprehensive about the future. Movers were significantly less well off financially than non-movers and may have moved to alleviate their financial situation. Few of either group wanted to move in with other family members.

CONCLUSIONS: The authors argue that older adults would prefer to remain in their own local communities, even if there is a deficiency in some services and a lack of options. They conclude that policies must be enacted that build more creative support systems for rural seniors.

Hodge, G. (1987). *The elderly in Canada's small towns: Recent trends and their implications.* **Vancouver, BC: The Centre for Human Settlements, University of British Columbia.**

OBJECTIVES: To examine recent trends in small towns in Canada in terms of age structure, male-to-female ratios, and mobility.

METHODS: Data were from the 1971, 1976, and 1981 Censuses of Canada.

DEFINITION OF RURAL: Small towns were defined as incorporated or unincorporated communities with < 10,000 population.

RESULTS RELATED TO RURAL AGING: In 1981, approximately 35% of Canadians aged 65+ were rural dwellers. The number and proportion of older adults on farms decreased from 1961 to 1971 while the number and proportion in towns and villages increased comparably to the national average. The proportion of older adults was negatively associated with the size of the town in all regions of Canada, with the exception of Newfoundland and British Columbia. There were proportionately more men among small town older residents than in the cities, particularly in towns with populations of < 2,500 and in the western provinces. In terms of mobility, older adults in small towns were less likely to change residence from 1976 to 1981 than those living elsewhere. Older in-migrants to small towns were most likely to be moving from the same census division or another area of the province; only 14% moved from another province.

CONCLUSIONS: The author identifies four areas that require attention to improve the quality of life of rural and small town older adults, namely health care services, home support services, home maintenance services, and transportation. While recognizing these issues exist in urban areas, the small town context with its small numbers, few alternative sources of services/amenities, and larger distances to travel provide unique challenges.

Joseph, A. E., & Cloutier, D. S. (1991). Elderly migration and its implications for service provision in rural communities: An Ontario perspective. *Journal of Rural Studies, 7*(4), 433-444.

OBJECTIVES: To provide an improved understanding of rural elderly migration and the implications for service provision, drawing on a case study in the province of Ontario.

METHODS: Canadian Census data on migration (1971 - 1976, 1976 - 1981, 1981 - 1986) were examined; communities were aggregated into Owen Sound, towns, villages, and townships. The survey involved a stratified random sample of 202 residents of Meaford (n = 126) and Markdale (n = 76) aged 65+, drawn from school support lists. During Summer 1987, in-person interviews on health and social service use in the past 2 years, demographic characteristics, and residential histories were conducted. Respondents were categorized as non-movers (resided in the same home for 15+ years), local movers (changed residence within the same community), county movers (relocated to Meaford or Markdale from another location within Grey County), and long distant movers (migrated to either location from outside Grey County). Females accounted for 65% of the sample; 60% were aged 65 - 74. The authors stated that "no tests of significance are performed" due to the small number of service users (p. 440).

DEFINITION OF RURAL: Grey County is located in southwestern Ontario. Owen Sound (1986 population 19,805) is the largest community. There are six villages (1986 populations from 420 to 1,295) and four towns (1986 populations from 1,500 to 6,415), including Meaford (1986 population 4,380, 21.7% aged 65+) and Markdale (1986 population 1,226, 28.6% aged 65+).

RESULTS RELATED TO RURAL AGING: Census data indicated a consistent net in-migration of older adults and a net out-migration of younger adults aged 20 - 29. Owen Sound, towns, and villages gained older residents through migration whereas townships lost older adults. Among survey participants, 48% were non-movers, 15% were local movers, 22% were county movers, and 14% were long-distance movers. Local movers and county movers tended to be older and were more likely to live alone. The four groups were similar in the likelihood of using physician services in the past 2 years. Few reported the use of homemaker (n = 16) or VON [home nursing] (n = 16) services. About 1 in 3 had spent time in hospital during the two years. At least 25% of the non-movers, local movers, and long distance movers aged 75+ indicated that they had no one to turn to in time of illness.

CONCLUSIONS: The demographic analysis revealed varying patterns of migration according to the community type while the survey results suggested that residential history is a potentially important pre-condition of dependence on formal services intended for the maintenance of elderly persons in the community. The authors call for local analysis of migration impacts and of the relationship between such impacts and longstanding problems of rural service provision.

COMMENTS: **Nord, M., & Luloff, A. E. (1992). Applied policy relevant research: Theory and method (Comments on 'elderly migration and its implications for service provision in rural communities: An Ontario perspective').** *Journal of Rural Studies, 8*(1), 105-109. These authors discuss two major weaknesses in the article that "undermine its contribution to both policy debate and scholarly discourse" (p. 105). The first relates to conceptual linkages between concentrations of older adults and service provision, and methodological implications for this linkage to spatial aggregation, measurement of concentration, and measurement of migration. The second involves problems of sample bias and contingency table analysis of the survey data.

See also Joseph, A. E., & Cloutier, D. S. (1990) (2 abstracts); and Joseph, A. E. (1992).

MacKenzie, P., & Cloutier-Fisher, D. (2004). Home sweet home: Experiences of place for retirement migrants to small-town British Columbia. *Rural Social Work, 9*(Dec.), 129-136.

OBJECTIVES: To examine the experiences of retirement in-migrants living in the region of 'Oceanside' in the province of British Columbia.

METHODS: This three-phase case study involved in-depth personal interviews with residents and with local community representatives such as municipal clerks, planners, service providers, and realtors. Attention here focused on results from 27 in-depth taped interviews conducted in 2002/03 with in-migrants (defined as those living in the area for up to 10 years) to Qualicum Beach and Parksville. Individuals were identified through the local Newcomer Clubs.

DEFINITION OF RURAL: 'Oceanside' is located on the east coast of Vancouver Island. In 2001, Qualicum Beach had a population of 6,921 people, with 38% aged 65+. Parksville had a population of 10,323, with 31% aged 65+.

RESULTS RELATED TO RURAL AGING: Four themes emerged, including reasons for and satisfaction with the relocation decision, recreating personal identities and personal meaning, finding a sense of belonging and community, and concerns about the lack of health resources. The reasons for the move included availability and desirability of housing with reasonable property taxes and maintenance cost, warm year-round climate with mild seasons, personal security, service availability, and social environment. Migrants reported detaching themselves from previous roles and residences, and re-establishing themselves as members of a new community. Many pursued volunteerism as a way to make new acquaintances, thereby being a resource to their community. The Newcomer Clubs appeared to play an important role in facilitating connections, suggesting the need for further information on such organizations as social networks are constructed or re-constructed. There were worries and concerns about the need for good health and about access to income that allows purchasing of services, good quality housing, and private transportation. Concern was expressed about the lack of locally available health care, including the difficulty in obtaining physician services and the need to travel for hospitalization.

CONCLUSIONS: These older in-migrants consider themselves to be valuable additions to their new communities. The authors call for community leaders and those charged with health and social planning to devise innovative strategies to listen and respond to the needs and talents of this group.

Moore, E. G., & McGuinness, D. L. (1997). Adjustments of the elderly to declining health: Residential moves and social support. *Canadian Studies in Population, 24*(2), 163-187.

OBJECTIVES: To examine the context of moves by older Canadians and the changes in access to formal and informal support as a consequence of these moves.

METHODS: Data were from Statistics Canada's 1986 Health and Activity Limitation Survey (HALS), and the 1991 Survey on Aging and Independence (SAI). Only data from the SAI were used in the rural-urban comparisons. SAI was a survey of 25,000 Canadians aged 45+ focusing on health, social, and economic situations, and planning choices/preparations for aging. Moves were classified as support (e.g., to receive care/support from a relative, decline in health of self or spouse, to be close to family/friends, or to be close to services), amenity, housing, retirement, separated/divorced/widowed, financial, employment, and other. Moves to institutions were excluded from the analyses.

DEFINITION OF RURAL: Three categories of community size were compared: urban areas with populations > 500,000, 'other' urban areas, and rural areas.

RESULTS RELATED TO RURAL AGING: Support moves constituted 24% of the moves for individuals aged 65 - 74 and 36% for the 75+ age group. In the rural areas, the corresponding percentages were 17% and 38%, respectively.

CONCLUSIONS: The authors call for longitudinal data to more fully understand the selective nature of elderly migration.

Northcott, H. C. (1985). The geographic mobility of Canada's elderly. *Canadian Studies in Population, 12*(2), 183-201.

OBJECTIVES: To examine the five-year mobility status of older Canadians.

METHODS: Data were from the 1961, 1971, 1976, and 1981 Censuses of Canada. Mobility status was defined as the difference between current residence and residence five years previous as identified by responses to the Census question *Where did you live five years ago?* The rural-urban analyses were limited to 1961 and 1971 data.

DEFINITION OF RURAL: Comparisons were made between urban centres (> 1,000 population), rural non-farm, and rural farm locations.

RESULTS RELATED TO RURAL AGING: Overall, in 1961, 26% of males aged 65+ and 29% of their female counterparts reported a move in the previous 5 years. The percentages were higher in urban areas (30% males, 32% females) than in rural non-farm (24% males, 22% females) and in rural farm (10% males, 11% females) locations. Similar patterns were evident for 1971.

CONCLUSIONS: The author concludes that while rural older adults appear less mobile than those who reside in urban areas, these data have to be interpreted with caution given the definition of urban as > 1,000 population. The results may "simply reflect the fact that the movement tends to be toward rather than away from the city (that is, a person who moves from farm to a city is classified as an urban mover" (p. 199).

Rothwell, N., Bollman, R. D., Tremblay, J., & Marshall, J. (2002). Migration to and from rural and small town Canada. *Rural and Small Town Analysis Bulletin, 3*(6), 1-24.

OBJECTIVES: To examine migration to and from rural and small town Canada from 1971 to 1996.

METHODS: Data were from the 1971, 1976, 1981, 1986, 1991, and 1996 Canadian Censuses. Each Census included the question *Where did this person live 5 years ago?* Four migration groups were considered at the national level: rural and small town (RST) non-movers, larger urban centres (LUC) non-movers, RST out-migrants to LUC, and RST in-migrants from LUC. At the provincial level, eight groups were identified.

DEFINITION OF RURAL: Rural and small town (RST) refers to the population living outside the commuting zone of larger urban centres (LUC), and specifically outside census metropolitan areas (CMAs) and census agglomerations (CAs). RST includes all municipalities with urban populations of 1,000 to 9,999 and rural areas, where < 50% of the employed individuals commute to the urban core of a CMA/CA.

RESULTS RELATED TO RURAL AGING: In RSTs, there was a net gain of individuals aged 65 - 69 and a net loss in the 70 - 74, 75 - 79, and 80+ age groups. While more individuals in the 70+ group moved out of than moved into RSTs, the net rates of migration were relatively small on average.

CONCLUSIONS: The authors argue that RST areas were net losers of youth but net gainers of individuals aged 25 - 69.

ECONOMICS

Snell, M. L., & Brown, K. H. (1987). Financial strategies of the recently retired. *Canadian Journal on Aging, 6*(4), 290-303.

OBJECTIVES: To investigate the use of four financial strategies used by the recently retired to enhance their financial resources, in the southern section of the province of Ontario.

METHODS: Interviews were conducted with a random sample of 450 men and women aged 61+ who had been retired for one to five years. In 1980, a random sample of individuals who met the age criterion was first selected and then approached to determine if they met the retirement criterion; the resulting sample included 300 urban and 75 rural residents. The rural residents were interviewed in 1982. Information was collected regarding changes in total expenditures (food, clothing, household operation, transportation); changes in home production (housework, home repairs, vegetable gardening); changes in assets (RRSPs, life insurance, saving/investments); and post-retirement employment.

DEFINITION OF RURAL: A dichotomy of rural-urban was used. No specific definition was provided.

RESULTS RELATED TO RURAL AGING: Overall, for males, rural residence was associated with an increase in home production activities and a decrease in assets. There were no significant rural-urban differences among the females.

CONCLUSIONS: The authors suggest that strategies other than reducing expenditures may be used to satisfy needs which are not necessarily economic in nature.

Zimmer, Z., & Chappell, N. L. (1996). Distinguishing the spending preferences of seniors. *Canadian Journal on Aging, 15*(1), 65-83.

OBJECTIVES: To examine the characteristics that distinguish older adults uninterested in spending on consumer products from those with specific product preferences, in the province of Manitoba.

METHODS: A random sample of 1,406 residents aged 65+ (mean age 75.8) were asked: *If you had what you consider to be some additional or extra income, would you spend it on any of the following: better housing, house repairs, more or better food, more or better clothing, more or better furniture, medical needs, recreational equipment or activities, transportation or a new car, and trips and/or holidays*? In addition, respondents were asked whether there was something else, not named, that they would spend their money on. Those who reported a non-product interest such as giving money to charity or to family were classified as uninterested consumers, while those who reported at least one product interest were classified as interested consumers.

DEFINITION OF RURAL: A dichotomy of rural-urban was used. The eight rural communities ranged in size from 2,000 to 10,000. Winnipeg was the urban centre.

RESULTS RELATED TO RURAL AGING: Rural residence was not a significant factor in distinguishing the non-interested from the interested nor for discriminating between spending preferences.

CONCLUSIONS: The authors conclude that the diversity in spending preferences can be understood in terms of a desire to enhance quality of life. No rural-specific conclusions were presented.

EDUCATION/LEISURE

Education

Denton, F. T., Pineo, P. C., & Spencer, B. G. (1988). Participation in adult education by the elderly: A multivariate analysis and some implications for the future. *Canadian Journal on Aging, 7*(1), 4-16.

OBJECTIVES: To examine factors associated with older adults' participation in adult education courses and to project future increases in course enrollment in Canada.

METHODS: Drawing on data from Statistics Canada's 1984 Adult Education Survey, participation in several types of education programs in 1983 (including academic, skill-oriented, hobby and personal interest, language, and 'other' but excluding regular courses taken by full-time students) was examined for the 65+ age group. A dichotomy of overall participation versus no participation was created. The independent variables were region of residence, marital status, educational attainment, language of the home, labor force participation, place of birth (inside or outside Canada), and metropolitan versus non-metropolitan residence. Participation rates, and projected size and educational attainment of the 65+ age group were used to estimate future course enrollment.

DEFINITION OF RURAL: No definitions of rural were provided; distinctions were made between metropolitan and non-metropolitan areas. Reference was made to "low density rural and small city areas" in comparison to metropolitan areas (p. 12).

RESULTS RELATED TO RURAL AGING: Only 4% of the 65+ age group reported participation in adult education in 1983, or approximately 86,000 older Canadians (Deveraux, 1984). Analyses presented in this article revealed no metropolitan and non-metropolitan differences in the likelihood of participation. Post-secondary education was the strongest factor associated with participation; individuals with at least some post-secondary education were more likely to be involved in such courses than those with a lower level of educational attainment. Assuming a continuation of current behavior patterns (e.g., increases in number of older persons and increases in their average levels of education), course enrollment was predicted to increase by 94% by 2005 and by 141% by 2010. Projections specific to non-metropolitan areas were not provided.

CONCLUSIONS: The authors argue that their results support the view of the important impact of education often acquired in early years on subsequent life style.

Gettle, B. C. (1990). *Report on Saskatchewan's Older Adults Learning Needs Survey.* **Regina, SK: Seniors' Education Centre, University Extension, University of Regina.**

OBJECTIVES: To identify the learning needs of individuals aged 65+ in the province of Saskatchewan.

METHODS: This project involved one-day forums planned in co-operation with local seniors' activity centres and regional colleges. Participants were asked to complete a questionnaire that focused on demographic characteristics, participation in learning activities, and barriers to participation. Small-group discussion on learning needs, preferred learning styles, barriers to learning, and present educational activities followed. Four forum sites were selected based on location (urban/south, urban/north, rural/south, rural/north), having at least 17% of the location's population aged 65+, and being served by a different regional college district. Sufficient interest for the forum was generated in only one location (rural/north); it was not known whether insufficient registration reflected satisfaction with current opportunities or a lack of awareness about the forum and lifelong learning resources. The forum was held June 15, 1989; 38 participants attended and 34 completed questionnaires (68% female, 66% aged 65 - 74).

DEFINITION OF RURAL: Rural was defined as any Saskatchewan community identified as a town, village, or hamlet; urban was defined as a city. The forum took place in Canora (a rural/north location), where 36% of its population was aged 65+ and the community was served by the Parkland Regional College.

RESULTS RELATED TO RURAL AGING: Only 37% of the 34 participants indicted that they had participated in a learning activity in the last 12 months, with topics ranging from grief and grieving to weaving. Barriers to participation included not wanting to go by oneself, health problems, self-confidence, and lack of transportation. Few participants identified cost as a barrier. Learning needs included the development of interpersonal and self-improvement skills while learning interests often focused on leisure activities and hobbies.

CONCLUSIONS: The author calls for future research on older adults' learning needs and related learning processes.

James, G. G. (1992). *Report on Saskatchewan Seniors Needs Identification Survey.* **Saskatoon, SK: Extension Division, University of Saskatchewan.**

OBJECTIVES: To identify the desired type of university level courses or cultural programming, and preferred delivery techniques for rural older adults in the province of Saskatchewan.

METHODS: This survey was conducted from March to June, 1991. All rural seniors' organizations (n = 430) and individuals who were designated as contact persons (n = 59) on the Saskatchewan Seniors Mechanism's province-wide mailing list of seniors' activity groups were sent questionnaires. Responses were received from 131 organizations and 29 individuals.

DEFINITION OF RURAL: Saskatoon and Regina were considered as urban and were excluded from the study.

RESULTS RELATED TO RURAL AGING: Only 12% of the organizations reported participation in any type of education activity in the previous 12 months. These activities tended to be informational meetings/seminars and participation activities. Interest in traditional 'academic' subjects was expressed by 26% of the organizations, with geography, history, and music being the most popular. Results on delivery techniques also were presented; however, response rates to specific questions were low.

CONCLUSIONS: The author concludes that lack of interest is a major obstacle to university-level programming for rural older adults. Other barriers included a widely dispersed population, and the necessary funding, resources, and delivery of programs of this type. The author proposes five possible solutions.

James, G. G. (1999). Learning for life: Extending university-level education to older adults in rural Saskatchewan. *Canadian Journal of University Continuing Education, 25*(1), 31-44.

OBJECTIVES: To assess the University of Saskatchewan Extension Division's outreach to rural older adults in the province of Saskatchewan.

METHODS: This 1996 study involved structured interviews with 11 older rural residents who participated in at least one university-level outreach course. These courses were offered by the University of Saskatchewan in Watrous, Leask, or Marcelin. Ten individuals took courses with 12 contact hours, once a week for two hours over six weeks; one took an 8-week art course. The subject matter varied (e.g., comparative religion, water colour, history). Respondents were asked about awareness of the course, comfort levels with participation, academic level of the course materials, rates of attendance, education committee function, linkages to either university in the province, participation rates in educational events in the last 12 months, travel time, and demographic characteristics. Nine respondents were female; ages ranged from the < 55 age group to the 76 – 80 age group although older adults were the target. Seven had completed secondary school.

DEFINITION OF RURAL: The 1991 populations were 1,872 (Watrous), 442 (Leask), and 193 (Marcelin).

RESULTS RELATED TO RURAL AGING: All respondents indicated a strong interest and none were intimidated by university-level subject matter. Reasons for taking the course included an interest in the subject matter and an interest in learning in general. All were satisfied with the program; no one was bored. Most participants would travel up to 40 kilometres for a class but having the use of an automobile was critical as there was usually no alternative.

CONCLUSIONS: Participant satisfaction was high for these outreach courses. The authors argue that the identification of interests at grass-roots level and the encouragement of local ownership of outreach programs are keys to successful rural extension to older adults.

McLaren, L. (2002). Information and communication technologies in rural Canada. *Rural and Small Town Canada Analysis Bulletin, 3*(5), 1-26.

OBJECTIVES: To examine the incidence of personal computers within rural households and the use of the Internet from rural households in Canada.

METHODS: Data were from Statistics Canada's General Social Survey – 2000, Cycle 14 – *Access to and Use of Information Communications Technology*. The GSS involves Canadians aged 15+.

DEFINITION OF RURAL: Rural and small town (RST) refers to the population living outside the commuting zones of large urban centres – specifically, outside census metropolitan areas (CMAs) and census agglomerations (CAs). RST areas have a population of 1,000 - 9,999 where < 50% of the employed individuals commute to a CMA/CA, and < 25% commute from a CMA/CA. 'RST small towns' refers to the population living in towns of 1,000 to 9,999 and outside a CMA or CA. 'RST rural' refers to the population living outside centres of 1,000 to 9,999 and outside a CMA or CA (Statistics Canada, 2002).

RESULTS RELATED TO RURAL AGING: Only 10% of RST individuals aged 70+ had a computer while 33% of those aged 55 - 69 did so. This compared to a range of 55% to 63% among RST individuals aged 15 - 54. Less than 20% of the 55+ age group in the rural and small town areas were connected to the Internet. Within each age group, rural residents were less likely than their urban counterparts to have a computer or to have an Internet connection.

CONCLUSIONS: The authors conclude that rurality matters when considering computer ownership and Internet connectivity.

Seniors Education Centre. (1992, April). *Last Mountain learning opportunities for older adults and others. 1991-92 report.* **Regina, SK: Seniors Education Centre, University Extension, University of Regina.**

OBJECTIVES: To describe the development and co-ordination of extension courses designed primarily for older adults by a steering committee from the rural Last Mountain area in the province of Saskatchewan.

METHODS: The historical development of this initiative and course content were documented. The courses were developed under a grant and offered as a trial to determine whether extension courses designed primarily for senior citizens would be popular in the rural area. Topics included: Fall 1991 - creative writing, computers, and the history of Saskatchewan; and Spring 1992 - prairie gardening, drawing in color, computers, and the literature of Saskatchewan. Course evaluations were completed.

DEFINITION OF RURAL: No definition of rural was provided. Courses were offered in Raymore, Nokomis, Semans, and Govan in the Last Mountain area of Saskatchewan; no population figures for these locations were provided.

RESULTS RELATED TO RURAL AGING: A total of 121 individuals registered in the 1991 - 1992 courses; 76% were aged 50+. The Fall 1991 program served 56 individuals (47 aged 50+) at a total direct cost of $1,196.80, and the Spring 1992 program served 65 individuals (45 aged 50+) at a total direct cost of $2,178.57. Course evaluations indicated that the participants were challenged and very pleased by the content. Participants viewed the program as a valuable learning experience.

CONCLUSIONS: This project was viewed as a success due to the direction of the Last Mountain Committee and the assistance of the University of Regina's Seniors' Education Centre. It highlighted the importance of bringing educational programs to rural areas and working with local seniors to create courses suited to their needs and address potential barriers such as distance, age, income, and lack of past educational opportunities.

Seniors Education Centre. (1992, July). *Saskatchewan Older Adult Literacy Survey.*
Final Report. **Regina, SK: Seniors Education Centre, University Extension,**
University of Regina.

OBJECTIVES: To provide an overview of the current state of older adults' literacy in the province of Saskatchewan.

METHODS: The Saskatchewan Older Adult Literacy Survey involved 16 literacy programs offered by regional colleges, public libraries, and technical institutes throughout Saskatchewan. The survey was conducted between January 15 and March 15, 1992. It involved mailed questionnaires and structured telephone interviews with 14 literacy program coordinators. Coordinators were asked to record information on the demographic characteristics of older adults enrolled in their literary programs and to offer their perceptions of learning needs and resources for older adult literacy in Saskatchewan.

DEFINITION OF RURAL: No definition of rural was provided. Distinctions were made between large urban, small urban, and rural.

RESULTS RELATED TO RURAL AGING: Based on the information provided by the 14 coordinators, 177 adults aged 55+ were registered in literacy programs in the 1991 - 1992 academic year. Learners were aged 55+ (69% aged 55 - 60, 15% aged 61 - 64, 12% aged 65 - 69, and 4% aged 70 - 74). They resided in large urban (45%), small urban (34%), and rural (21%) areas. Reasons for participation stated by the older adult learners to the coordinators included independence, self-esteem, enhanced quality of life, and security. Barriers to older adults' participation in literacy programs were negative attitudes toward self and ability to learn, stigma, misconceptions of others about the learning abilities of older adults, and gaps in current literacy programming. The roots of illiteracy ranged from environmental factors to traditional gender roles.

CONCLUSIONS: The authors argue that older adults can be reached if literacy programs are made accessible and relevant, if a peer tutoring system is created, and if programs are promoted as lifelong learning. Ideas to meet older adult learners' needs are suggested, such as educational resource development, relevant learning and teaching approaches, and the centre's role as an educator and information clearinghouse on literacy and the older adult.

Williams, A. M., & Montelpare, W. J. (1998). Lifelong learning in Niagara: Identifying the educational needs of a retirement community. *Educational Gerontology, 24(8), 699-717.*

OBJECTIVES: To examine the educational needs/interests, educational approaches, and learning mediums of retirees who lived in Heritage Village, a retirement community located in the Niagara region in the province of Ontario.

METHODS: Five focus groups (individuals aged < 65, those aged > 65, previously a resident in the Niagara region, previously a resident outside the Niagara region, and single or widowed females) were conducted with residents in the Heritage Village Clubhouse in January and February 1997. Each group had approximately 6 participants. Questions addressed educational/training history, leisure pursuits/interests with an emphasis on those fulfilled by the university, appropriate delivery mechanisms, and possible barriers to participation in university-provided learning opportunities. All session were audiotaped and then transcribed.

DEFINITION OF RURAL: This newly developed retirement community had 473 residents in 1995. It was located within the town of Vineland.

RESULTS RELATED TO RURAL AGING: Most participants expressed an interest in the idea of having access to university-provided learning opportunities. Most were interested in education for leisure and personal development. Important delivery aspects were identified such as an on-site location; short courses; timing; a style that was interactive, group-oriented, and fun; and the expectation that learning was for the joy of it.

CONCLUSIONS: The authors argue that residents perceived university-provided learning opportunities as potentially enhancing their quality of life. Strategies to appropriately plan and implement educational programs specific to an elderly population living in a retirement community are discussed.

Leisure/Recreation

Bocksnick, J. G., & Hall, B. L. (1994). Recreation activity programming for the institutionalized older adult. *Activities, Adaptation & Aging, 19*(1), 1-25.

OBJECTIVES: To explore recreation activity participation and the extent of free choice in the decision to participate in activities, among institutionalized rural older adults in the province of Alberta.

METHODS: Conducted in six independently owned and operated nursing homes in southern rural Alberta, the study involved 53 residents, 6 administrators, and 6 recreation therapists. Residents had been in the nursing home at least six months. Their mean age was 84 years; "nearly all" were female (p. 8). Residents were classified into two groups: 34 regularly participated in activities offered and organized by the recreation therapist, and 19 did not participate in organized activities. Both participating (74%) and non-participating (90%) residents were likely to have a minimum of one physical disability. No information on cognitive functioning was provided. Open-ended interviews were audiotaped, transcribed, and content analyzed.

DEFINITION OF RURAL: No definition of rural was provided.

RESULTS RELATED TO RURAL AGING: Outings and trips (41%) and exercise (41%) were the top two activities in which the participating residents engaged. The non-participating residents were involved in passive and solitary activities such as TV viewing (37%) and reading (26%). Physical limitation and not perceiving a potential benefit were given as reasons for not participating in a program. Fifty-three percent of the participating residents and 68% of the non-participating residents viewed the primary purpose of the recreation program as killing time and alleviating boredom. The recreation therapists viewed the purpose as improving quality of life. Residents reported that they had a choice regarding participation but also felt a sense of pressure to participate. The therapists agreed that individuals should have free choice but also indicated that they used persuasive techniques to encourage participation. This latter perspective also was evident among the administrators.

CONCLUSIONS: The authors argue that differing opinions on the value and operationalization of the goals of therapeutic recreation present serious implications for consumer choice, education, and functional status of the nursing home resident.

See also Hall, B. L., & Bocksnick, J. G. (1995).

Hall, B. L., & Bocksnick, J. G. (1995). Therapeutic recreation for the institutionalized elderly: Choice or abuse. *Journal of Elder Abuse & Neglect, 7*(4), 49-60.

OBJECTIVES: To examine freedom of choice in recreational activity participation, from the perspectives of residents, recreation therapists, and administrators in six rural nursing homes in the province of Alberta, and to explore whether therapeutic recreation therapists played a role in elder abuse.

METHODS: Conducted in six independently owned and operated nursing homes in rural Alberta, the study involved 53 residents, 6 administrators, and 6 recreation therapists. Residents had been in the nursing home at least six months. Their mean age was 84 years; "the majority" were female (p. 54). Residents were classified into two groups: 34 regularly participated in activities offered and organized by the recreation therapist, and 19 did not participate in organized activities. Both groups had a minimum of one physical disability. Information on cognitive functioning was not provided. Open-ended interviews were audiotaped, transcribed, and content analyzed.

DEFINITION OF RURAL: No definition of rural was provided.

RESULTS RELATED TO RURAL AGING: Content analysis showed that some residents felt externally pressured or coerced to participate in activities and that they had no say in evaluating and modifying the programs (percentages were not provided). Administrators and recreation specialists believed that they were allowing residents to make participation decisions independently.

CONCLUSIONS: The authors suggest that residents who feel pressured to attend activities may be experiencing a form of psychological abuse, despite therapists' and administrators' perceptions that residents had a choice. The challenge of identifying the degree of acceptable external control and the difficult role of the recreation therapist in a long-term care facility are discussed.

See also Bocksnick, J. G., & Hall, B. L. (1994).

Losier, G. F., Bourque, P. E., & Vallerand, R. J. (1993). A motivational model of leisure participation in the elderly. *Journal of Psychology, 127*(2), 153-170.

OBJECTIVES: To develop a motivational model of leisure participation in order to examine the factors that may encourage leisure involvement in later life, in the province of New Brunswick.

METHODS: Mailed questionnaires were completed by 102 French-speaking elderly Canadians in the Moncton area. Respondents were selected through the proportional stratified sampling method. Their mean age was 73.8; 65% were female. "Roughly half lived in an urban setting and half in a rural community" (p. 159). Information was collected on leisure motivation, satisfaction, participation, opportunities, and constraints as well as health and demographic characteristics.

DEFINITION OF RURAL: No definition of rural was provided.

RESULTS RELATED TO RURAL AGING: The results supported the three propositions of the motivational model of leisure participation: (1) perceptions of leisure opportunities and perceptions of leisure constraints both predict leisure motivation; (2) leisure motivation is a predictor of leisure satisfaction; and (3) leisure satisfaction is a predictor of leisure participation. There were no rural-urban differences in leisure participation, leisure satisfaction, intrinsic motivation, self- or non-self determined extrinsic motivation, amotivation, perceptions of leisure opportunities, or perceptions of leisure constraints.

CONCLUSIONS: The authors argue that their results support a self-determination theory, which suggests that the perception of having choices and freedom to choose should have positive effects on one's self-determined motivation. Place of residence (rural vs. urban) did not emerge as a critical factor.

Nilson, R., Mazur, P., & Weaver, D. (1990). *Leisure and aging in Saskatchewan: A report to the Saskatchewan Department of Culture, Multiculturalism and Recreation*. Regina, SK: Faculty of Physical Activity Studies, University of Regina.

OBJECTIVES: To assess the leisure/physical activity involvement of older adults in the province of Saskatchewan.

METHODS: A stratified random sample of individuals aged 65+ (by geographic region, settlement type, and gender) was selected from a computer-generated list of names from the 1988 Saskatchewan Health Covered Population. Data were collected through a mail-out questionnaire focusing on leisure participation, barriers, volunteer involvement, travel and transportation, leisure activities, exercise/fitness/life satisfaction, and demographic characteristics. A total of 4,799 questionnaires were mailed and 2,969 (62%) were returned and useable (cities, n = 1,359; towns, n = 811; villages, n = 304; and rural municipalities, n = 495). A spatial analysis of the distribution and concentration of older adults also was completed.

DEFINITION OF RURAL: Settlement type included rural municipalities, villages, towns, and cities.

RESULTS RELATED TO RURAL AGING: Results were presented for the total sample; summary statements regarding differences by settlement type were included. Overall, leisure activity participation did not differ substantially between rural and urban residents during the winter months. However, during the summer, city dwellers were more likely to watch television and listen to the radio than those in rural areas. There were differences in the importance of leisure by place of residence in that city dwellers placed more value on physical health and exercise. Distance from facilities was the number one barrier for residents of rural municipalities and villages. Place of residence did not have an appreciable effect on the perception of physical imitations on leisure activity. For volunteer participation, residents of villages were more likely to volunteer than were residents of other settlement types. Shortage of time and transportation, a lack of someone to volunteer with, and a lack of information on volunteering opportunities were more frequent barriers for volunteer participation for residents of farms and rural municipalities. Health was the most important barrier for all groups. Finally, residents of cities appeared to have, overall, a more positive attitude toward leisure time activities.

CONCLUSIONS: The authors provide a number of recommendations directed to the Sport and Recreation Branch of the Saskatchewan Department of Culture, Multi-Culturalism and Recreation.

Ouellette, P. (1986). The leisure participation and enjoyment patterns of French and English-speaking members of senior citizens' clubs in New Brunswick, Canada. *Canadian Journal on Aging, 5*(4), 257-268.

OBJECTIVES: To examine leisure participation and enjoyment patterns of French- and English-speaking members of senior citizens' clubs in the province of New Brunswick.

METHODS: A Likert-type questionnaire tapping participation and enjoyment in aesthetic, civic, intellectual, mass-media, physical, social, spiritual, and tourist-related leisure activities was completed by 1,080 members of 229 senior citizens' clubs affiliated with the New Brunswick Senior Citizens' Federation. Demographic characteristics included sex, age, marital status, socioeconomic index (SEI), geographical location (urban vs. rural), maternal language, home language, participation in a New Horizon project, perceived health, and obstacles to leisure participation. There were 405 urban respondents and 675 rural respondents. Canonical correlation analyses were used.

DEFINITION OF RURAL: No definition of rural was provided.

RESULTS RELATED TO RURAL AGING: Geographical location (urban vs. rural) did not emerge as significant. Members of rural senior clubs were no more likely than their urban counterparts to participate in and enjoy various types of activities.

CONCLUSIONS: The authors call for future research to develop standardized instruments of participation, to explore individual activities and differences between participation and enjoyment, and to involve more diverse groups of older adults.

Reid, C. (1999). *Time to Preserve: A Study of Two Generations of Food Preservers in Rural Wellington County.* **Master's thesis, University of Guelph, Guelph, ON. Retrieved from:** http://proquest.umi.com/pqdweb?index=0&did=732074021&SrchMode=1&sid =3&Fmt=13&VInst=PROD&VType=PQD&RQT=309&VName=PQD&TS=1172605 202&clientId=12301

OBJECTIVES: This thesis explores the practice of food preservation for two generations of rural women in Wellington County in the province of Ontario.

METHODS: Eighteen women (9 born before the Second World War, and 9 born during or after the Second World War) were interviewed. Government documents on food preservation also were examined.

DEFINITION OF RURAL: Wellington County had a 1996 population of 171,365, with 42,884 considered rural. All participants described themselves as rural.

RESULTS RELATED TO RURAL AGING: All participants learned about food preservation through informal sources and used similar techniques. Older women tended to preserve for economic savings and for preventing food waste. Younger women mentioned self-sufficiency and the superior taste of home preserves but also spoke of how time prevented them from preserving.

CONCLUSIONS: The author provides recommendations for home economists and extension workers, and calls for research on the role that families and friends play in the development of local food systems, the time it takes to preserve food, and the sustainability of various food preservation practices.

Strain, L. A. (2001). Senior centres: Who participates? *Canadian Journal on Aging,*
20(4), 471-491.

OBJECTIVES: To examine the likelihood of senior centre participation, the frequency of attendance among participants, changes in use/non-use over a 4-year period, and associated characteristics in the province of Manitoba.

METHODS: Data were from the 1991/92 and 1995 Canadian Aging Research Network Group A study. This quantitative study involved a two-stage sampling approach. Purposive sampling was used to select eight rural Manitoba communities, based on distance to Winnipeg, the proportion of older adults in the community, and having/not having a Provincial Department of Health office. Within each community, a random sample of individuals aged 65+ was selected, stratified by age and gender. In 1991/92, in-person interviews were conducted with 1,406 older adults (50% in Winnipeg and 50% in the rural communities). All but 7 respondents answered the question on senior centre participation and were included in these analyses (n = 1,399). Follow-up interviews were conducted with 962 respondents in 1995. Information on senior centre participation at both time periods was available for 956 individuals. All respondents were asked: *Have you used a senior centre in the past 6 months? If yes, how often?* Individuals defined a senior centre themselves and were not asked to indicate a specific location or type of centre.

DEFINITION OF RURAL: All eight rural communities had populations of < 15,000. Winnipeg was the urban centre.

RESULTS RELATED TO RURAL AGING: In 1991/92, 21% of participants reported that they had visited a senior centre at least once in the 6 months prior to the interview. Urban residents (16%) were less likely to report participation than rural residents (27%). Place of residence was the strongest characteristic associated with participation in 1991/92. Being female, having a monthly household income of < $1,000, having fewer limitations in instrumental activities of daily living, and living alone also were associated with a greater likelihood of participation. However, when considering the rural sample only, none of the characteristics emerged as significant. No rural-urban differences were evident in the number of visits by participants. Four years later, only 8% had joined a senior centre and 13% ceased their participation. Again, place of residence did not emerge as significant.

CONCLUSIONS: The author suggests that the lack of variability among the rural sample in characteristics associated with the likelihood of participation, the frequency of attendance, or changes in participation may reflect a broad community appeal, and acceptance of the senior centre/drop-in centre as a meeting place in rural areas. Unlike urban senior centres that may have had to identify specific target groups and designed their services accordingly, rural centres may not have been challenged to serve the needs of specific sub-groups of the older population.

See also Strain, L. A., & Greenslade, L. (1996).

Strain, L. A., & Greenslade, L. (1996). *Senior centre participation in Manitoba.* **Winnipeg, MB: Centre on Aging, University of Manitoba.**

OBJECTIVES: To examine sociodemographic and health characteristics of senior centre participants in the province of Manitoba.

METHODS: Data were from two studies conducted by researchers at the University of Manitoba. The 1991/92 CARNET study involved data collection with a random sample of 1,406 individuals aged 65+ living in Winnipeg or eight smaller communities; a follow-up study was conducted in 1995. The 1991/92 Manitoba Study of Health and Aging (MSHA) was undertaken with a stratified random sample of 1,763 Manitobans aged 65+. Both studies included questions about senior centre participation and factors related to participation.

DEFINITION OF RURAL: Winnipeg/non-Winnipeg comparisons were made. In CARNET, the eight small communities all had populations of < 15,000. Winnipeg is the major urban centre in the province. In MSHA, community size varied.

RESULTS RELATED TO RURAL AGING: Approximately 20% of individuals indicated that they had used a senior centre at least once in the six months prior to the interview. In both CARNET and MSHA, senior centre participation rates were higher outside Winnipeg than in Winnipeg. The age profiles of Winnipeg and non-Winnipeg participants were virtually identical. Senior centre participants residing outside Winnipeg were more likely to be male (MSHA), married (CARNET, MSHA), living with others (MSHA), have less education (MSHA), and lower monthly household income (CARNET, MSHA) than their Winnipeg counterparts. Few differences in the health status of participants according to Winnipeg/non-Winnipeg residence were evident. Some of these differences reflected differences between the Winnipeg/non-Winnipeg sample as a whole and were not specific to senior centre participants.

CONCLUSIONS: The authors conclude that there are significant Winnipeg/non-Winnipeg differences in senior centre participation rates. They call for future research with focused questions on senior centres.

See also Strain, L. A. (2001).

West, G. E., Delisle, M.-A., Simard, C., & Drouin, D. (1996). Leisure activities and service knowledge and use among the rural elderly. *Journal of Aging and Health,* *8*(2), 254-279.

OBJECTIVES: To examine the relationship between leisure activities and knowledge/use of health and social services, among older adults in the province of Quebec.

METHODS: The study draws on data from an evaluation of two physical conditioning programs designed for rural residents aged 55+ in a rural county in southern Quebec. Self-administered questionnaires were completed in small group settings by 641 active program participants and a control group of non-participants who were selected from a comprehensive list of community dwelling residents aged 55+. In order to reflect proportional representation, a random sub-sample of program participants aged 65+ was then selected, and the sample was weighted to give a more accurate sex ratio. The final sample size was 418, with 55% being female and a mean age of 74 years. Health and social service use included consultations with professional social service providers (psychologist, social worker, or other counselor); consultations with professional health service providers (doctor, nurse, physiotherapist, chiropractor, dentist, optometrist); use of social service programs (income maintenance, rent subsidies, senior centres, community meals, adult education classes); use of health programs (Red Cross, adult day centre, local health care centre); and knowledge of the existence of 16 services. Using Andersen's service utilization model, predisposing, enabling, and need characteristics associated with use were examined. Leisure activity was considered as an enabling characteristic, with five measures to tap group versus solitary and physical versus sedentary dimensions.

DEFINITION OF RURAL: No definition of rural was provided.

RESULTS RELATED TO RURAL AGING: The effect of leisure participation varied according to the nature of the participation and by type of service. Use of professional social services was related to participating in formal group activities and not participating in either group sedentary or solitary physical activities. Use of professional services was associated with taking part in formal group activities and not participating in either group or solitary sedentary activities. Use of social programs was related to participating in physical group activity and not engaging in solitary sedentary activity. No characteristics emerged as significant for the use of health programs. Knowledge of services was associated with both formal and sedentary group participation. Marital status was the only significant predisposing characteristic but this was evident only for the use of social programs. The need characteristic was significant only for use of professional health services.

CONCLUSIONS: The authors argue that their most controversial finding was that leisure activity patterns explained a greater amount of the variation in the use of services provided by health and social service professionals than did need characteristics. This finding raises the question of whether certain types of leisure activity patterns may be related to a more judicious or appropriate use of health and social services. However, the potential overlap between some of the leisure activities and the services was not discussed.

Witcher, C. S. G. (2005). *Exploring older adults' perceptions of physical activity and current leisure activity participation in rural Newfoundland.* **Master's thesis, University of Alberta, Edmonton, AB. Retrieved from:** http://proquest.umi.com/pqdweb?index=0&did=1034630531&SrchMode=1&sid=4&Fmt=13&VInst=PROD&VType=PQD&RQT=309&VName=PQD&TS=1172605297&clientId=12301

OBJECTIVES: To explore the nature of physical activity participation and perceptions of being physically active among older adults in rural Newfoundland and Labrador.

METHODS: This thesis involved qualitative research with a purposive sample of individuals aged 65+ residing on Fogo Island, Newfoundland. In 2004, semi-structured, taped interviews were conducted with 10 participants (5 males, 5 females, mean age = 82); member checking was completed with 5 of these individuals. Discussion focused on leisure culture, leisure choices when young, life course activity change, current health interpretation, and community culture.

DEFINITION OF RURAL: Fogo Island is located off the northeast coast of Newfoundland and accessible only by ferry. The nine communities on the Island have a combined population of approximately 3,500.

RESULTS RELATED TO RURAL AGING: Three main themes emerged from these interviews: the historical context of physical activity, current leisure-time activity participation, and strategies for a successful old age. In their youth, participants spent most of their time working and little time engaged in leisure activity. Beliefs about aging and age-appropriate activity affected participants' current levels of physical activity.

CONCLUSIONS: The author argues that this study draws attention to contextual and local cultural considerations of physical activity participation. Suggestions for future research are provided.

EPIDEMIOLOGY

Cancer

Brophy, J. T., Keith, M. M., Gorey, K. M., Laukkanen, E., Hellyer, D., Watterson, A., Reinhartz, A., & Gilbertson, M. (2002). Occupational histories of cancer patients in a Canadian cancer treatment center and the generated hypothesis regarding breast cancer and farming. *International Journal of Occupational and Environmental Health, 8*(4), 346-353.

OBJECTIVES: To compare lifetime occupational histories of women with newly diagnosed breast cancers and women with other cancers in the Windsor-Essex County in the province of Ontario.

METHODS: The preliminary study involved the use of data from the Computerized Recording of Occupations Made Easy (CROME) at the Windsor Regional Cancer Centre (WRCC). Structured interviews were used to obtain detailed occupational histories. A convenience sample of 299 females with primary malignant breast cancer between January 1, 1995 and December 31, 1998 was selected from CROME. The control group consisted of 237 women with other cancers who were receiving treatment at the WRCC. There were 135 cases and 107 controls over the age of 65. Farming person-years were calculated; farming included field crop production, crop spraying and dusting, vineyard or fruit farming, greenhouse or nursery operations, livestock farming, other agricultural jobs, and other farm services. Only 14% of the cases and 11% of the controls had farm exposures. Odds ratios were calculated using logistic regression, adjusting for age, social class, and education.

DEFINITION OF RURAL: No definition of rural was provided. Having ever farmed was examined as a risk factor.

RESULTS RELATED TO RURAL AGING: No statistically significant differences between breast cancer and farming exposure emerged for the 56+ age group. Females aged 66 - 75 had the highest percentage of cancer for both breast cancer and other cancers.

CONCLUSIONS: The authors argue that patients' occupational histories can help to inform understanding of cancer etiology and prevention. They call for an investigation of the possible association between breast cancer and agricultural hazards such as pesticides.

Godon, D., Lajoie, P., Thouez, J.-P., & Nadeau, D. (1989). Pesticides et cancers en milieu rural agricole au Québec: Interpretation geographique. (Pesticides and cancers in rural agricultural contexts in Quebec: Geographical interpretation). *Social Science & Medicine, 29*(7): 819-833.

OBJECTIVES: To examine the potential relationship between the incidence of cancer and the agricultural use of pesticides among the rural agricultural population in the province of Quebec.

METHODS: Data on the 1982 – 1983 agricultural use of pesticides and three types of cancer (brain cancer, cancer of lymphatic tissues, and leukemia) among the rural farm population were compiled for 34 rural agricultural drainage basins in Quebec. Basins were divided into 3 categories of exposure (low, intermediate, high) on the basis of pesticide sales levels. Data on the incidence of new cases of cancer by age and gender were from the Tumors Database of Quebec.

DEFINITION OF RURAL: The rural agricultural population included all municipalities that had at least 10 farms and had 3.3% or more of its total 1981 population as agricultural rural population. The municipalities were grouped into drainage basins as information on pesticide sales was available only for drainage basins. The total rural agricultural population was 1,012,010; drainage basis populations ranged from 15,125 to 79,180.

RESULTS RELATED TO RURAL AGING: Women living in highly exposed basins were 1.62 times more likely to have cancers of the lymphatic tissues than women in low exposure basins, and 1.63 times more likely than those in basins with intermediate exposure. For adults aged 65+, significant associations between pesticides utilization and geographic variations were evident for women in cancers of the lymphatic tissues and leukemia, while no significant associations were found for men aged 65+. Socioeconomic factors were significant only for the following: lymphatic tissues - men aged 65+, cancer of the brain - women of all ages, and leukemia – women aged 1 - 14 and 65+.

CONCLUSIONS: The authors urge caution in the interpretation of the results. The goal was to describe potential relationships between pesticide use in agriculture and the incidence of certain types of cancer, but not to confirm the causal relationship. Future individual-level epidemiological research is needed to examine the relationship between cancers and exposure to pesticides used in rural agricultural contexts.

Rosenberg, T., & Martel, S. (1998). Cancer trends from 1972-1991 for Registered Indians living on Manitoba reserves. *International Journal of Circumpolar Health, 57*(Suppl 1), 391-398.

OBJECTIVES: To determine the incidence of and mortality from cancer from 1972 to 1991, and to describe the distribution of cancer sites and survival for Registered Indians living on-reserve in the province of Manitoba.

METHODS: Data were abstracted from the computerized cancer registry of the Manitoba Cancer Treatment and Research Foundation for the period 1972 to 1991. Cases were reported to the registry through mandatory physician notification, pathology reports, health insurance claim records, and death certificates. Postal codes from the 38 of 61 Manitoba reserves with unique codes were used to identify cases; status as a Registered Indian with a treaty number was not recorded on the registry. Treaty Status was verified using a population registry kept by Health Canada's Medical Services Branch. On-reserve population figures were obtained from the federal Department of Indian Affairs.

DEFINITION OF RURAL: No definition of rural was provided. The population on the 38 reserves was 28,409 in 1972 and 49,152 in 1991, representing a 73% increase. The authors suggest that the reserves with unique postal codes may have been more isolated than the more urbanized reserves sharing a postal code with adjacent towns.

RESULTS RELATED TO RURAL AGING: A total of 700 cases of cancer and 308 cancer deaths were reported during the study period. Cancer incidence rates rose with age. The incidence rates per 100,000 per year were 1,135.4 for males aged 60 - 69 and 2,048.6 for males aged 70+. The corresponding figures for females were 738.0 and 1,464.4, respectively. Cancer mortality rates also increased with age (541.2 for males 60 - 69; 988.6 for males 70+; 418.2 for females 60 - 69; 599.7 for females 70+). Lung, prostate, and colorectal cancers were the most frequent among males whereas, for females, these were breast, cervix, colorectal, and lung cancers. No specific information on the cancer site was provided for the 60+ group.

CONCLUSIONS: Cancer incidence and mortality appear to be increasing on reserves. The authors argue that these trends will likely continue unless there is reduction in the high rate of smoking, and a change in dietary habits. They call for the implementation of more widespread and effective Pap screening on reserves.

Schechter, M. T., Spitzer, W. O., Hutcheon, M. E., Dales, R. E., Eastridge, L. M., Steinmetz, N., Tousignant, P., & Hobbs, C. (1989). Cancer downwind from sour gas refineries: The perception and the reality of an epidemic. *Environmental Health Perspectives, 79*, 283-290.

OBJECTIVES: To investigate the cancer incidence in a rural population living downwind from natural gas refineries, in southern areas of the province of Alberta.

METHODS: As part of a large field epidemiologic study undertaken during Summer 1985 to investigate possible health effects in the rural area (referred to as the Index Area), a residential cohort study was carried out to investigate cancer incidence. The cohort was defined as all those individuals who resided in the area in 1970. A total of 30,175 person-years of risk within Alberta were experienced by this cohort from 1970 to 1984. The incident cancers during this period were enumerated by computerized record linkage with the Alberta Cancer Registry. The three referent populations were from the Census Division 2 excluding the metropolitan area of Lethbridge; the Census Division 6 excluding the metropolitan area of Calgary, both located in southern Alberta; and all of rural southern Alberta with the exclusion of Lethbridge, Calgary, and Medicine Hat.

DEFINITION OF RURAL: The Index Area is a rural area located southeast of the town of Pincher Creek and east of the Rocky Mountains. It consists primarily of ranchland surrounding small communities (Twin Butte, Glenwood, Mountain View, Hill Spring, and Willow Creek). Two natural gas refineries that emit primarily sulfur began production in the area in 1957.

RESULTS RELATED TO RURAL AGING: Age- and sex-standardized incidence ratios excluding nonmelanotic skin cancer, based on expected rates from the three referent populations were 0.91, 0.93, and 0.89, respectively. Those same ratios including nonmelanotic skin cancer were 1.05, 1.09, and 1.03, respectively, none of which was significantly different from unity.

CONCLUSIONS: The findings suggest that the overall cancer experience for this cohort, during the study period, was remarkably similar to what should have been expected and offered reassurance to a community that was convinced it had experienced an epidemic of cancer.

See also Schechter, M. T., Spitzer, W. O., Hutcheon, M. E., Dales, R. E., Eastridge, L. M., Hobbs, C., Suissa, S., Tousignant, P., & Steinmetz, N. (1990).

Cardiovascular

Bussey, L. A., & Rothfels, P. (2003). Vitamin B$_{12}$ deficiency and megaloblastic anemia in elderly female patients in a rural community. *Canadian Journal of Rural Medicine, 8*(3), 179-181.

OBJECTIVES: To determine whether macrocytic anemia is a useful indicator of vitamin B$_{12}$ deficiency in older adults in the province of Nova Scotia.

METHODS: A retrospective chart review was completed on 102 females aged 65+ who were patients in one author's family practice in the town of Noel. Vitamin B$_{12}$ levels prior to treatment and corresponding mean corpuscular volume (MCV), hemoglobin level, and age at time of testing were recorded. Only 50 of the 102 charts (49%) contained information on vitamin B$_{12}$ levels and were used in the analysis. Patients with vitamin B$_{12}$ levels less than 116 pmol/L were considered deficient; normal range was 116 to 781 pmol/L. Patients with hemoglobin levels less than 110g/L were considered anemic; the normal range was 110 to 150g/L. Patients with MCVs higher than 100 fl were considered to have macrocytosis; nomal range was 76 to 100 fl.

DEFINITION OF RURAL: At the time of the study, Noel's population was 200 - 250, with a catchment area of 4,000 and there was only one family physician practicing in the area. Described as a "remote community", the nearest community hospital was 45 minutes away (p. 180).

RESULTS RELATED TO RURAL AGING: A deficiency in vitamin B$_{12}$ was evident for 10 of the 50 female patients aged 65+. Only 1 was anemic and 1 had macrocytosis. There were no differences between the groups with and without a vitamin B$_{12}$ deficiency in terms of age, hemoglobin level, or MCV.

CONCLUSIONS: These results suggest that vitamin B$_{12}$ deficiency often is present without macrocytic anemia. The authors argue for the importance of testing older patients for vitamin B$_{12}$ deficiency, given the severe and irreversible neurological damage that can occur with such deficiencies.

Chen, Y., Rennie, D. C., Lockinger, L. A., & Dosman, J. A. (1998). Association between obesity and high blood pressure: Reporting bias related to gender and age. *International Journal of Obesity, 22,* **771-777.**

OBJECTIVES: To examine the validity of self-reported information on obesity and high blood pressure (HBP) and to explore the impacts of misclassification on the association between obesity and HBP in the province of Saskatchewan.

METHODS: Data were from a 1993 community based cross-sectional study conducted in Humboldt, Saskatchewan. The analysis was limited to 1,791 individuals aged 18+, including 659 participants aged 55 - 74. A questionnaire and clinical assessment were completed with each participant. Objectively measured HBP was positive if systolic blood pressure (BP) was $\geq$ 140 mm Hg, diastolic BP was $\geq$ 90 mm Hg, or the subject was currently using antihypertensive medication. Self-reported HBP was positive if the respondents answered affirmatively to the question: *Has a doctor ever said you had high blood pressure*? Body mass index (BMI) was calculated as weight (kg)/height (m^2). Obesity was defined as a BMI > 27 kg/m^2. Measured obesity and reported obesity were based on measured and self-reported information on height and weight, respectively.

DEFINITION OF RURAL: No information was provided although the reader is directed to other publications from this study.

RESULTS RELATED TO RURAL AGING: The prevalence of reported HBP among both males and females aged 55 - 74 was lower than that of objectively measured HBP. Overall, males were more likely to underreport than were females, and younger participants were more likely to underreport compared to older participants. A similar pattern was evident for obesity. Age- and gender-specific sensitivity, specificity, positive and negative predictive values, and relative risk were provided.

CONCLUSIONS: The bias in self-reporting, which is related to gender, age, and obesity status, has important implications for relative risk estimates for HBP.

See also Chen, Y., Rennie, D. C., & Reeder, B. A. (1995).

Chen, Y., Rennie, D. C., & Reeder, B. A. (1995). Age-related association between body mass index and blood pressure: The Humboldt study. *International Journal of Obesity and Related Metabolic Disorders, 19*(11), 825-831.

OBJECTIVES: To investigate how age modifies the relation between body mass and blood pressure among residents in the town of Humboldt, in the province of Saskatchewan.

METHODS: In 1993, a community-based, cross-sectional study was conducted with 2,865 residents aged 6 to 74 years in the town of Humboldt (response rate of 86%). All households in the community were approached; questionnaires were left at the home for completion and returned during a pre-arranged clinic visit. Information was gathered on sociodemographic characteristics; smoking; alcohol consumption; exercise; the home environment; and individual/family history of diabetes, and pulmonary and cardiovascular disease. During a clinic visit or in the school, lung function, blood pressure, height, and weight were measured. Body mass index [weight (kg)/height (m^2)] was calculated. The analyses focused on the 2,326 respondent aged 18+; 153 males and 228 females were aged 65+.

DEFINITION OF RURAL: Humboldt is a service centre for an agricultural trading area. Population figures were not provided.

RESULTS RELATED TO RURAL AGING: The mean blood pressure and body mass index rose with increasing age among females. A similar pattern was evident for males, with the exception of a leveling off of diastolic blood pressure and body mass index in those aged 65 - 74. In the 55 - 74 age group, the mean blood pressure for a 1-unit increase in body mass index (kg/m^2) was 0.47 mm Hg for males and 0.43 mm Hg for females. In females, age also modified the relation between body mass index and the prevalence of high blood pressure. The odds ratios for high blood pressure for a 1-unit increase in body mass index were 1.10 for both males and females in the 55 - 74 age group.

CONCLUSIONS: The relationship of body mass index with diastolic blood pressure in both males and females appeared stronger in young children and adults than in older persons. These results suggest that age has a modifying effect on this relationship, but that the modifying effect may vary between populations with different relative body weights.

See also Chen, Y., Rennie, D. C., Lockinger, L. A., & Dosman, J. A. (1998).

McIntyre, L., & Shah, C. P. (1986). Prevalence of hypertension, obesity and smoking in three Indian communities in northwestern Ontario. *Canadian Medical Association Journal, 134*(4), 345-349.

OBJECTIVES: To determine community levels of blood pressure and to document the prevalence of hypertension, obesity, and cigarette smoking in non-urban Indians in three northwestern communities in the province of Ontario.

METHODS: A cross-sectional blood pressure survey was conducted over 7 days in July and August 1983 in three isolated communities. Blood pressure was measured and chart reviews for a previous diagnosis of hypertension and evidence of control were completed. All but 10 of the 678 individuals present in the communities at the time of the survey (99%) participated. Age- and sex-specific mean diastolic and systolic blood pressure readings were calculated.

DEFINITION OF RURAL: The three communities were located in the Sioux Lookout Zone which was a health service area of the Medical Services Branch, Department of National Health and Welfare. About 10,000 Cree and Ojibwa Indians lived in approximately 30 remote settlements in the sub-arctic boreal forest.

RESULTS RELATED TO RURAL AGING: Systolic blood pressure generally rose with increasing age while diastolic blood pressure was lower in the 55 - 64 and 65+ age groups than in the 45 - 55 age group for both males and females. However, all of the mean systolic and diastolic blood pressure readings by age and sex were below the cut points for elevated blood pressure (diastolic pressure of $\geq$ 95 mm Hg; systolic pressure of $\geq$ 160 mm Hg). The overall prevalence rate of hypertension was 13%. Females aged 65+ were more likely to be hypertensive than males in this age group. The risk factors for hypertension (obesity and smoking) were investigated. Obesity was significantly related to hypertension, but the relationship was age-dependent (no further details provided). Longer duration of smoking (usually an effect of age) was positively related to hypertension.

CONCLUSIONS: The results support the need for improved screening for hypertension in this population, particularly for males.

Monsalve, M. V., Thommasen, H. V., Pachev, G., & Frohlich, J. (2005). Differences in cardiovascular risks in the aboriginal and non-aboriginal people living in Bella Coola, British Columbia. *Medical Science Monitor, 11*(1), CR21-CR28.

OBJECTIVES: To establish the relative prevalence of cardiovascular disease (CVD) risk factors among people of aboriginal and non-aboriginal descent living in Bella Coola in the province of British Columbia.

METHODS: A retrospective review of the 2,378 charts located in the Bella Coola Medical Clinic was conducted in Fall 2002. Anthropometric, biochemical, and clinical information was obtained for 1,120 people of Nuxalk descent and 1,258 people of mainly European descent. Children and adults of either sex, pre- and post-menopausal women, and patients with hyperlipidaemia, Type 2 diabetes, and hypertension were included in the review.

DEFINITION OF RURAL: Bella Coola is a rural and remote community located in the central coast region of British Columbia. In 2001, the population was 2,289. The hospital is one of the most isolated physician-staffed hospital facilities in the province, with the closest referral hospital being over 450 kilometres by road or a two-hour flight by air. Approximately 47% of the population is aboriginal, mostly of Nuxalk decent.

RESULTS RELATED TO RURAL AGING: Among individuals aged 65+ of aboriginal descent, 60% had cardiovascular disease (22% - coronary heart disease, 17% - transient ischemic attacks or cerebrovascular accidents, 12% - peripheral vascular disease, 36% - hypertension). The percentages for the non-aboriginal aged 65+ age group were 58% (15% - coronary heart disease, 8% - transient ischemic attacks or cerebrovascular accidents, 5% - peripheral vascular disease, 47% - hypertension). There was no indication of whether these were statistically significant differences. Coronary artery disease appeared to be more prevalent in older aboriginal people whereas hypertension appeared to be more prevalent in older non-aboriginal people.

CONCLUSIONS: The majority of older adults have some form of cardiovascular disease although it is more prevalent in older aboriginal people. The authors call for a prospective randomized trial controlling for dietary habits and other lifestyle factors.

Dementia/Cognition

Émard, J.-F., Thouez, J.-P., Mathieu, J., Boily, C., Beaudry, M., Cholette, A., Robitaille, Y., Bouchard, R., & Gauvreau, D. (1992). Répartition géographique de la maladie d'Alzheimer au Saguenay–Lac-Saint-Jean, Québec (Projet IMAGE) : Résultats préliminaires. (Geographical distribution of Alzheimer's disease in Saguenay – Lac-Saint-Jean, Quebec (IMAGE Project): Preliminary findings). *Cahiers de Géographie du Québec, 36*(97), 61-75.

OBJECTIVES: To present preliminary findings of the IMAGE Project (an acronym for Research into Genetics and Epidemiology of Alzheimer's disease [AD]), the geographical distribution of AD cases, and the initial measurements on the rural-urban variations in prevalence rates, in one region of the province of Quebec.

METHODS: The IMAGE Project involved screening and establishing a registry of AD cases since 1986 in the Saguenay – Lac-Saint-Jean territory. Data presented were based on 221 'definite', 'probable', and 'possible' cases in six areas of the region. 'Possible' cases were patients who presented at least one illness that complicated the diagnosis of AD. 'Probable' cases were patients whose neuropsychological changes closely corresponded to the clinical template describing the onset and development of AD and whose medical history did not present any exclusion criteria. Both 'possible' and 'probable' cases were confirmed as 'definite' by means of the autopsy and neuropathological examination after death. Prevalence rates were calculated for: (1) all 'definite', 'probable', and 'possible' cases; and (2) for 'definite' and 'probable' cases only. Observed prevalence rates were estimated by comparing cases to the general population aged 45+ in 1981. Rates were calculated for each of the six geographic areas; odds ratios were used to estimate rural-urban differences.

DEFINITION OF RURAL: Situated approximately 225 kilometres north of Quebec City, the Saguenay – Lac-Saint-Jean territory covers about 23,000 square kilometres. The rural-urban classification was based on the municipality and took into account modifications of legal status and boundaries of the municipalities in the province of Quebec.

RESULTS RELATED TO RURAL AGING: The risk of AD tended to be higher in urban zones for the spheres of La Baie, Chicoutimi, and Roberval. In the spheres of Jonquiere, Alma, and Dolbeau, the risk of AD tended to be higher in rural zones. For all spheres except Alma, these results were not statistically significant. The findings were consistent when all 'definite', 'probable', and 'possible' cases were considered and when only the 'definite' and 'probable' cases were examined.

CONCLUSIONS: The finding that the risk of AD in urban zones was not statistically different from the risk observed in rural zones, with the exception of the sphere of Alma, is in contrast to the findings of other studies. The authors recognize the difficulty of studying environmental risks that may affect AD and call for a comparison of the distribution of AD cases taking into account the place of birth in addition to place of residency at the moment of appearance of first symptoms.

See also Jean, H., Emard, J.-F., Thouez, J.-P., Houde, L., Robitaille, Y., Mathieu, J., Boily, C., Daoud, N., Beaudry, M., Cholette, A., Bouchard, R., Veilleux, F., & Gauvreau, D. (1996).

Frecker, M. F. (1991). Dementia in Newfoundland: Identification of a geographical isolate? *Journal of Epidemiology & Community Health, 45*(4), 307-311.

OBJECTIVES: To identify geographical regions in the province of Newfoundland with an increased incidence of dementia mortality and to confirm whether there was an excess of patients with Alzheimer's disease originating from a small geographical area.

METHODS: All 1985 and 1986 death certificates registered at the Vital Statistics Division of the Newfoundland Department of Health were reviewed for immediate, antecedent, underlying, or contributing causes of death that could be attributed to dementia (Alzheimer's disease, chronic/organic brain syndrome, dementia, senile dementia/senile confusion, or senility). Age, sex, place of birth, and place of death were recorded for all eligible cases. Birthplaces of those aged 70+ with dementia were compared to those aged 70+ who died without dementia. Two Census Divisions (03 and 07) were compared in order to test the significance of a geographical isolate of persons. The frequency of family names was analyzed to examine a possible genetic component of the excess while standard measures of drinking water quality were used to test for a possible environmental component.

DEFINITION OF RURAL: Census Division 03 is a relatively isolated region on the southwest coast of Newfoundland; Census Division 07 includes Bonavista Bay and the north shore of Trinity Bay.

RESULTS RELATED TO RURAL AGING: The overall prevalence of dementia at death for 1985 and 1986 was 34 and 37/100,000, respectively, with a significant excess of persons originating from a small area. Differences in age, sex, ethnic origin, and mobility patterns did not explain the excess. A high concentration of aluminum in the drinking water was found in the small areas. An analysis of the family names gave inconclusive evidence of a clustering among the dementia cases.

CONCLUSIONS: The author indicates that it is possible that environmental factors, as yet undefined, can produce a dementing illness. He argues that areas smaller than census districts need to be studied in order to identify subpopulation variation in the prevalence of dementia, and calls for future research to determine the genetic and environmental factors.

Gauthier, E., Fortier, I., Courchesne, F., Pepin, P., Mortimer, J., & Gauvreau, D. (2001). Environmental pesticide exposure as a risk factor for Alzheimer's Disease: A case control study. *Environmental Research, 86*, 37-45.

OBJECTIVES: To evaluate the influence of pesticide exposure on the development of Alzheimer's disease (AD), taking into account potentially confounding factors (genetic, occupational exposure, and sociodemographic) in the province of Quebec.

METHODS: An age-gender stratified random sample of 1,924 individuals aged 70+ in the Saguenay - Lac-Saint-Jean region was selected from the files of the provincial health plan of Quebec. The AD diagnosis was established in three steps according to recognized criteria. Sixty-eight AD cases were paired with a non-demented control for age (± 2 years) and sex. Structured questionnaires were used to collect information on sociodemographic characteristics, lifestyle characteristics, and residential, occupational, familial, and medical histories. Assessment of environmental exposure to pesticides was based on residential histories and the agriculture census histories of Statistics Canada (1971 - 1991) for herbicide and insecticide spraying in the area.

DEFINITION OF RURAL: The Saguenay – Lac-Saint-Jean region is in a geographically isolated area of Quebec. No additional information about the region was provided.

RESULTS RELATED TO RURAL AGING: Long-term exposure to herbicides, insecticides, and pesticides did not emerge as a significant risk factor for AD.

CONCLUSIONS: While the development of AD was not associated with exposure, the authors caution that the risk may be underestimated and offer a number of reasons for this. They call for future investigations to establish more precisely the identification, measurement, mobility, and bioavailability of neurotoxic pesticide residues in relation to AD.

Hébert, R., Lindsay, J., Verreault, R., Rockwood, K., Hill, G., & Dubois, M.-F. (2000). Vascular dementia: Incidence and risk factors in the Canadian Study of Health and Aging. *Stroke, 31*(7), 1487-1493.

OBJECTIVES: To determine incidence rates of vascular dementia (VaD) and associated risk factors in Canada.

METHODS: Data were from the Canadian Study of Health and Aging (CSHA). CSHA-1 was conducted in 1991/92 and involved data collection with an age-stratified random sample of 10,263 Canadians aged 65+. The incidence cohort sample consisted of 8,623 subjects who participated in CSHA-1 and were followed up in 1996. Risk factors were examined with a nested, prospective, case-control study. Exposure was determined by means of a risk factor questionnaire administered to the subject or a proxy at the beginning of the study.

DEFINITION OF RURAL: No definition of rural was provided. The sample was from 36 urban centres and the surrounding areas.

RESULTS RELATED TO RURAL AGING: On the basis of 38,476 person-years at risk, the annual incidence rate was estimated to be 2.52 per thousand undemented Canadians. When an estimation of the probability of VaD among the decedents was added, the figure rose to 3.79. For the risk factors study, 105 incident cases of VaD (based on the NINCDS-AIREN* criteria) were compared with 802 control subjects. A larger proportion of cases lived in rural (18%) than in urban areas (11%). Individuals residing in rural areas were 2 times more likely to develop VaD. Other significant risk factors were age, living in an institution, diabetes, depression, apolipoprotein E epsilon4, hypertension for women, heart problems for men, taking aspirin, and occupational exposure to pesticides or fertilizers. Protective factors were eating shellfish and regular exercise for women. Sex, education, and alcohol consumption were not significant.

CONCLUSIONS: The authors claim that this is the largest population-based incidence study on VaD and also the largest risk factor study in this field. In terms of rural aging, the risk associated with exposure to pesticides and fertilizers may explain in part the heightened risk for rural residents. Prospective studies that include exposure data are needed to provide more insight into these associations.

* National Institute of Neurological Communicative Disorders and Stroke - Association Internationale pour la Recherché et l'Enseignement en Neurosciences.

Jean, H., Emard, J.-F., Thouez, J.-P., Houde, L., Robitaille, Y., Mathieu, J., Boily, C., Daoud, N., Beaudry, M., Cholette, A., Bouchard, R., Veilleux, F., & Gauvreau, D. (1996). Alzheimer's disease: Preliminary study of spatial distribution at birth place. *Social Science & Medicine, 42*(6), 871-878.

OBJECTIVES: To explore the hypothesis that risk factors acting at, or around, birth place and time play a role in the etiology of Alzheimer's disease (AD). The study involved participants from the province of Quebec.

METHODS: Data were from Projet Image, a population-based study that integrated genetic and epidemiological data on AD. A registry of cases in the area of Saguenay – Saint-Lac-Saint Jean (SLSJ), Quebec began in 1986. Data on AD cases were collected from 1986 to 1994. Cases were classified based on NINCDS/ADRDA criteria. In this preliminary study, the rural and urban distribution of the birth places of a sample of 235 AD cases born in a specific region of Quebec between 1895 and 1935 was examined. A reference population of live births was used to compute odds ratios.

DEFINITION OF RURAL: The area of SLSJ, located in central Quebec, had a total population of approximately 300,000 across 12,000 square kilometres and a population density of approximately 25 persons per square kilometre. Urban municipalities included municipalities classified as cities or villages in the 1991 Statistics Canada Census Tract data, with > 2,500 residents concentrated in a well-defined urban agglomeration. Other municipalities were considered rural.

RESULTS RELATED TO RURAL AGING: There was a statistically significant excess of AD cases in the rural area as compared to the reference population. However, when stratified for sex, the rural-urban differences were accounted for by an excess of female AD cases in both the rural and the urban areas. For men, only the urban area presented a statistically significant deficit. An analysis of the structures of the genealogical kinships of the rural and urban sub-groups found that removal of the kin pairs had little effect on the rural/urban distribution of cases.

CONCUSIONS: The results revealed a higher number of AD cases born in the rural sub-group as compared to the reference population. It suggests the existence of confounders or social and/or environmental differences between rural and urban areas. However, the authors caution that potential biases such as a higher rate of report for women, differential migration between birth places, or a differential mortality ratio between sexes could produce spurious results in the direction of the findings from this preliminary study.

See also Émard, J.-F., Thouez, J.-P., Mathieu, J., Boily, C., Beaudry, M., Cholette, A., Robitaille, Y., Bouchard, R., & Gauvreau, D. (1992).

MSHA Research Group. (1995). *Manitoba Study of Health and Aging Final Report: Executive Summary and Technical Section.* **Winnipeg, MB: Centre on Aging, University of Manitoba.**

OBJECTIVES: To examine the prevalence of dementia among individuals aged 65+ in the province of Manitoba.

METHODS: Data were from the 1991/92 Manitoba Study of Health and Aging (MSHA). In-person interviews were conducted with a random sample of older adults aged 65+ in the community and clinical assessments with those whose screening assessment indicated possible cognitive impairment were undertaken. In addition, clinical assessments were completed with 189 institutionalized residents aged 65+. Institutions were first stratified into three groups based on bed size and then a random sample of institutions was chosen for each size stratum. Within each selected institution, a random sample of residents was selected. The screening interview included the Modified Mini Mental State Examination (3MS). The clinical assessment consisted of the Cambridge Examination for Mental Disorder of the Elderly (CAMDEX), a brief questionnaire and re-administration of the 3MS, a neuropsychological assessment, and a physician examination. Diagnostic criteria were based on the Diagnostic and Statistical Manual of Mental Disorders (DMS-III-R), and the NINCDS-ADRDA recommendation for the diagnosis of dementia of the Alzheimer's type. The International Classification of Diseases (ICD-10) was used to define sub-categories of vascular and 'other' dementias. Weighted estimates of the prevalence of dementia of all types for Manitoba, for Winnipeg, and for non-Winnipeg by age and gender were calculated.

DEFINITION OF RURAL: Winnipeg/non-Winnipeg comparisons were made. Winnipeg is the major urban centre in the province; non-Winnipeg was defined as all areas outside of Winnipeg.

RESULTS RELATED TO RURAL AGING: Slightly more individuals with dementia (all types) lived in Winnipeg (56%) than outside Winnipeg (44%). While the crude rate outside Winnipeg was slightly higher (83/1,000) than in Winnipeg (81/1,000), there was no difference when the rate was age- and sex-standardized (76/1,000 vs. 76/1,000). This suggests that the difference in the number and in the crude rate of dementia (all types) between Winnipeg and the rest of the province was due to differences in the age and sex distribution of the population within Manitoba. In both Winnipeg and the rest of the province, similar proportions of individuals with dementia (all types) resided in institutions (51% vs. 49%, respectively). The age-standardized rate of Alzheimer's disease was lower in Winnipeg (52/1,000) than in the rest of the province (62/1,000). The difference was consistent for both males and females overall, although not for age groups. There was virtually no difference between Winnipeg and the rest of the province with respect to the prevalence of vascular dementia (age-standardized rates of 12/1,000 and 11/1,000, respectively) while the prevalence of 'other' dementia was higher in Winnipeg (11/1,000) than in the rest of the province (4/1,000). This difference was greater for females (14/1,000 vs. 3/1,000) than for males (9/1,000 vs. 6/1,000).

CONCLUSIONS: The results underscore the importance of factors such as type of dementia, and age and sex distribution in studies examining the prevalence of dementia.

See also MSHA-2 Research Group. (1998). Follow-up to the Manitoba Study of Health and Aging (MSHA-2): Changes in Cognitive Status in Later Life; MSHA-2 Research Group. (1998). Follow-up to the Manitoba Study of Health and Aging (MSHA-2): Factors related to the risk of developing Alzheimer's Disease; and Strain, L. A., Blandford, A. A., & St. John, P. D. (2003).

MSHA-2 Research Group. (1998). *Follow-up to the Manitoba Study of Health and Aging (MSHA-2): Changes in Cognitive Status in Later Life.* **Winnipeg, MB: Centre on Aging, University of Manitoba.**

OBJECTIVES: To explore changes in cognitive status from 1991/92 to 1996/97, and to identify characteristics associated with the development of cognitive impairment in the province of Manitoba.

METHODS: Data were from the 1991/92 and 1996/97 Manitoba Study of Health and Aging (MSHA), an expansion of the Canadian Study of Health and Aging (CSHA). The sample consisted of 1,763 community-dwelling older adults and 189 individuals in institutional settings in 1991/92. Cognitive status was assessed in 1991/92 and in 1996/97 in two stages, first using the Modified Mini-Mental State Examination (3MS) and then based on clinical assessments with those scoring below the cutoff point. The diagnosis was based on established criteria. Cognitive status categories were cognitively intact, possible cognitive impairment, cognitive impairment-no dementia (CIND), and dementia.

DEFINITION OF RURAL: Winnipeg/non-Winnipeg comparisons were made. Winnipeg is the major urban centre in the province; non-Winnipeg was defined as all areas outside of Winnipeg.

RESULTS RELATED TO RURAL AGING: No Winnipeg/non-Winnipeg differences emerged in the likelihood of becoming cognitively impaired over the five-year period. This held for both the community-dwelling and institutional samples.

CONCLUSIONS: The authors caution that their findings cannot be generalized to all Manitobans aged 65+. They discuss the difficulty of studying changes in cognitive status and call for future research, service delivery, and policy development.

See also MSHA Research Group. (1995); MSHA-2 Research Group. (1998). Follow-up to the Manitoba Study of Health and Aging (MSHA-2): Factors related to the risk of developing Alzheimer's Disease; and Strain, L. A., Blandford, A. A., & St. John, P. D. (2003).

MSHA-2 Research Group. (1998). *Follow-up to the Manitoba Study of Health and Aging (MSHA-2): Factors related to the risk of developing Alzheimer's Disease.* **Winnipeg, MB: Centre on Aging, University of Manitoba.**

OBJECTIVES: To identify factors that influence the risk of developing Alzheimer's disease (AD) in the province of Manitoba.

METHODS: Data were from the 1991/92 and 1996/97 Manitoba Study of Health and Aging (MSHA), an expansion of the Canadian Study of Health and Aging (CSHA). These analyses were limited to 694 community-dwelling individuals aged 65+ who were cognitively intact in 1991/92, who completed a risk factor questionnaire in 1991/92, and who were re-interviewed in 1996/97. Cognitive status was assessed in 1991/92 and 1996/97 in two stages, first using the Modified Mini-Mental State Examination (3MS) in a screening interview and then through clinical assessments with those scoring below the cutoff point. The diagnosis was determined, using established criteria.

DEFINITION OF RURAL: Place of residence (Winnipeg/non-Winnipeg) was considered as a risk factor. Winnipeg is the major urban centre in the province; non-Winnipeg was defined as all areas outside of Winnipeg.

RESULTS RELATED TO RURAL AGING: Only 36 individuals were diagnosed with AD in 1996/97. Place of residence (Winnipeg/non-Winnipeg) did not emerge as a risk factor for AD. Occupation exposure to fumigants/defoliants did increase the risk of AD.

CONCLUSIONS: Given the limited number of new cases of AD, the authors urge caution in the interpretation of their findings.

See also MSHA Research Group. (1995); MSHA-2 Research Group. (1998). Follow-up to the Manitoba Study of Health and Aging (MSHA-2): Changes in Cognitive Status in Later Life; and Strain, L. A., Blandford, A. A., & St. John, P. D. (2003).

Strain, L. A., Blandford, A. A., & St. John, P. D. (2003). Who remains cognitively intact among the 80+ age group? *Geriatrics Today, 6,* 141-145.

OBJECTIVES: To examine change in cognitive status over a 5-year period among individuals aged 80+ in the province of Manitoba.

METHODS: Data are from the 1991/92 and 1996/97 Manitoba Study of Health and Aging (MSHA), an expansion of the Canadian Study of Health and Aging (CSHA). The sample for these analyses consisted of 611 cognitively intact individuals aged 80+ and living in the community at the time of the 1991/92 screening interview. Cognitive status was assessed in two stages, first using the Modified Mini-Mental State Examination (3MS) and then based on clinical assessments with those scoring below the cutoff point. The diagnosis was based on established criteria. Cognitive status categories were cognitively intact, possible cognitive impairment, cognitive impairment-no dementia (CIND), and dementia.

DEFINITION OF RURAL: Winnipeg/non-Winnipeg comparisons were made. Winnipeg is the major urban centre in the province; non-Winnipeg was defined as all areas outside of Winnipeg.

RESULTS RELATED TO RURAL AGING: Among the 453 individuals who were cognitively intact at baseline, 38% remained intact five years later, 24% were diagnosed with cognitive impairment (11% - CIND, 13% dementia), and 36% had died since 1991/92. Changes from a 1991/92 status of possible cognitive impairment, CIND, or dementia also were presented. A comparison of the 170 individuals who remained cognitively intact and the 283 who did not revealed no Winnipeg/non-Winnipeg differences.

CONCLUSIONS: Remaining cognitively intact is associated with younger age, more education, and better physical functioning. Study limitations and directions for future research are discussed.

See also MSHA Research Group. (1995); MSHA-2 Research Group. (1998). Follow-up to the Manitoba Study of Health and Aging (MSHA-2): Changes in Cognitive Status in Later Life; and MSHA-2 Research Group. (1998). Follow-up to the Manitoba Study of Health and Aging (MSHA-2): Factors related to the risk of developing Alzheimer's Disease.

Worrall, G., & Moulton, N. (1993). Cognitive function: Survey of elderly persons living at home in rural Newfoundland. *Canadian Family Physician, 39, 772-777.*

OBJECTIVES: To estimate the prevalence of cognitive dysfunction among elderly, rural community-dwelling residents in the province of Newfoundland.

METHODS: The study involved a community sample of 233 patients aged 70+ on June 1, 1990. Data were collected between June and September 1990. Patients were interviewed in random order. The Canadian Mental Status Questionnaire (CMSQ) was used to measure cognitive function and was administered to participants in their own homes. Medical records also were reviewed. Of the 233 respondents, 52% were female; 45% were aged 70 to 74.

DEFINITION OF RURAL: Located in rural north-eastern Newfoundland, the town of Glovertown had a population of 2,188 at the time of the study. There was a medical clinic served by 2 physicians.

RESULTS RELATED TO RURAL AGING: The prevalence rates for moderate and severe cognitive impairment as measured by the CMSQ were 6.8% and 2.3%, respectively. The rate of moderate/severe impairment for men in the community was 8.7% while for women, it was 9.3%. Caution is needed in interpreting the results given the small sample size. In addition, a number of limitations are associated with the CMSQ including a tendency to underestimate the prevalence of cognitive impairment (see original article by Robertson, Rockwood, & Stolee. (1982). A short mental status questionnaire. *Canadian Journal on Aging, 1*, 16-20).

CONCLUSIONS: The authors indicate that the physicians in the community had recognized those with severe impairment, but had not recognized those with moderate impairment. They suggest that cognitive function testing should be part of the periodic health examination of older patients.

COMMENTS: **Clarfield, A.M. (1993). Recognizing cognitive impairment.** *Canadian Family Physician, 1993, 39, 2107.* The author, Chair of the Canadian Consensus Conference on the Assessment of Dementia, alerts the reader to the publication of the *Canadian Conference on the Assessment of Dementia.* A summary of that report is available in: Organizing Committee, Canadian Consensus Conference on the Assessment of Dementia. (1991). Assessing dementia: The Canadian Consensus (editorial). *Canadian Medical Association Journal, 144*, 851-853.

Depression

Patten, S. B., Sedmak, B., & Russell, M. L. (2001). Major depression: Prevalence, treatment utilization and age in Canada. *Canadian Journal of Clinical Pharmacology, 8*(3), 133-138.

OBJECTIVES: To determine the relationships between age, the prevalence of major depression, and antidepressant treatment in the province of Alberta and nationally.

METHODS: Data were from two Alberta surveys and Statistics Canada's 1996 National Population Health Survey (NPHS). The two Alberta surveys were population-based, random-digit dial telephone surveys with 2,542 and 796 respondents, respectively. The first study was conducted in Calgary, with data collection between February 1, 1998 and July 1, 1999. The second study was undertaken in a predominantly rural Alberta health region, with data collection between May and August 1999. The NPHS involved 73,402 Canadians and relied on both in-person and telephone-based data collection methods. In all three studies, major depression was evaluated using the WHO Composite International Diagnostic Interview Short Form for Major Depression (CIDI-SFMD). Diagnostic status was examined in relation to current use of antidepressant medications, age, and other relevant factors. Unequal selection probabilities and clustering inherent in the sampling procedures were accounted for in all analyses.

DEFINITION OF RURAL: The predominantly rural health region had a population of approximately 74,000 at the time of the study and covered the area from Calgary south to the border with the United States and west to the British Columbia border. Predominant industries were agriculture, oil, and tourism. The urban centre, Calgary, had a population of 850,000. The NPHS analyses did not include a rural-urban distinction.

RESULTS RELATED TO RURAL AGING: In the rural sample, the prevalence of major depression was found to be highest among the 16 - 29 age group and lowest in the 65+ group. However, the prevalence of antidepressant use was highest for the 65+ group (7%) and lowest (< 1%) for the 16 - 29 age group. Younger rural respondents were less likely to have been given a diagnosis of a depressive disorder than their urban counterparts. The pattern of a decrease in the prevalence of major depression with age was evident in the Calgary study and the NPHS. The pattern of antidepressant use in the NPHS was similar to that for the rural Alberta study. In Calgary, the prevalence of antidepressant use was lower for the 65+ group than for the 45 - 64 age group.

CONCLUSIONS: The data presented indicate that antidepressant medications tend to be used less frequently in younger than older age groups in Canada. However, the authors note that there is a potential for antidepressant medication to be used more frequently for indications other than major depression in the older age group. The authors call for ongoing research in both rural and urban areas to confirm optimal use rates in relation to age.

See also Patten, S. B., Stuart, H. L., Russell, M. L., Maxwell, C. J., & Arboleda-Flórez, J. (2003).

Patten, S. B., Stuart, H. L., Russell, M. L., Maxwell, C. J., & Arboleda-Flórez, J. (2003). Epidemiology of major depression in a predominantly rural health region. *Social Psychiatry and Psychiatric Epidemiology, 38,* 360-365.

OBJECTIVES: To evaluate the prevalence and incidence of major depression in a predominantly rural health region in the province of Alberta.

METHODS: Data were from a cross-sectional general health survey that involved telephone interviews with 801 respondents. Random digit dialing was used to select one resident from each household. Respondents were invited to participate in a second telephone interview 6 months later. Of 801 subjects initially enrolled, 666 (83%) consented to be re-contacted, and 501 (75%) were successfully reached. Among the 65+, 135 participated in the initial interview and 76 completed the follow-up interview. The WHO Composite International Diagnostic Interview Short Form for Major Depression (CIDI-SFMD) was used in both waves. Numerous other variables relevant to the epidemiology of major depression were measured. The identical procedure was used in the urban sample.

DEFINITION OF RURAL: The predominantly rural health region had a population of approximately 74,000 at the time of the study and covered the area from Calgary south to the border with the United States and west to the British Columbia border. Predominant industries are agriculture, oil, and tourism. The urban centre was Calgary, with a population of 850,000.

RESULTS RELATED TO RURAL AGING: Among the 65+ age group, 7 (5%) of the respondents were depressed at the initial interview while 6 (8%) of those in the follow-up sample showed signs of depression 6 months later. The weighted prevalence of major depression for all age groups at baseline was 10.4% while the weighted incidence was 3.8%. Having a past history of depression and having a high level of perceived stress were predictors of risk. An exploratory comparison with data collected using similar methods in Calgary revealed that rural prevalence (10.5%) was lower than urban (15.2%), when adjusted for age and sex.

CONCLUSIONS: The 6-month cumulative incidence of depressive disorder was higher than that reported in most previous studies. This may reflect the diagnostic instrument used in the study and that subjects with previous depressive episodes during their lifetime were not excluded from the study. The authors argue that geographic differences in the prevalence of mental disorders have important implications for service planning and delivery.

See also Patten, S. B., Sedmak, B., & Russell, M. L. (2001).

Wang, J. L. (2004). Rural-urban differences in the prevalence of major depression and associated impairment. *Social Psychiatry & Psychiatric Epidemiology, 39*(1), 19-25.

OBJECTIVES: To examine the rural and urban difference in the 12-month prevalence of major depressive episode(s) (MDE) in Canada, and whether participants in rural and urban areas differed in the impairment levels due to depressive symptoms and in mental health service utilization.

METHODS: Data were from 1998/99 Canadian National Population Health Survey (NPHS). MDE was measured by the Composite International Diagnostic Interview-Short Form for Major Depression (CIDI-SFMD). Two-week disability and daily life interference due to depressive symptoms were used as indicators of impairment. The prevalence of MDE in rural and urban areas, at national and regional levels, was calculated. Impairment levels and mental health service utilization also were compared between the rural and urban groups. Three age groups (12 - 19, 20 - 54, 55+) were studied.

DEFINITION OF RURAL: All territories outside urban areas were considered as rural. Urban was defined as minimum population of 1000 with a population density of at least 400 per square kilometre (Statistics Canada, 1999).

RESULTS RELATED TO RURAL AGING: Among the 55+ age group, a significant rural-urban difference in the prevalence of MDE was evident, with a lower rate among the rural group. This trend also was evident for the non-immigrant group. No age specific analyses were conducted with regard to rural-urban differences in 2-week disability, daily life interference due to depressive symptoms, or contact with health professionals for mental health problems.

CONCLUSIONS: The authors call for consideration of rural and urban differences in future mental health service planning, particularly at provincial levels.

Diabetes

Brassard, P., Robinson, E., & Lavallée, C. (1993). Prevalence of diabetes mellitus among the James Bay Cree of northern Quebec. *Canadian Medical Association Journal, 149*(3), 303-307.

OBJECTIVES: To determine the prevalence of diabetes mellitus among the James Bay Cree in six remote and two northern rural communities in the province of Quebec.

METHODS: During July and August 1989, a chart survey of physician-diagnosed cases of diabetes was undertaken. Cases were identified from a chronic disease registry or from the diabetes clinic list kept at each community clinic. Eligible cases were Cree residents of eight James Bay Cree communities. The biochemical criteria of the World Health Organization were used to confirm the diagnoses. Prevalence rates, both crude and standardized to the 1986 Canadian population, were estimated by sex, age group, and type of diabetes.

DEFINITION OF RURAL: The eight villages varied in population from 384 to 2,419 in 1989. The five coastal communities and the inland community of Nemaska were defined as remote; the other two inland communities were considered as rural. Remote communities were accessed primarily by air; rural communities were accessible by road.

RESULTS RELATED TO RURAL AGING: A total of 235 cases of diabetes were confirmed, for a crude prevalence of 2.7%. The age-standardized rate of Non-Insulin-Dependent Diabetes Mellitus (NIDDM) was 6.6% among individuals aged 20+. The prevalence increased with age until age 60 - 69 and then decreased. The rate for the 60 - 69 age group was approximately 20% (information provided in a Figure; exact rate not given). An examination of gender differences revealed that the prevalence rate was highest for females aged 60 - 69 and for males aged 50 - 59. The mean rate of NIDDM was significantly higher in the two rural communities than in the six remote communities (8.8% vs. 3.4%, respectively). The overall prevalence for Insulin Dependent Diabetes Mellitus (IDDM) was 0.06%, indicating that IDDM is still infrequent in the native population.

CONCLUSIONS: The crude prevalence rates were comparable to those reported for similar native linguistic and cultural groups elsewhere in Canada. The decrease in rates after age 60 may reflect a survivor effect; the overrepresentation of individuals without diabetes in the older groups may be due to the survivor's better health or a resistance in the older age groups to adopt a Western lifestyle. The authors argue that a better understanding of the sociocultural changes in this population is necessary.

COMMENTS AND AUTHORS' REPONSE: **Worrall, G. (1994). Diabetes among native people. *Canadian Medical Association Journal, 150*(5), 644-645.** Worrall agreed that diabetes is becoming an important disease among the native population but argues that it is equally prevalent among non-native people. He disputed the authors' claim that the prevalence of diabetes is "now two to five times higher the rate in the remaining population" (p. 644). In the authors' response (pp. 645-646), they indicated that they "still believe that there is a higher prevalence among native people of North America (excluding the Inuit)."

Delisle, H. F., & Ekoé, J.-M. (1993). Prevalence of non-insulin-dependent diabetes mellitus and impaired glucose tolerance in two Algonquin communities in Quebec. *Canadian Medical Association Journal, 148*(1), 41-47.

OBJECTIVES: To assess and compare the prevalence of non-insulin-dependent diabetes mellitus (NIDDM) and impaired glucose tolerance (IGT) in two Algonguin communities in the province of Quebec.

METHODS: All native Indian residents aged 15+ residing in River Desert and Lac Simon were eligible for this population-based study, conducted between March and December 1989. Of the 621 participants, 68 (11%) were aged 65+ (53 River Desert, 15 Lac Simon). They attended a central survey site where measures of blood glucose level and serum glucose level 2 hours after a 75-g oral glucose tolerance test (except those with confirmed diabetes), body mass index (BMI), fat distribution, and blood pressure were obtained. Personal interviews were conducted at the site the same day or within a week in the participant's home; information was gathered on sociodemographic characteristics, ethnic background, personal and family medical history, diet, and level of physical activity.

DEFINITION OF RURAL: River Desert and Lac Simon are the two largest Alonquin communities in Quebec. River Desert is located 128 kilometres north of Hull and adjacent to Maniwaki, and had a population of approximately 1,200. Lac Simon, with a population of approximately 600, is further north and 32 kilometres from Val d'Or.

RESULTS RELATED TO RURAL AGING: The age-sex standardized prevalence rate of NIDDM was 19% in Lac Simon and 9% in River Desert. The highest rate for any age-gender group was reported for females aged 65+ in River Desert. In Lac Simon, the highest rate was for females aged 50 - 64. Considering all age groups, the 65+ had lower rates than the 50 - 64 age group, with the exception of females in River Desert. In both communities, females aged 65+ had a higher prevalence of marked obesity (BMI greater than 30), with the rates for the 65+ being the greatest for females in Lac Simon.

CONCLUSIONS: The prevalence of NIDDM was high in these Algonquin communities and varied between communities. The authors call for longitudinal research to further explore decline in the rate for the 65+ compared to the 50 - 64 age group. They speculate that this trend may represent a survival effect or reflect the relatively recent appearance of diabetes.

Fox, C., Harris, S. B., & Whalen-Brough, E. (1994). Diabetes among native Canadians in northwestern Ontario: 10 years later. *Chronic Diseases in Canada, 15*(3), 92-96.

OBJECTIVES: To estimate the 1992 rate of non-insulin-dependent diabetes mellitus (NIDDM) in an isolated First Nations population in the province of Ontario.

METHODS: All resident native Canadians who received health care from the Sioux Lookout Zone Hospital and who had been diagnosed with NIDDM were included in the study. Potential participants were identified from chronic diabetic patient lists at the nursing stations and from community-based physician lists at the hospital. Retrospective chart reviews were undertaken to confirm a fasting blood sugar ≥ 7.8 mmol/L or a 2-hour post 75-g glucose load of greater ≥ 11.1 mmol/L.

DEFINITION OF RURAL: The Sioux Lookout Zone, as defined by Health Canada's Medical Services Branch, includes 28 isolated northern communities throughout a 385,000 square kilometre area covering 1/3 of Ontario. There are over 14,000 Cree and Ojibway treaty native Canadians in the region. An accredited 43-bed hospital is located in Sioux Lookout (population 4,000). In 16 of the 28 communities, there are nursing stations and on-site nurse practitioners; the remaining communities have health representatives who are supported by visiting nurse-practitioners and physicians.

RESULTS RELATED TO RURAL AGING: Among the 65+ age group, the prevalence rate per 1,000 was 154.4. The rate for females (210.5) was more than double the rate for males (93.2). Overall, age-specific rates peaked in the 55 - 64 age group (174.7).

CONCLUSIONS: The rate of NIDDM in the Sioux Lookout Zone had increased by 45% over a five year period. The authors suggest this may be accounted for, in part, by increased awareness and improved health care delivery. They call for future research to accurately determine incidence rates and associated risk factors.

See also Young, T. K., McIntyre, L. L., Dooley, J., & Rodriguez, J. (1985).

Maberley, D. A. L., King, W., & Cruess, A. F. (2000). The prevalence of diabetes in the Cree of Western James Bay. *Chronic Diseases in Canada, 21*(3), 128-133.

OBJECTIVES: To determine the prevalence of diabetes among the Cree of Moose Factory, Ontario.

METHODS: Data were collected in 1998 during a retrospective review of the local hospital's diabetes registry and all patient charts in the outpatient clinic. All known cases of diabetes in the community were cared for by this clinic. A diagnosis of diabetes was confirmed based on chart information; only 1 case of Type I diabetes was identified and was excluded from the analysis.

DEFINITION OF RURAL: Moose Factory is located on an island in the mouth of the Moose River. The 1997 Cree population aged 15+ numbered 1,900. Health care is provided at the local hospital or at an outpatient family medicine clinic based at the hospital. Travel to the community is primarily by air.

RESULTS RELATED TO RURAL AGING: The prevalence rates per 1,000 population for the 65 - 74 age group (n = 87) were 131.2 for males and 265.3 for females. For the 75 - 84 age group (n = 38), the rates were 285.7 for males and 411.8 for females. Among the 85+ (n = 19), there were no cases for males and a rate of 307.7 for females.

CONCLUSIONS: The authors view this study as a baseline for further surveillance projects and suggest the need for increased understanding of diabetes, its related complications, and sex/geographical variability in the James Bay Cree.

Orr, P. H., Martin, B. D., Patterson, K., & Moffatt, M. E. K. (1998). Prevalence of diabetes mellitus and obesity in the Keewatin district of the Canadian Arctic. *International Journal of Circumpolar Health, 57*(Suppl 1), 340-347.

OBJECTIVES: To determine the prevalence of diagnosed diabetes mellitus in Inuit of the Keewatin District of the Northwest Territories.

METHODS: In Spring 1996, a medical chart review was completed for all cases diagnosed with diabetes mellitus. Information was gathered on height, weight, diabetes type, duration, treatment, and diagnosed complications. The prevalence and pattern of obesity were determined from measurements of body mass index (BMI), skinfold thickness, and waist-hip ratio obtained during the 1990/91 Keewatin Health Assessment Study of 414 individuals aged 18+.

DEFINITION OF RURAL: The Keewatin District with its seven communities covers approximately 200,000 kilometres in the Canadian Central Arctic. The total population at the time of the study was 5,834, of whom 90% were Inuit. Primary care is provided in health centres by local nurse practitioners and visiting family physicians, and secondary and tertiary care by family physicians in Churchill and visiting consultants.

RESULTS RELATED TO RURAL AGING: Thirty-eight cases of diabetes mellitus were identified in the chart reviews (13% Type I, 87% Type II). Caucasians were more likely to have the disease (55%) than were Inuits (37%). The prevalence rate for the Keewatin District was calculated to be .24% (0.03% Type I, .21% Type II). For those aged 15+, the prevalence was 0.47% (0.07% Type I, 0.40% Type II). All cases were in adults, and no cases of gestational diabetes were noted. Thirty-one percent of 414 randomly identified adults (29% of males, 37% of females) were overweight (BMI > 27). Central fat patterning was more prevalent in women and less prevalent in men from the Keewatin compared to the general Canadian population. Among the 65 - 74 age group, the mean triceps skinfold thickness values were 13.6 for males and 21.9 for females while the mean subscapular skinfold thickness values were 18.1 for males and 20.7 for females. These values, with the exception of that for females in this age group, were higher than published measurements from national U.S. data.

CONCLUSIONS: The authors call for longitudinal studies that confirm the prevalence trends and assess the impact of obesity, diet, and physical activity on the incidence and prevalence of diabetes.

Patenaude, J., Tildesley, H., MacArthur, A., Voaklander, D. C., & Thommasen, H. V. (2005). Prevalence of diabetes mellitus in aboriginal and nonaboriginal people living in the Bella Coola Valley. *BC Medical Journal, 47*(8), 437-445.

OBJECTIVES: To determine the prevalence rate of diabetes, and the relationship of age, gender, weight, body mass index, and aboriginal status with having diabetes mellitus, among residents of the Bella Coola Valley in the province of British Columbia.

METHODS: A retrospective population-based medical chart review was conducted using the charts at the Bella Coola Medical Clinic as of September 2001 (n = 2,377). There were no other primary care health facilities in the area. The presence of diabetes was based on a physician's diagnosis of diabetes. Among the aboriginal sample, 58 were aged 65+ while 160 of the non-aboriginal sample were in this age group.

DEFINITION OF RURAL: Bella Coola Valley, a rural and remote community in the central coast region of British Columbia, had a 2001 Census population of 2,260 and 44% of its population were of aboriginal descent (p. 440). It is part of the traditional territory of the Nuxalk Nation.

RESULTS RELATED TO RURAL AGING: Among the 218 individuals aged 65+, 20% had a diagnosis of Type 2 diabetes. Prevalence rates were higher for aboriginal males aged 65+ (40%) than non-aboriginal males aged 65+ (18%). Among females aged 65+, the rates were higher for aboriginals (33%) than for non-aboriginals (12%).

CONCLUSIONS: The authors call for individual study of different First Nations Groups, given the wide variation in prevalence rates observed and reported for aboriginal people residing in British Columbia.

See also Thommasen, H. V., Patenaude, J., Anderson, N., McArthur, A., & Tildesley, H. (2004).

Pioro, M. P., Dyck, R. F., & Gillis, D. C. (1996). Diabetes prevalence rates among First Nations adults on Saskatchewan reserves in 1990: Comparison by tribal grouping, geography and with non-First Nations people. *Canadian Journal of Public Health, 87*(5), 325-328.

OBJECTIVES: To determine prevalence rates of diabetes mellitus among First Nations adults and to compare these rates by tribal grouping, geography, and with non-First Nations people in the province of Saskatchewan.

METHODS: This point prevalence study was conducted for all Saskatchewan reserves in 1990, using data from a Chronic Disease Registry and from Family Files of the Medical Services Branch.

DEFINITION OF RURAL: The First Nations population is limited to those living on reserves.

RESULTS RELATED TO RURAL AGING: Age-adjusted rates of diabetes mellitus were higher among First Nations adults (9.7%) than among non-First Nations adults (6.1%). These differences were greater between women (12.1% vs. 6.6%) than men (7.2% vs. 5.6%). First Nations diabetes rates were highest among individuals with Saulteaux and Sioux ancestry, and among those living on southern reserves.

CONCLUSIONS: The prevalence of diabetes mellitus among Saskatchewan First Nations people has risen from 0% to almost 10% within the adult population since 1934 and more than doubled from 1980 to 1990. This trend was more evident among women and certain tribal groups, possibly due to differences in exposure to non-traditional lifestyles.

Thommasen, H. V., Patenaude, J., Anderson, N., McArthur, A., & Tildesley, H. (2004). Differences in diabetic co-morbidity between aboriginal and non-aboriginal people living in Bella Coola, Canada. *Rural and Remote Health, 4*(4), 1-13.

OBJECTIVES: To examine whether there were differences in diabetes related co-morbidity prevalence rates between aboriginal and non-aboriginal diabetics living in Bella Coola Valley, an isolated, rural community in the province of British Columbia.

METHODS: A population-based retrospective chart review was conducted for individuals having a chart at the Bella Coola Medical Clinic as of September 2001. Aboriginal status was determined from the Nuxalk Band lists, a locally available genealogy, clinic charts, and a recent survey. The presence/absence of known diabetes related co-morbidities (retinopathy, nephropathy, coronary artery disease, peripheral vascular disease, and neuropathy) was noted.

DEFINITION OF RURAL: Bella Coola Valley is a remote community located in the central coast region of British Columbia. In 2001, there were 2,285 people living in the Valley; 46% were of aboriginal descent (p. 4).

RESULTS RELATED TO RURAL AGING: There were 126 adult (> 18 years old) diabetics living in the Bella Coola Valley; their average age was 60.2 years. Prevalence rates for the various co-morbidities varied from 7% to 54% (history of alcohol issues [44%], retinopathy [14%], coronary artery disease [19%], cerebrovascular disease [8%], peripheral vascular disease [7%], peripheral neuropathy [10%], hypertension [54%], hypercholesterolemia [47%], and nephropathy [7%]). All were significantly higher than the rates for non-diabetics living in the Bella Coola Valley. The overall screening rate for non-insulin dependent diabetes mellitus was approximately 62%. The charts of the 65+ age group were the most likely to have glucose screening results (97% aboriginal, 86% non-aboriginal).

CONCLUSIONS: The development of diabetes in both aboriginal and non-aboriginal residents of the Bella Coola Valley was associated with the presence of multiple co-morbidities. Rates of diabetes associated co-morbidities were similar for both populations. The authors speculate that a diet rich in fish oils (omega-3 fatty acids) may explain the lower than expected rates of cardiovascular disease among this aboriginal population.

See also Patenaude, J., Tildesley, H., MacArthur, A., Voaklander, D. C., & Thommasen, H. V. (2005).

Young, T. K., McIntyre, L. L., Dooley, J., & Rodriguez, J. (1985). Epidemiologic features of diabetes mellitus among Indians in northwestern Ontario and northeastern Manitoba. *Canadian Medical Association Journal, 132*(7), 793-797.

OBJECTIVES: To estimate the prevalence of diabetes mellitus among Indians in the northwestern portion of the province of Ontario and the northeastern portion of the province of Manitoba.

METHODS: This descriptive epidemiologic study included all cases of diagnosed diabetes mellitus among Indians living in the study area on January 1, 1983. Cases in northwestern Ontario were identified through the records of the Sioux Lookout Zone hospital, ambulatory care visits to outpost nurses and visiting physicians, peripheral health units where follow-up occurred, and the Zone hospital pharmacy. Cases in northeastern Manitoba were identified through records maintained by community outpost nurses and a central list from the Zone office of the Medical Services Branch.

DEFINITION OF RURAL: The area included 30 isolated communities, with a population of 14,000 Algonkian-speaking Cree and Ojibwa (Saulteaux) Indians. Health services were primarily provided by the Medical Services Branch of the Department of National Health and Welfare.

RESULTS RELATED TO RURAL AGING: A total of 56 of the 385 cases were aged 65+ (17 males, 39 females). The prevalence rate per 1,000 population was 95.7 for the 65+ age group.

CONCLUSIONS: The authors argue that their study provides baseline epidemiologic data in one group of Canadian Indians. They call for research in different regions in both urban and rural areas, standardized glucose tolerance testing in screening surveys, and longitudinal designs.

See also Fox, C., Harris, S. B., & Whalen-Brough, E. (1994).

Young, T. K., Schraer, C. D., Shubnikoff, E. V., Szathmáry, E. J. E., & Nikitin, Y. P. (1992). Prevalence of diagnosed diabetes in circumpolar indigenous populations. *International Journal of Epidemiology, 21*(4), 730-736.

OBJECTIVES: To compare the prevalence of diagnosed diabetes among indigenous populations in the circumpolar Arctic and sub-Arctic regions of Russia, Alaska, and Canada.

METHODS: Data on clinically diagnosed and physician treated cases of diabetes mellitus were obtained from official health services agencies in the different countries. In Canada, this included data for Inuit and Athapaskan Indians who lived in the Yukon Territory and/or the Northwest Territories (NWT). Clinical and demographic data on all indigenious diabetes cases in mid-1987 were collected as part of a national survey.

DEFINITION OF RURAL: The territories are located above the 60th parallel. The populations of the Yukon and NWT Indians were 4,249 and 11,194, respectively, compared to 18,733 NWT Inuit. The numbers of individuals aged 65+ were 218, 552, and 501, respectively.

RESULTS RELATED TO RURAL AGING: The prevalence rates per 1,000 aged 65+ ranged from 64.2 for Yukon Indians to 16.3 for NWT Indians to 10.0 for NWT Inuit. In comparison, the rates for Alaska 65+ age groups were 119.5 for Alaskan Aleuts, 44.9 for Alaskan Eskimos, and 107.8 for Alaskan Indians.

CONCLUSIONS: The authors speculate that environmental factors are likely responsible for differences between these indigenous populations. They call for glucose tolerance surveys and examination of potential risk factors such as diet, physical activity, obesity, insulin resistance, and genetic admixture.

Gastro-intestinal

Pinchbeck, B. R., Kirdeikis, J., & Thomson, A. B. R. (1988). Inflammatory bowel disease in northern Alberta. An epidemiologic study. *Journal of Clinical Gastroenterology, 10*(5), 505-515.

OBJECTIVES: To identify the prevalence and incidence of chronic inflammatory bowel disease, and to examine the relative rates and the age/sex distribution of Crohn's disease and ulcerative colitis in northern rural and urban areas in the province of Alberta.

METHODS: The Medical Record departments of five Edmonton teaching hospitals and 37 rural community hospitals in northern Alberta were contacted, and a search was made for all patients with a discharge diagnosis of inflammatory bowel disease (Crohn's disease, Crohn's enteritis, Crohn's disease of the small intestine, Crohn's colitis, regional enteritis, granulomatous colitis, ulcerative colitis, and ulcerative proctitis). The patient records of all Edmonton gastroenterologists were reviewed to discover patients with Crohn's disease or ulcerative colitis who had never been hospitalized within the census areas. All records from January 1, 1977 to December 31, 1981 were reviewed. A total of 2,419 patients had a diagnosis of inflammatory bowel disease; there were 1,716 (71%) for whom demographic data were available.

DEFINITION OF RURAL: The rural area of northern Alberta is comprised of seven census areas and had a total population of 1,295,360 at the time of the study. It was served by 37 small and general hospitals. The urban centre, Edmonton, had a population of 532,246 at the time of the study and was served by five teaching hospitals.

RESULTS RELATED TO RURAL AGING: Of the 2,419 patients with inflammatory bowel disease, 98% had been admitted to hospital at some point since their diagnosis; 25% of the patients were admitted to rural facilities. A diagnosis of definite Crohn's disease was recorded for 49% of the patients; 33% had definite ulcerative colitis. The prevalence of Crohn's disease was higher in urban than in rural areas and in females than in males, whereas the prevalence of ulcerative colitis was unaffected by these variables. The prevalence of Crohn's disease peaked below age 29 in males and females, and decreased steadily with age. The peak for ulcerative coilitis was at age 49 but a decrease was not evident until the 70+ age group.

CONCLUSIONS: Several features of the patients groups suggest that Crohn's disease and ulcerative colitis are not the same disease. There were rural-urban differences for the former but none for the latter. The authors argue that these rural-urban differences may point to environmental factors in the etiology of inflammatory bowel disease.

Raina, P. S., Pollari, F. L., Teare, G. F., Goss, M. J., Barry, D. A. J., & Wilson, J. B. (1999). The relationship between *E. coli* indicator bacteria in well-water and gastrointestinal illnesses in rural families. *Canadian Journal of Public Health, 90*(3), 172-175.

OBJECTIVES: To determine the relationship between consumption of *E. coli* contaminated well-water and gastrointestinal illness in rural families in the province of Ontario.

METHODS: Data were from the 1-year follow-up of the 1991/92 Ontario Farm Groundwater Quality Survey. A total of 181 families with well-water as a drinking source participated in the follow-up. Well-water collected from tap water was tested for *E. coli* bacteria 5 times (February, March, June, and October 1994, and February 1995). One contact person per household completed a daily family health diary booklet for each family member between February 1994 and February 1995. Interviewers telephoned the contact person monthly to collect the diary information, including illness episodes (nausea, vomiting, diarrhea, fever, cramps, muscle pain, cold or flu, earache, and sore throat). Well factors (construction, depth, and distance from septic tank) were determined by a site visit. A self-administered questionnaire was used to gather information about the household (age, gender, occupation, etc.). Data were available for 531 individuals.

DEFINITION OF RURAL: No definition of rural was provided and no information on farm size was available.

RESULTS RELATED TO RURAL AGING: There were 117 individuals (22%) who had wells that tested positive for *E. coli*; 8% of these individuals were aged 66+. Among the 66+ age group, 9 of the 117 (8%) had wells with positive results. *E. coli* in well-water was significantly associated with gastrointestinal illness in family members; however, the relationship was modified by the distance from the septic tank to the well. No other age-based analyses were presented.

CONCLUSIONS: Consumption of contaminated well-water was found to be associated with gastrointestinal illness. The authors argue that *E. coli* can be a useful marker for detecting wells that pose a potential public health problem in rural areas.

Immunity

Karmali, M. A., Mascarenhas, M., Petric, M., Dutil, L., Rahn, K., Ludwig, K., Arbus, G. S., Michel, P., Sherman, P. M., Wilson, J., Johnson, R., & Kaper, J. B. (2003). Age-specific frequencies of antibodies to *Escherichia coli* verocytotoxins (Shiga toxins) 1 and 2 among urban and rural populations in southern Ontario. *The Journal of Infectious Diseases, 188*(11), 1724-1729.

OBJECTIVES: To investigate the age-specific frequencies of antibodies to *Escherichia coli* verocytotoxins (Shiga toxins) 1 and 2 among urban and southern rural populations in the province of Ontario. Verocytotoxin (VT)-producing *Escherichia coli* (VTEC), also referred to as Shiga toxins, are causes of a potentially fatal foodborne illness.

METHODS: Serum samples were obtained from 232 dairy farmers aged 1 - 70 years, from July 1992 to February 1993. As age was not recorded for 8 individuals, the age-specific frequency for the farm population was based on 224 samples; 15 were from the 61 - 70 age group. Samples were obtained in 1987 from 173 urban residents in Toronto aged < 1 - 79 years; 11 samples were from those aged 61 - 70. Lab tests were completed twice on each sample.

DEFINITION OF RURAL: No information on the location or the farm size was provided.

RESULTS RELATED TO RURAL AGING: For the rural population, the overall frequency of antiverocytotoxin 2 antibodies (VT2 Abs) was significantly higher than that of VT1 Abs (65% vs. 39%) in dairy farmers aged 1 - 70. The peak frequency of both VT1 Abs and VT2 Abs was evident during the 1st decade of life, remained roughly similar until the 4th decade of life, and then declined thereafter (ages 51 - 60 and 61+). This was in contrast to the age-specific pattern seen in the urban residents where there was a decrease in the frequency the 1st to 2nd decade of life, followed by a progressive increase to the 5th decade (for VT1 Abs) and 4th decade (VT2 Abs), and a decline thereafter. Overall frequency of VT1 Abs was 3 times higher in the rural than in the urban population (39% vs. 12%), and 1.5 times higher for VT2 Abs (65% vs. 46%). No patients aged 64+ had hemolytic uremic syndrome (HUS). There were significant differences between urban and rural residents with regard to the prevalence and age-specific patterns of VT antibodies.

CONCLUSIONS: This pattern, which inversely reflects the age-related incidence of HUS, is consistent with a role for antiverocytotoxin antibodies in protective immunity. In dairy-farm residents, peak frequencies of antibodies to both toxins occurred during the first decade of life and remained elevated for 3 decades before decreasing. This pattern is consistent with frequent exposure to bovine VTEC from an early age.

Reymond, D., Johnson, R. P., Karmali, M. A., Petric, M., Winkler, M., Johnson, S., Rahn, K., Renwick, S., Wilson, J., Clarke, R. C., & Spika, J. (1996). Neutralizing antibodies to *Escherichia coli* Vero cytotoxin 1 and antibodies to O157 lipopolysaccharide in healthy farm family members and urban residents. *Journal of Clinical Microbiology, 34*(9), 2053-2057.

OBJECTIVES: To develop and evaluate an enzyme-linked immunosorbent assay (ELISA) for antibodies to 0157 lipopolysaccharide (LPS) and to compare overall and age-stratified frequencies of 0157 antibodies and Vero cytotoxin 1-neutralizing-antibody (VT1-NAb) in the sera of control urban residents and dairy farm residents in the province of Ontario

METHODS: The ELISA was developed with sera from 63 children with confirmed recent *E. coli* O157 infection and from 256 age-stratified urban controls. The O157 LPS assay and the VT1-NAb assay were used to compare the relative frequencies of O157 LPS antibodies and VT1-NAbs in the age-stratified urban controls and in 216 healthy family members from dairy farms.

DEFINITION OF RURAL: The rural sample resided on dairy farms in southern Ontario; farm size was not provided. The urban sample was from Toronto.

RESULTS RELATED TO RURAL AGING: The median ELISA values were significantly higher for dairy farm residents (0.25) than the urban controls (0.05). The frequency of O157 LPS antibodies was also significantly higher for dairy farmer residents (12.5%) compared to urban controls (4.7%). The urban group had a low frequency of the 0157 LPS antibodies over the years as opposed to a high frequency in the dairy population. In terms of the VT1-NAb, 42% of dairy farmers were VT1-NAb positive versus 8% for the urban controls. The age-related frequency distribution of VT1-NAb positive subjects indicated a decreasing trend for dairy farm residents versus relatively constant low frequencies in the urban group.

CONCLUSIONS: The high rate of seropositivity to VT1 in farm residents likely reflects the booster effect of repeated VTEC exposures and argues against a sustained generalized immunosuppressive effect of VT1. The authors argue that seroepidemiological studies may help in assessing the level of exposure of different populations to VTEC strains.

Neurological

Thiessen, B., Rajput, A. H., Laverty, W., & Desai, H. (1990). Age, environments, and the number of substantia nigra neurons. *Advances in Neurology, 53*, 201-206.

OBJECTIVES: To examine rural-urban differences in the number of neurons in the substantia nigra (SN) among residents of the province of Saskatchewan. The pathology of Parkinson's disease (PD) is characterized by a loss of these neurons and a greater risk of PD has been identified in rural areas.

METHODS: A review of all autopsy cases at University Hospital, Saskatoon from 1984 to 1987 was conducted. Forty-eight midbrain sections from normal brains containing SN at the level of the exiting fibers of the IIIrd cranial nerve were examined and neuron counts were obtained. Interviews were conducted with the next-of-kin regarding the case's residence. Cases were classified into three groups based on at least 80% life exposure to a rural environment, an urban environment, or a mix of urban and rural residences (22 rural, 12 urban, and 14 mixed residences). There were 36 males and 12 females.

DEFINITION OF RURAL: Rural was defined as a population of < 500 while urban was 500+.

RESULTS RELATED TO RURAL AGING: An age-related decline in SN neuronal counts was obtained for all three residential groups, with a 23% mean decline from age 20 through 80. Although the SN count was 18% lower in the rural group at age 20, the difference in decline with age across the groups was not significant.

CONCLUSIONS: Given the lack of a statistically significant difference in neuron counts between the rural and urban groups, the authors suggest that SN neuron numbers in the general rural and urban populations may be similar and the causal agent for PD is only present in certain rural locations. However, their other studies have not identified significantly higher incidence rates for PD in specific rural communities.

Warren, S., & Warren, K. G. (1992). Prevalence of multiple sclerosis in Barrhead county, Alberta, Canada. *Canadian Journal of Neurological Sciences, 19*(1), 72-75.

OBJECTIVES: To determine the prevalence of multiple sclerosis (MS) in the town of Barrhead and surrounding County of Barrhead, in the province of Alberta.

METHODS: Records of the University of Alberta's Multiple Sclerosis Patient Care and Research Clinic (MS Clinic) located in Edmonton were reviewed to identify MS patients in Barrhead County. Local health professionals were asked to contact their MS patients and request permission for the research team to contact them. Neurological examinations and the collection of personal and disease characteristics were conducted with non-hospitalized patients in the local public health clinic and with hospitalized patients in the facility. January 1, 1990 was set as the prevalence date, and all data were collected between that date and April 30, 1990.

DEFINITION OF RURAL: Barrhead County is a rural area located 90 miles northwest of Edmonton. Encompassing several small towns, the 1986 population of the County and the town of Barrhead was 9,720. There were nine general practitioners in the community but no neurologists. The primary referral centre for suspected/diagnosed MS patients in north-central Alberta is the University of Alberta's MS Clinic in Edmonton.

RESULTS RELATED TO RURAL AGING: A total of 20 cases were identified (1 possible, 4 probable, and 15 definite). There were 6 cases between the ages of 55 and 64, and only 1 in the 65+ age group. The prevalence rate for clinically probable/definite multiple sclerosis on January 1, 1990 was 196/100,000. It was highest in the 55 - 64 age group and lowest in the 65+ group, with the exception of the < 20 and the 20 - 24 age groups where there were no cases. The average annual incidence rates per 100,000 were 1.31 in 1950 - 1959, 4.97 in 1960 - 1969, 3.77 in 1970 -1979, and 4.22 in 1980 - 1989. No age-specific incidence rates were provided. The results related to patient and disease characteristics, a family history of MS, and the impact of MS were not age-specific.

CONCLUSIONS: The authors conclude that further studies are needed to clarify the typical MS prevalence rates in Alberta.

Yiannakoulias, N., Svenson, L. W., Hill, M. D., Schopflocher, D. P., Rowe, B. H., James, R. C., Wielgosz, A. T., & Noseworthy, T. W. (2004). Incident cerebrovascular disease in rural and urban Alberta. *Cerebrovascular Diseases, 17*(1), 72-78.

OBJECTIVES: To examine the pattern of incidence and health service use of cerebrovascular disease cases in urban and rural areas of the province of Alberta.

METHODS: This population-based study relied on population-wide administrative health data (physician claims, ambulatory emergency department, and hospital in-patient) from the publicly-funded health care system. Mortality data were from Alberta's Vital Statistics death registration file. Cases of cerebrovascular disease included ischaemic stroke, subarachnoid haemorrhage, intracerebral haemorrhage, and transient ischaemic attack. Age- and sex-standardized incidence and mortality rates were calculated for rural and urban areas. Final status (discharge or death), place of service, and place of residence were reported for all cases. Incident cases of cerebrovascular disease (stroke and transient ischaemic attack) and 4 different definitions of incident stroke were identified from data on emergency department admissions in the 1999/2000 fiscal year.

DEFINITION OF RURAL: Rural was identified as residing in an area with a postal code with the second digit being 0 (Statistics Canada, 1996). Residence in any other postal code was categorized as urban.

RESULTS RELATED TO RURAL AGING: The overall rates of cerebrovascular disease per 10,000 were similar for urban (13.24) and rural (13.82) areas. Sex-specific rates were reported for the 60 - 69, 70 - 79, 80 - 89, and 90+ age groups. For example, among the 70 - 79 age group, the rates were 91.43 for urban males, 77.15 for urban females, 103.24 for rural males, and 71.58 for rural females. Rural residents frequently reported their incident episode to urban emergency departments; no age-specific information was provided. Rural dwellers died more frequently in the emergency department setting than urban dwellers, who died more often as in-patients. Again, age-specific information was not available. Patients with haemorrhagic forms of stroke (intra-cerebral and subarachnoid haemorrhage) presenting to rural emergencies were more likely to die acutely.

CONCLUSIONS: Overall mortality is similar between urban and rural residents. However, rural residents had a higher 30-day mortality rate, and were more likely to die in, or enroute to the emergency department. The service use pattern differed according to rural and urban residence. The authors call for more research to determine how accessibility and diagnosis affects the incidence across geographical areas.

Respiratory

Dickinson, H., Denis, W., & Li, P. (1988). Respiratory disease in Saskatchewan: Some regional and social variations. In G. S. Basran & D. A. Hay (Eds.), *The political economy of agriculture in western Canada* **(pp. 125-132). Toronto, ON: Garamond Press.**

OBJECTIVES: To compare the frequency of respiratory diseases, and to assess how gender and age groups may be differentially affected in the province of Saskatchewan.

METHODS: Data were from the Saskatchewan Medical Care Insurance Commission (MCIC) records of physician visits in 1981, and a special data tape from the 1981 Agricultural Census for Saskatchewan. Age-gender rates of diagnosed respiratory disease (ICD-9 codes) were calculated for city regions and outside city areas. Census data provided information on farming such as farm income, size, and type.

DEFINITION OF RURAL: The 726 postal code areas were categorized as areas with a population of < 5,000 and city regions with a population > 5,000.

RESULTS RELATED TO RURAL AGING: The prevalence rates for respiratory disease were highest among individuals residing in areas outside cities with cropland and lowest for those residing outside cities in areas with no cropland. Among males aged 65+, the rates were 284.14 for city areas, 78.88 for areas outside cities with no cropland, and 321.36 for areas outside cities with cropland. The corresponding rates for females aged 65+ were 237.33, 117.65, and 297.85, respectively. In terms of age differences, the 65+ had the second highest rate, after the group under the age of 15.

CONCLUSIONS: The authors conclude that, while their rates are underestimates as individuals who do not go to a doctor and those with multiple respiratory problems are not taken into account, the location of residence, age, and gender have an effect on the likelihood of being diagnosed with respiratory disease. They call for further research to examine possible causal mechanisms that lead to these differential rates.

Dosman, J. A., Graham, B. L., McDuffie, H. H., Hall, D., Van Loon, P., Bhasin, P., & Froh, F. (1989). Respiratory health in farmers: Symptoms and pulmonary function. In J. A. Dosman & D. W. Cockcroft (Eds.), *Principles of health and safety in agriculture* (pp. 50-54). Boca Raton, FL: CRC Press.

OBJECTIVES: To determine whether farmers had more respiratory symptoms and/or poorer pulmonary function than non-farmers in the province of Saskatchewan.

METHODS: Data were from a respiratory health survey of 1,824 male farmers in 16 municipalities in Saskatchewan and a control group of 556 non-farming residents of a large town in central Saskatchewan. A technician-administered questionnaire focused on a history of employment, respiratory health, and tobacco smoking as well as an assessment of working conditions. Three maximum exhalation maneuvers were performed by each participant, including forced vital capacity (FVC), forced expired volume (FEV), and maximum midexpiratory flow rate (MMFR). In the 50 - 70 age group, there were 769 farmers (mean age 58.0) and 136 controls (mean age 56.4).

DEFINITION OF RURAL: No definition of rural was provided.

RESULTS RELATED TO RURAL AGING: There were no significant differences in smoking habits between farmers and controls for any of the age groups. In the 50 – 70 age group, farmers were significantly more likely than non-farmers to report wheezing (29% vs. 15%) and shortness of breath (42% vs. 32%). No differences were reported for morning phlegm (16% vs. 14%) or chronic bronchitis (12% for both groups). Farmers had significantly lower FVC and lower FEV than non-farmers but no differences emerged for MMFR or a calculated rate (FEV/FVC x 100).

CONCLUSIONS: The authors conclude that farmers have more respiratory symptoms and poorer pulmonary function than non-farmers. They call for further epidemiological studies to confirm their findings and to delineate possible mechanisms.

FARM TRANSFERS/WORK

Hay, D. A., & Basran, G. S. (1988). The western Canadian farm sector: Transitions and trends. In G. S. Basran & D. S. Hay (Eds.), *The political economy of agriculture in western Canada* (1st Ed.) (pp. 3-25). Toronto, ON: Garamond Press.

OBJECTIVES: To present and discuss major trends in farming that have occurred in Canada and the four western provinces since 1986, including farm population numbers and ages.

METHODS: Data were from the 1961, 1971, 1981, and 1986 Canadian Censuses of Population and Censuses of Agriculture.

DEFINITION OF RURAL: No definitions of rural or farm operator were provided.

RESULTS RELATED TO RURAL AGING: The average age of farm operators nationally and across the four western provinces remained relatively constant across the 4 time periods. Farm operators in British Columbia, compared to the other western provinces and Canada, were approximately 2 - 3 years older. The relative stability of farmers aged 50+ represented a reversal in the trend from 1941 and 1971 when there was a decrease in the relative number of younger farmers and an increase in farmers aged 50+.

CONCLUSIONS: The authors conclude that, despite the trend reversal (e.g., an increase in younger farmers relative to older farmers) since 1971, there is a need for programs and policies that would attract and retain young people in farming.

Keating, N. C., & Munro, B. (1988). Farm women/farm work. *Sex Roles, 19*(3/4), 155-168.

OBJECTIVES: To discuss the family, business, and historical context of women's farm work and to present data on the nature of farm work for a group of farm women in western Canada.

METHODS: Data were from a larger study of Alberta grain farm owner-operators and their spouses. A sample of 3,000 grain farm owners who reported at least 51% of gross income from grain and oilseed crop sales was drawn by Statistics Canada from the 1981 Census data on farm owners. A survey focusing on farm operation, work roles, satisfaction with work, barriers to involvement in work, stress, and satisfaction with various relationships was mailed to the registered farm owners. Responses were received from 414 units, including 326 females and 392 males. The analyses presented focus on the 326 females (mean age 42.5); the number of women aged 61+ varied from 22 to 29 for the three measures examined.

DEFINITION OF RURAL: The study focused on grain farmers who were the largest commodity group in Alberta.

RESULTS RELATED TO RURAL AGING: Among the 61+ age group, 80% reported an involvement in farm work, with a mean of 404 hours per year. They reported an average of 1.3 barriers (e.g., lack of physical strength, poor health, lack of interest, knowledge, skill, time) to involvement in farm work. Overall, older women were less likely to have a farm work role and saw fewer barriers to farm work than younger women.

CONCLUSIONS: The authors argue that variations in women's farm work may be a result of cohort differences in socialization for farm work, of farm cycle, or of family cycle. They call for research that takes off-farm and household work into account.

Keating, N. C., & Munro, B. (1989). Transferring the family farm: Process and implications. *Family Relations, 38*(2), 215-219.

OBJECTIVES: To describe the process of exit from farm businesses of a group of older farmers, and to determine the relationship between goals of family succession and behaviors in the exit phase in the province of Alberta.

METHODS: A mailed questionnaire was completed in Fall 1985 by 315 Alberta farm owners aged 50+ who were owner operators of farms with sales of more than $2,500 in 1981. The initial sample of 1,500 farmers was drawn by Statistics Canada, using the 1981 Census of Canada (response rate 21%). Questions focused on the owner operator's current and prior involvement in work, management, and ownership; involvement of other people in the business; and attitudes toward retirement and continuity of the operation. Responses to the questions related to the sequence of the exit were dichotomized into decrease/no decrease in involvement during the past 5 years. Virtually all (99%) of the respondents were male; 89% were married and 7% were childless.

DEFINITION OF RURAL: The farms included grain/seed (60%), livestock (21%), mixed (17%), and dairy (2%) farms; 48% were individually owned.

RESULTS RELATED TO RURAL AGING: A sequence of exit from work, management, and ownership was identified. The overall pattern began with reductions in farm work, followed by reduction in livestock holdings; in production, marketing, and financial decisions; in land; and lastly in equipment. Farmers who expected the farm to remain in the family and those who shared decisions with a son were more likely to have decreased their involvement at the exit stage. No age breakdowns were provided.

CONCLUSIONS: The authors suggest that programs for two-generation farm families may be useful in the early part of the exit phase while estate planning information and programs may be more appropriate to those in the latter part of the process. They argue that an awareness of the elements of the process could assist educators as they help farmers make informed decisions about movement out of the farm business.

Keating, N. C., & Munro, B. (1991). *Generations in Alberta farming families*. Edmonton, AB: University of Alberta, Report to the Seniors Advisory Council for Alberta and Alberta Agriculture.

OBJECTIVES: To examine the 'stake' or investment in family and farm by older and younger farmers, the nature of retirement from farming, the stress experienced in succession process, and the plans and provisions made by older farm couples in their retirement in the province of Alberta.

METHODS: In-person interviews were conducted in 1990 with 74 farm families. More specifically, each parent, one child who was involved in the farm, and the child's spouse participated. Information was gathered on the history of work, management and ownership of the farm, retirement plans, personal investment in farming, and family relationships.

DEFINITION OF RURAL: No definition of rural was included; the farms were located across Alberta.

RESULTS RELATED TO RURAL AGING: Younger men who were 'receiving' the farm expected to be fully integrated into the business by their late thirties while their female counterparts either expected to be homemakers providing support to their farmer-husbands or to be full partners. Older men and women who were 'retiring' expected the transfer to be completed by their late sixties. Retiring men and women did not see transfer of ownership as an important element of retirement although it was for the receiving generation. Five stakes in farm and family were identified: in the farm, in the success of the business, in the family, in farming with the family, and in 'throwing off the stake'.

CONCLUSIONS: The authors argue that the exit phase of family farms is a lengthy process experienced differently by various family members. Both generations are highly invested in the success of the transfer but not all use the same criteria to determine when the transfer is complete.

Kimhi, A., & Bollman, R. (1999). Family farm dynamics in Canada and Israel: The case of farm exits. *Agricultural Economics, 21,* **69-79.**

OBJECTIVES: To understand behavioral aspects of farm exits in Canada and Israel, the possible effect of the institutional setup on exit decisions, and the dependence of farmers' mobility on the institutional setup.

METHODS: The Canadian data were from the 1966 and 1971 Agricultural Censuses of Canada. Analyses were restricted to farms in Prince Edward Island, Nova Scotia, and New Brunswick. A total of 24,288 observations were available from the 1966 Census.

DEFINITION OF RURAL: No definition of rural was provided. Type of farm was divided into 12 categories (cattle, dairy, hog, poultry, other livestock, field-crop, feed-crop, citrus, other fruit, vegetable, flower, and specialty).

RESULTS RELATED TO RURAL AGING: In both Canada and Israel, farmers over a certain age (e.g., 54 years) were more likely to exit as they became older, but exit probability rose much faster in Canada than in Israel. Farm size also was a factor, with Canadian operators of large farms having a lower tendency to exit. The reverse was evident for Israeli farmers.

CONCLUSIONS: The authors conclude that reduced advanced planning and institutional constraints in Israel my play a role in farm exits.

Ouellet, E., Tondreau, J., Parent, D., & Perrier, J.-P. (2003). La transmission de la ferme Québécoise d'une génération à l'autre: Au-delà des considérations économiques, une question d'échanges, d'intégration aux tâches et de délégation du pouvoir. (The transmission of a Quebec farm from one generation to another: beyond economic considerations, a question of exchange, of integration of tasks, and of delegation of power). *Recherches Sociographiques, 44*(1), 141-164.

OBJECTIVES: To explore the relational aspects in family farm transfers from one generation to the next, and specifically the process when a younger person identified as a successor has to be gradually integrated into the decision-making process and given responsibilities for the agricultural enterprise, in the province of Quebec.

METHODS: This article draws on examples from various published studies and on a survey of 114 pairs of farm proprietors aged 45 to 65 and their chosen successors. The vast majority of the pairs (95%) were fathers-sons.

DEFINITION OF RURAL: No definition of rural was provided. Attention was given to farms as part of the agricultural landscape.

RESULTS RELATED TO RURAL AGING: Due to the frequent lack of clarity between the family farm proprietor and the chosen successor regarding the timing, process, and conditions of transferring property and decision-making powers, conflicts emerged between some older farmers and their younger successors. Conflicts also arose from the differences in expectations and the lack of openness on both sides. Two factors involved in the transfer of a family farm between generations were the degree of preparedness and the internal dynamic of interpersonal relations during the farm transfer. This dynamic was impacted by the younger generation's degree of involvement in the management of the business, and with the power distribution between proprietor and successor. The focus tended to be on implications for the younger generation, not the older one.

CONCLUSIONS: Further research is required to determine if similar problems of communication and expectations may arise when the farm proprietor and/or the successor are female. The influence of a spouse and mother on the process of farm transfer between father and son also needs to be examined.

Selles, R. O. (1988). *The process of retirement among Dutch-Canadian farmers in Neerlandia, Alberta.* **Master's thesis, University of Alberta, Edmonton, AB.**

OBJECTIVES: To determine the process of retirement among farmers of Dutch-Canadian descent in Neerlandia in the province of Alberta.

METHODS: Twelve two-generation farm families consisting of father, mother, son, or daughter and his/her spouse residing on original homesteads in the region of Neerlandia participated in the study. Joint couple interviews were completed, with participants asked about the meaning of retirement, the circumstances of retirement in their family, and their perception of ideal retirement for themselves.

DEFINITION OF RURAL: The farm region surrounded the hamlet of Neerlandia and consisted of Townships 60 and 61 of the County of Barrhead. This area was homesteaded in 1911 by 50 Dutch immigrants.

RESULTS RELATED TO RURAL AGING: Among these farmers, retirement was a process in which some work, management, and ownership was transferred between generations. Participants identified three phases of retirement - partial, semi, and complete, based on the interest and involvement of fathers and sons in the family enterprise. Context issues included the number of sons, the meaning of the land, the meaning of community, the role of farm women, and intergenerational relationships.

CONCLUSIONS: The author argues that the process used by these farmers resulted in early retirement for parents and early entry into farming for children, and reflected the beliefs and traditions of their ethnic group.

See also Selles, R., & Keating, N. (1989).

Selles, R., & Keating, N. (1989). La transmission des fermes par les Albertains ages d'origine hollandaise. (Generational relations and farm transfer among Dutch Canadian farmers in Alberta). In R. Santerre, & D. Meintel (Eds.), *Vieillir au Quebec, en Afrique et Ailleurs*. Quebec City, PQ: University of Laval Press.

OBJECTIVES: To begin to explore the process of farm transfer of western Canadian farmers, drawing on a study of Dutch-Canadians living in a farming community in the northwestern portion of Alberta.

METHODS: The sample was limited to two-generation farm families that had continuous ownership of the land for at least two generations. Twelve pairs of two-generation families (n = 24 families) participated in joint couple interviews that focused on changes in work, management, and ownership; the meaning of retirement; the circumstances of a retirement in their family; and their ideal retirement. A model of the process of retirement was developed and tested.

DEFINITION OF RURAL: The farm region surrounded the hamlet of Neerlandia and was homesteaded in 1911 by 50 Dutch immigrants.

RESULTS RELATED TO RURAL AGING: For these farm families, retirement and transfer was a three-stage process from partial retirement to semi-retirement to complete retirement. Women were not directly involved in the transfer process; girls were expected to remain in farming by marrying a farmer rather than doing farm work or becoming involved in farm management.

CONCLUSIONS: Retirement among these farm families was a process of transfer that occurred within the context of individual, family, and farm enterprise development, and was part of the cycle of life. The authors call for future research to explore transfer practices with a more general population of farmers.

See also Selles, R. O. (1988).

FUNCTIONAL/PHYSICAL HEALTH

Nutrition

Barr, S. I., & Kuhnlein, H. V. (1985). High density lipoprotein and total serum cholesterol levels in a group of British Columbia native Indians. *Nutrition Research, 5,* 827-837.

OBJECTIVES: To evaluate the high density lipoprotein (HDL) and total serum cholesterol levels in members of the Nuxalk Nation in the province of British Columbia.

METHODS: In May 1983, residents of the Nuxalk Nation in Bella Coola were invited to participate in a nutrition and health assessment. For 202 residents, cholesterol was measured enzymically in non-fasting serum, and HDL cholesterol was measured following precipitation of very-low and low-density lipoproteins with polyethylene glycol. Only 6 males and 12 female participants were aged 60+.

DEFINITION OF RURAL: Bella Coola is located on the central B.C. coast. Band members totalled 592.

RESULTS RELATED TO RURAL AGING: Cholesterol levels averaged 202.6 ± 45.7 mg/dl, and HDL cholesterol levels averaged 57.5 ± 17.3 mg/dl. For males aged 60+, serum level averaged 260.3 ± 26.6 and HDL level averaged 61.5 ± 11.4. For females aged 60+, the corresponding levels were 232.6 ± 9.1 and 51.1 ± 6.2, respectively. Cholesterol levels were positively correlated with age while HDL levels were not.

CONCLUSIONS: Based on serum cholesterol levels, a greater proportion of Nuxalk native people would be classified as being at high risk for heart disease using age- and sex-specific standards. However, caution is advised in interpreting the findings due to small sample size.

See also Kuhnlein, H. V. (1989).

Campbell, M. L., Diamant, R. M. F., Macpherson, B. D., Grunau, M., & Halladay, J. (1994). Energy and nutrient intakes of men (56-74 years) and women (16-74) years in three northern Manitoba Cree communities. *Journal of the Canadian Dietetic Association, 55*(4), 167-174.

OBJECTIVES: To examine the energy and nutrient intake of individuals in three northern Cree communities, two of which were affected by the Churchill River Diversion hydroelectric project in the province of Manitoba.

METHODS: Data were from a random sample of men (56 - 74 years) and women (16 - 74 years) in three communities. Twenty-four hour recalls were obtained in Fall 1990 and Winter 1991 by trained Cree interviewers under the supervision of a nutritionist.

DEFINITION OF RURAL: The communities located in Canada's sub-Arctic varied in their degree of isolation. God's River was located 585 kilometres northeast of Winnipeg, had a population of 400, and was accessible by air or winter road. Nelson House, population 3,000, had year-round access to Thompson 75 kilometres away (Thompson is approximately 700 kilometres north of Winnipeg). South Indian Lake, population 845, is 130 kilometres northwest of Thompson and could be reached by air, by winter road, and by a gravel road and ferry in the summer.

RESULTS RELATED TO RURAL AGING: The median percent energy intakes for males aged 56 - 74 were 41% from fat, 22% from protein, and 34% from carbohydrates. The corresponding figures for females aged 56 - 74 were 38%, 22%, and 39%, respectively. The probability of inadequate calcium and vitamin C intakes was higher for older men and older women (56 - 74 years) than younger women (16 - 54 years), while the probability of inadequate intakes of vitamin A and folate was only slightly higher. By contrast, the risk of inadequate iron intakes was greater for younger women than older men and women.

CONCLUSIONS: The nutrients of primary concern were calcium, iron, and vitamins A, C, and folate. The authors suggest that the low intake of nutrients likely reflects the lack of availability or the use of traditional food sources, and the high price and limited availability of marketed foods that are rich in these nutrients.

Doolan, N. E. (1991). *Selected nutrients and PCBs in the food system of the Sahtú (Hareskin) Dene/Metis.* **Master's thesis, McGill University, Montreal, QC.**

OBJECTIVES: To study vitamin A, protein, iron, zinc, and polychlorinated biphenyls (PCBs) in the food system of the Sahtú (Hareskin) Dene/Métis of Fort Good Hope and Colville Lake, Northwest Territories.

METHODS: This thesis research consisted of four related components. The first involved secondary data analysis of a cross-sectional dietary survey in Fort Good Hope and Colville Lake conducted in Summer 1988. The second consisted of a further cross-sectional dietary survey of adult women in Fort Good Hope and Colville Lake in Spring 1990. In the third component, measures of weights and heights were obtained in Spring 1990. The fourth was a compilation into a statistical database. Information was provided for different age groups, including the 50+. Data were compared for the summer, winter, spring, and seasonal average. Sample sizes for Fort Good Hope ranged from 17 to 83 for the 50+ group; the corresponding numbers for Colville Lake were 3 to 14.

DEFINITION OF RURAL: Fort Good Hope is located just below the Artic Circle and on the banks of the Mackenzie River. The Hare Dene/Métis population numbered 518 in 1988. Colville Lake is located about 100 miles from Fort Good Hope and is just above the Artic Circle; the Hare Dene/Métis population was 54.

RESULTS RELATED TO RURAL AGING: Among females aged 50+, traditional foods contributed significantly more protein, iron, and zinc to their diet than did market foods. There was a trend for women aged 50+ in Fort Good Hope to consume greater amounts of protein, iron, and zinc in each season and less Vitamin A than women aged 19 - 49. Older women in Colville Lake had the same patterns of nutrient consumption, with the exception of Vitamin A intake in the winter which was higher for younger women, and of protein, iron, and zinc intakes in the spring which were lower for the younger age group. This difference may reflect small sample sizes. The seasonal average daily PCB intake of women aged 50+ in Fort Good Hope was significantly greater than that of women aged 19 - 49, presumably due to the higher traditional food intake; no age group differences were evident for the Colville Lake sample.

CONCLUSIONS: The author calls for more research to improve information gaps on the benefits and risks of the contemporary Sahtú (Hareskin) Dene/Métis food system. He calls for more food sampling to precisely define age, sex, body part, and preparation technique differences in PCB isomer levels in food species consumed.

See also Barr, S. I., & Kuhnlein, H. V. (1985); Doolan, N., Appavoo, D., & Kuhnlein, H. V. (1991); Kinloch, D., Kuhnlein, H., & Muir, D. C. G. (1992); Kuhnlein, H. V. (1989); Kuhnlein, H. V. (1995); Kuhnlein, H. V., Receveur, O., Morrison, N. E., Appavoo, D. M., Soueida, R., & Pierrot, P. (1995); Kuhnlein, H.V., Receveur, O., Muir, D. C. G., Chan, H. M., & Soueida, R. (1995); Kuhnlein, H. V., Soueida, R., & Receveur, O. (1996); and Morrison, N. E., Receveur, O., Kuhnlein, H. V., Appavoo, D. M., Soueida, R., & Pierrot, P. (1995).

Doolan, N., Appavoo, D., & Kuhnlein, H. V. (1991). Benefit-risk considerations of traditional food use by the Sahtu (Hare) Dene/Metis of Fort Good Hope, N.W.T. *Circumpolar Health, 90,* **747-751.**

OBJECTIVES: To examine the benefits and risks of traditional food use among the Hare Dene/Métis in Fort Good Hope and Colville Lake, Northwest Territories.

METHODS: Data were collected in July and August 1988, using a 24-hour recall and a food frequency questionnaire. In November and December 1988, recall and food frequency questionnaires were administered. The food intake information was converted to nutrient intake data using a food composition database adapted to Canadian fortifications and modified to include Dene traditional food composition data.

DEFINITION OF RURAL: Fort Good Hope is located just below the Arctic Circle and on the banks of the Mackenzie River. The Hare Dene/Métis population numbered 518 in 1988. Colville Lake is located about 100 miles from Fort Good Hope and is just above the Arctic Circle; the Hare Dene/Métis population was 54.

RESULTS RELATED TO RURAL AGING: Mean percentages of Dene food contribution to adult Recommended Nutrient Intakes (RNI) for protein, iron, and zinc indicate that most of the values were well over the RNI. This pattern held for both males and females 50 - 74 and 75+. On any one day during periods of high traditional food consumption, more than 95% of men and 98% of women consumed less than 25% of the tolerable daily intake level for PCBs, values that indicated a low risk circumstance to PCB intake. Age-specific tolerable daily intake levels for PCBs were not provided.

CONCLUSIONS: Traditional Dene foods make a substantial contribution to the adult RNI for protein, iron, and zinc. Adults consuming a variety of Dene foods at the current average level of consumption during high traditional food use periods are not at risk of exceeding the provisional tolerable daily intake for PCBs.

See also Barr, S. I., & Kuhnlein, H. V. (1985); Doolan, N. (1991); Kinloch, D., Kuhnlein, H., & Muir, D. C. G. (1992); Kuhnlein, H. V. (1989); Kuhnlein, H. V. (1995); Kuhnlein, H. V., Receveur, O., Morrison, N. E., Appavoo, D. M., Soueida, R., & Pierrot, P. (1995); Kuhnlein, H.V., Receveur, O., Muir, D. C. G., Chan, H. M., & Soueida, R. (1995); Kuhnlein, H. V., Soueida, R., & Receveur, O. (1996); and Morrison, N. E., Receveur, O., Kuhnlein, H. V., Appavoo, D. M., Soueida, R., & Pierrot, P. (1995).

Kinloch, D., Kuhnlein, H., & Muir, D. C. G. (1992). Inuit foods and diet: A preliminary assessment of benefits and risks. *The Science of the Total Environment, 122,* 247-248.

OBJECTIVES: To examine the nutritional benefits of Inuit traditional foods in Broughton Island, Northwest Territories.

METHODS: Dietary assessments were conducted in Broughton Island from July 1987 to August 1988. Trained bilingual (Inuktitut-English) local assistants collected 135 food samples that were subjected to analysis for contaminants and nutrients. Nutrient analyses were performed for protein, total lipid, and moisture, using standard techniques. A food frequency questionnaire also was used.

DEFINITION OF RURAL: Broughton Island is a community in the Northwest Territories. In 1985, it appeared to have the highest potential per capita intake of Inuit foods among Baffin Island communities. No additional community information was provided.

RESULTS RELATED TO RURAL AGING: Traditional foods formed a substantial part of the Inuit diet and were a major source of energy and essential nutrients. The pattern of Inuit food choices differed by age and gender, with larger amounts of traditional choices consumed by males and older residents. Both groups consumed larger amounts of fat (blubber from sea mammals and fats from other species) and mattock (sea mammal skin). These foods were of interest because of their major contribution to PCB intake. However, the consequences of contaminant intake from dietary sources, at the observed levels, cannot be authoritatively stated nor explicitly quantified.

CONCLUSIONS: The implications of long-term contaminant intake, even for single contaminants, are not known and will be difficult or impossible to determine in the foreseeable future. Limiting the intake of traditional foods to avoid potential but unknown hazards of contaminant intake carries nutritional risks of its own. The social and cultural benefits associated with traditional food use also are an important consideration. The authors provide recommendations for future work, including collaborative education programs.

See also Barr, S. I., & Kuhnlein, H. V. (1985); Doolan, N. (1991); Doolan, N., Appavoo, D., & Kuhnlein, H. V. (1991); Kuhnlein, H. V. (1989); Kuhnlein, H. V. (1995); Kuhnlein, H. V., Receveur, O., Morrison, N. E., Appavoo, D. M., Soueida, R., & Pierrot, P. (1995); Kuhnlein, H.V., Receveur, O., Muir, D. C. G., Chan, H. M., & Soueida, R. (1995); Kuhnlein, H. V., Soueida, R., & Receveur, O. (1996); and Morrison, N. E., Receveur, O., Kuhnlein, H. V., Appavoo, D. M., Soueida, R., & Pierrot, P. (1995).

Kuhnlein, H. V. (1989). Factors influencing use of traditional foods among the Nuxalk People. *Journal of the Canadian Dietetic Association, 50*(2), 102-106.

OBJECTIVES: To describe patterns of food use and factors influencing the traditional food system of the Nuxalk People of Bella Coola in the province of British Columbia.

METHODS: In 1982, interviews were completed with 61 Nuxalk women who represented three generations (20 'grandmothers' – birthdates 1904 - 1930; 21 'mothers' – birthdates 1931 - 1950; and 20 'daughters' – birthdates 1951 - 1963). Two Nuxalk women carried out the interviews that focused on the extent of present and previous use of 70 food species used in the Nuxalk tradition, taste appreciation, food availability, and harvest time.

DEFINITION OF RURAL: The Nuxalk Nation, with approximately 800 people, is located around Bella Coola, a rural area on the central west coast of British Columbia.

RESULTS RELATED TO RURAL AGING: The most commonly used foods in the traditional food system were seafoods, game, and berries. Among the 12 females > 60, the average daily consumption in grams was 94 for fish, 84 for meat, and 125 for fruit. The percentage of energy was 37.2% for carbohydrate, 21.6% for protein, and 41.3% for fat. Compared to 'daughters' and 'mothers', the 'grandmothers' were moderate in their taste appreciation scores for three seafood groups.

CONCLUSIONS: The authors argue for the importance and consideration of generational differences in taste appreciation and food availability in the local environment.

See also Barr, S. I., & Kuhnlein, H. V. (1985).

Kuhnlein, H. V. (1995). Benefits and risks of traditional food for Indigenous Peoples: Focus on dietary intakes of Arctic men. *Canadian Journal of Physiology and Pharmacology, 73,* 765-771.

OBJECTIVES: To examine the extent of use of traditional food by age, gender, and season, the nutrient density of traditional and market food used by men, and contaminant risks for men from traditional food use in the eastern and western Arctic.

METHODS: This review paper summarizes research by Kuhnlein and colleagues in three communities: Broughton Island, Fort Good Hope, and Colville Lake.

DEFINITION OF RURAL: Broughton Island, an Inuit community, had a 1987/88 population of approximately 400. Fort Good Hope had a 1990 population of approximately 600. Colville Lake had a 1990 population of approximately 45. Both Fort Good Hope and Colville Lake are Sahtú Dene/Métis communities.

RESULTS RELATED TO RURAL AGING: Males and females aged 60+ consumed more total traditional food than younger individuals. Older males consumed more traditional fat than did younger men, with older Inuit men consuming greater amounts than the Sahtú Dene/Métis. Among the 60+ males, PCB contaminant daily intake was much higher for the Inuit males (21.0 grams) than for the Sahtú Dene/Métis males (5.6 grams). This pattern of higher average daily intake rates for the Inuit holds for other contaminants.

CONCLUSIONS: The authors concluded that there are both benefits and risks associated with traditional food systems of indigenous peoples in the Canadian Arctic.

See also Barr, S. I., & Kuhnlein, H. V. (1985); Doolan, N. (1991); Doolan, N., Appavoo, D., & Kuhnlein, H. V. (1991); Kinloch, D., Kuhnlein, H., & Muir, D. C. G. (1992); Kuhnlein, H. V. (1989); Kuhnlein, H. V., Receveur, O., Morrison, N. E., Appavoo, D. M., Soueida, R., & Pierrot, P. (1995); Kuhnlein, H.V., Receveur, O., Muir, D. C. G., Chan, H. M., & Soueida, R. (1995); Kuhnlein, H. V., Soueida, R., & Receveur, O. (1996); and Morrison, N. E., Receveur, O., Kuhnlein, H. V., Appavoo, D. M., Soueida, R., & Pierrot, P. (1995).

Kuhnlein, H. V., Receveur, O., Morrison, N. E., Appavoo, D. M., Soueida, R., & Pierrot, P. (1995). Dietary nutrients of Sahtú Dene/Métis vary by food source, season and age. *Ecology of Food and Nutrition, 34*, 183-195.

OBJECTIVES: To examine nutrient intake from traditional and market food of Sahtú Dene/Métis people from two communities of the Canadian sub-Arctic.

METHODS: Interviews were conducted by local resident interviewers from July to August 1988, November to December 1998, and May to June 1990. Dietary intake was assessed using 24-hour recall. A total of 709 useable 24-hour recalls by 483 individuals were collected. Two food composition databases were used: a database of the composition of traditional Dene/Métis food and a market food database adjusted for Canadian nutrient fortification. Results were presented for the age groups 3 - 12, 13 - 19, 20 - 40, 41 - 60, and > 60.

DEFINITION OF RURAL: The populations of Fort Good Hope and Colville Lake were approximately 693 and 57, respectively, at the time of the study.

RESULTS RELATED TO RURAL AGING: Dietary nutrient intake was shown to vary by source of food, age, gender, and season. Among females aged > 60, market food contributed significantly more carbohydrate, total fat, saturated and polyunsaturated fat, vitamin A, calcium, and sodium while traditional foods did so for protein, phosphorus, iron, and copper. There were no differences for energy intake or dry food. A similar pattern emerged for men > 60. The only exception was for magnesium, where there was no significant difference for males according to the source of food.

CONCLUSIONS: Both traditional and market food sources provide important energy and nutrient components to the diets of the Sahtú Dene/Métis people. The authors speculate that delocalization of the food supply may compromise additional nutrients, with iron and zinc being particularly compromised.

See also Barr, S. I., & Kuhnlein, H. V. (1985); Doolan, N. (1991); Doolan, N., Appavoo, D., & Kuhnlein, H. V. (1991); Kinloch, D., Kuhnlein, H., & Muir, D. C. G. (1992); Kuhnlein, H. V. (1989); Kuhnlein, H. V. (1995); Kuhnlein, H.V., Receveur, O., Muir, D. C. G., Chan, H. M., & Soueida, R. (1995); Kuhnlein, H. V., Soueida, R., & Receveur, O. (1996); and Morrison, N. E., Receveur, O., Kuhnlein, H. V., Appavoo, D. M., Soueida, R., & Pierrot, P. (1995).

Kuhnlein, H. V., Receveur, O., Muir, D. C. G., Chan, H. M., & Soueida, R. (1995). Arctic indigenous women consume greater than acceptable levels of organochlorines. *Journal of Nutrition, 125,* 2501-2510.

OBJECTIVES: To examine exposure to polychlorinated biphenyls and organochlorine (OC) pesticides through traditional food resources among Arctic indigenous women living in the Canadian Arctic.

METHODS: Data were collected in a Baffin Island Inuit community in the eastern Arctic from 1987 to 1988 and in two Sahtú Dene/Métis communities in the western Arctic from 1988 to 1990. Dietary recall interviews were completed. Polychlorinated biphenyls, toxaphene, chlorobenzenes, hexachlorocyclohexanes, dichlorodiphenyltrichloroethane, chlordane-related compounds, and dieldrin were determined in local food resources as normally prepared and eaten. Results were presented for women aged 20 - 49, 41 - 60 and > 60. Records were available for 11 Baffin Inuit females and 28 Sahtú Dene/Métis females.

DEFINITION OF RURAL: In 1988, the Baffin Island community had a registered population of 451 and the two Sahtú Dene/Métis communities had registered populations of 586 and 52.

RESULTS RELATED TO RURAL AGING: There was wide variation of intake of all OC contaminants in both areas and among age groups for the Sahtú Dene/Métis. Comparison across age groups in the two cultural areas showed generally higher intake of all OCs for Sahtú Dene/Métis women in the 41 - 60 age group in comparison with both younger (20 - 49) and older (> 60) women. A similar age effect was not present among Baffin women, with OC intakes uniformly high across age groups.

CONCLUSIONS: The authors indicate that, due to the multifactorial and multidisciplinary nature of both risk and benefit analysis of the use of traditional Arctic foods, it is difficult to reach definitive conclusions. They call for continuing research on food contaminants and their sources, body burden, and potential health effects, and ways to reduce the presence and bioavailability of contaminants.

See also Barr, S. I., & Kuhnlein, H. V. (1985); Doolan, N. (1991); Doolan, N., Appavoo, D., & Kuhnlein, H. V. (1991); Kinloch, D., Kuhnlein, H., & Muir, D. C. G. (1992); Kuhnlein, H. V. (1989); Kuhnlein, H. V. (1995); Kuhnlein, H. V., Receveur, O., Morrison, N. E., Appavoo, D. M., Soueida, R., & Pierrot, P. (1995); Kuhnlein, H. V., Soueida, R., & Receveur, O. (1996); and Morrison, N. E., Receveur, O., Kuhnlein, H. V., Appavoo, D. M., Soueida, R., & Pierrot, P. (1995).

Kuhnlein, H. V., Soueida, R., & Receveur, O. (1996). Dietary nutrient profiles of Canadian Baffin Island Inuit differ by food source, season, and age. *Journal of the American Dietetic Association, 96*(2), 155-162.

OBJECTIVES: To compare the effect of traditional and market food sources, season, and age on dietary nutrient patterns of Inuit living on Baffin Island, Northwest Territories.

METHODS: Twenty-four hour recall interviews were conducted with all residents who had lived $\geq$ 3 years in the community. A total of 1,410 recalls were collected from 366 residents. Energy, total dry weight of food, and dietary nutrients (i.e., carbohydrate, protein, total fat, saturated fat, polyunsaturated fat, vitamin A, iron, copper, zinc, calcium, phosphorus, magnesium, and sodium) were measured. Nutrient density (nutrient per 1,000 kcal) was calculated in traditional and market food sources. Selected nutrients were computed in total diets and compared with Recommended Dietary Allowances (RDAs).

DEFINITION OF RURAL: Broughton Island is an Inuit community on Baffin Island.

RESULTS RELATED TO RURAL AGING: Among the > 60 age group, the percentage of total energy provided by traditional foods was 51% for women and 47% for men. Increasing age was associated with increased proportions of energy coming from traditional sources. Among women > 60, traditional food contributed a higher amount of vitamin A, iron, phosphorus, magnesium, zinc, and copper. Market food contributed greater amounts of carbohydrate, polyunsaturated fat, calcium, and sodium. No differences were evident for dry weight, energy, protein, fat, or saturated fatty acids. The results for males > 60 were similar with two exceptions. Traditional foods contributed significantly more to protein content for males > 60 than market foods while there were no difference for magnesium.

CONCLUSIONS: The authors argue that their comprehensive view of nutrient profiles, food source, and seasonality of Inuit diets will assist health professionals in developing nutrition promotion and education programs for all age groups of this population.

See also Barr, S. I., & Kuhnlein, H. V. (1985); Doolan, N. (1991); Doolan, N., Appavoo, D., & Kuhnlein, H. V. (1991); Kinloch, D., Kuhnlein, H., & Muir, D. C. G. (1992); Kuhnlein, H. V. (1989); Kuhnlein, H. V. (1995); Kuhnlein, H. V., Receveur, O., Morrison, N. E., Appavoo, D. M., Soueida, R., & Pierrot, P. (1995); Kuhnlein, H.V., Receveur, O., Muir, D. C. G., Chan, H. M., & Soueida, R. (1995); and Morrison, N. E., Receveur, O., Kuhnlein, H. V., Appavoo, D. M., Soueida, R., & Pierrot, P. (1995).

Morrison, N. E., Receveur, O., Kuhnlein, H. V., Appavoo, D. M., Soueida, R., & Pierrot, P. (1995). Contemporary Sahtú Dene/Métis use of traditional and market food. *Ecology of Food and Nutrition, 34,* 197-210.

OBJECTIVES: To determine variation in food and food group intake defined by traditional and market food sources, season, and age group for the Sahtú Dene/Métis in the Northwest Territories.

METHODS: Local resident interviewers completed food frequency interviews and 24-hour recalls from July to August 1988, November to December 1998, and May to June 1990. A total of 709 useable 24-hour recalls by 483 individuals were collected.

DEFINITION OF RURAL: Fort Good Hope is located in the northwestern area of the Northwest Territories, on the banks of the Mackenzie River, and 27 kilometres south of the Arctic Circle. Colville Lake is a more 'traditional' satellite community approximately 170 kilometres from Fort Good Hope. The population at the time of the study was 693 in Fort Good Hope and 57 in Colville Lake.

RESULTS RELATED TO RURAL AGING: Land mammals and fish comprised a total of 68% of traditional food items mentioned. There was no significant difference in the intake of market food compared to traditional food by individuals aged > 60. Traditional food groups accounted for 43.4% of the total daily energy for women aged > 60; the corresponding percent for males was 41.6%. Among older women, traditional meat/organs accounted for the higher average daily intake, followed by birds. The reverse was evident for older males. Coffee/tea contributed the most to the average daily intake of market foods for both older males and females. This was followed by fruit/juices for older females and cola/alcohol for older males.

CONCLUSIONS: Differences in food use by age and gender were evident. The authors argue that implementation of dietary interventions need to take into account the traditional diet, taste and food preferences, and the general cultural milieu.

See also Barr, S. I., & Kuhnlein, H. V. (1985); Doolan, N. (1991); Doolan, N., Appavoo, D., & Kuhnlein, H. V. (1991); Kinloch, D., Kuhnlein, H., & Muir, D. C. G. (1992); Kuhnlein, H. V. (1989); Kuhnlein, H. V. (1995); Kuhnlein, H. V., Receveur, O., Morrison, N. E., Appavoo, D. M., Soueida, R., & Pierrot, P. (1995); Kuhnlein, H.V., Receveur, O., Muir, D. C. G., Chan, H. M., & Soueida, R. (1995); and Kuhnlein, H. V., Soueida, R., & Receveur, O. (1996).

Phaneuf, R. A. (1994). Surveillance of a community's fat consumption using a food frequency questionnaire. *Canadian Journal of Public Health, 85*(6), 397-401.

OBJECTIVES: To initiate a community surveillance of fat consumption, using a food frequency questionnaire in Lanaudière in the province of Quebec.

METHODS: Telephone interviews were conducted with a random sample of 584 French-speaking adults who were identified as area residents from a listing purchased from Bell Canada. Information on the daily consumption of 13 food items was obtained. The fat content was calculated and an index was computed that indicated the grams of fat consumed per day.

DEFINITION OF RURAL: The Lanaudière region is situated northeast of Montreal and had a population of approximately 300,000. The southern half of the region is primarily suburban and home to about one-half of the adult population. The north zone is mostly rural and serves as a summer residence for many individuals.

RESULTS RELATED TO RURAL AGING: The index's median value was 39.5 grams (g) of fat per day. Among the 60+ age group, the median values were 30g for men in the north, 34g for men in the south, 27g for women in the north, and 23g for women in the south. Using a weighted least squares regression analysis, sex, level of education, age, and residency in the northern predominantly rural zone were independently associated with the index.

CONCLUSIONS: While fat consumption appeared to be higher among residents of more rural zones, this difference was minimal for the 60+ age group. The authors argue that their index is sufficiently sensitive for community surveillance purposes.

Ritenbaugh, C., Szathmáry, E. J. E., Goodby, C.-S., & Feldman, C. (1996). Dietary acculturation among the Dogrib Indians of the Canadian Northwest Territories. *Ecology of Food and Nutrition, 35,* 81-94.

OBJECTIVES: To identify patterns of dietary acculturation that may be associated with the appearance of hyperglycemia and diabetes in a population that currently has low prevalence of these conditions in the Northwest Territories.

METHODS: The study involved a stratified random sample of adults aged 27+ registered to the Rae Band. Dietary data were collected in June 1985, using a 24-hour recall, a report of intake on a usual winter day, and a food-frequency questionnaire. Food intake was coded as grams of each food per person per day, with all foods categorized as traditional or nontraditional. Traditional foods included market foods but a limited number of fruits and no vegetables. The sample size was 145, with 31 aged 65+.

DEFINITION OF RURAL: No definition of rural was provided. Respondents were from four villages: Rae, Lac LaMarte, Rae Lakes, and Snare Lake.

RESULTS RELATED TO RURAL AGING: Typical Dogrib dietary patterns for the 65+ age group revealed fairly traditional dietary patterns. The percentage of calories obtained from traditional sources of meat was highest (31%) for those in the 65+ age group. Overall, dietary change involved addition to the diet of non-traditional foods rather than replacement of traditional foods by non-traditional foods. Such change was less evident among the Dogrib aged 65+ than among the younger age groups.

CONCLUSIONS: The authors conclude that, with acculturation, the macronutrient composition changes from a hunting-based diet (high protein, moderate fat, low carbohydrate) to one with relatively more carbohydrate and fat, and less protein. Such dietary acculturation was less prominent among the 65+ age group. In terms of methodology, the authors argue that the food frequency questionnaire appeared to overestimate consumption of the nontraditional food components while accurately estimating the traditional portion of the diet.

Roebothan, B. V., Friel, J. K., & Healey, L. (1994). Diet and drug consumption in a group of elderly residing in rural Newfoundland. *Canadian Journal of Public Health, 85*(5), 313-316.

OBJECTIVES: To examine dietary intake and drug consumption for older adults in Grand Banks, Newfoundland.

METHODS: This descriptive study involved a volunteer sample from a senior citizens' club in Grand Banks. The study was explained to the entire group and 24 individuals agreed to be interviewed in-person. Information was collected on socioeconomic status, polypharmacy (all drugs consumed, frequency of use, dosage administered, duration of use each day), and dietary intake.

DEFINITION OF RURAL: No definition of rural was provided. Grand Banks is a fishing outport.

RESULTS RELATED TO RURAL AGING: In terms of food consumption, 71% of these older adults did not consume the recommended daily minimum intake of grain products and 67% did not meet the minimum intake recommended for meat and alternatives. Inadequate consumption levels of milk products and vegetables/fruit were reported by 33% and 29% of the respondents, respectively. All respondents used at least one medication on a regular basis. The number of regularly consumed prescription and nonprescription drugs ranged from 1 to 8. Antihypertensives and antianginals had the highest reported usage.

CONCLUSIONS: The authors suggest that many seniors simultaneously experience two factors with potentially negative effects on their nutritional status, namely poor dietary intake and high drug use. Recognizing the limitations due to small sample size, they call for a larger scale study to examine these issues.

Wein, E. E., Sabry, J. H., & Evers, F. T. (1989). Food health beliefs and preferences of northern native Canadians. *Ecology of Food and Nutrition, 23*, 177-188.

OBJECTIVES: To examine beliefs about the health value of selected country and store-bought foods and preference for these foods among northern native populations living in the vicinity of Wood Buffalo National Park, on the border of Alberta and the Northwest Territories.

METHODS: The purposive sample consisted of 208 men and women aged 13 to 86 from Cree and Chipewyan Indian and Métis households. Individuals aged 50 to 86 accounted for 22% of the sample. Ratings for health value and for preference were obtained for 22 foods, using 5-point Likert-type scales presented in pictorial format.

DEFINITION OF RURAL: Wood Buffalo National Park covers 44,000 square kilometres. The population is concentrated in two ethnically mixed communities with populations of 1,200 and 2,300 at the time of the study.

RESULTS RELATED TO RURAL AGING: The 50 - 86 age group assigned the highest health value scores to vegetables, fruits, fish, and country meats, and the lowest to modern snack foods. Preference scores were highest for moose, bannock, and caribou, and lowest for luncheon meat. Comparisons across three age groups (13 - 24, 25 - 49, and 60+) revealed statistically significant differences in the health scores of nine foods and in the preference scores of eight foods. Older adults were least skeptical of the health value of modern snack foods.

CONCLUSIONS: Northern native people prefer traditional foods and believe that their traditional foods are high in food value. The authors argue that the high nutritional value and preferences for country food should be recognized in land use policy decisions in order to ensure that availability of country food is not diminished.

See also Wein, E. E., Sabry, J. H., & Evers, F. T. (1991).

Wein, E. E., Sabry, J. H., & Evers, F. T. (1991). Food consumption patterns and use of country foods by native Canadians near Wood Buffalo National Park, Canada. *Arctic, 44*(3), 196-205.

OBJECTIVES: To examine food consumption patterns and the distribution of dietary energy intakes as meals and snacks, and to compare the consumption of food groups by frequent and infrequent users of country foods among native Canadians living in Fort Smith, Northwest Territories and in Fort Chipewyan in the province of Alberta.

METHODS: The frequency of use by season of 48 country foods by 120 households was examined. Interviews were conducted with female household heads between September 1985 and August 1986. Twenty-four hour recalls of individual food consumption on four separate days over two seasons (late August to mid-November 1986 and late April to mid-July 1987) were obtained for 178 persons aged 13 - 86 years (25% aged 50 - 86).

DEFINITION OF RURAL: Fort Smith is located on Slave River and is an ethnically mixed community with a population of 2,300 at the time of the study; 45% of the residents were status Indian or Métis. Fort Chipewyan is located on Lake Athabasca and is a predominantly native community; at the study of the study, its population was 1,200, with 92% status Indians or Métis.

RESULTS RELATED TO RURAL AGING: The mean daily frequency of consumption of country food by older females and older males was .97 and .70, respectively. For older females, country meat, birds, and fish accounted for 34% of the frequency and 42% of the weight of total meat, bird, and fish consumption. The corresponding figures for older males were 37% and 46%, respectively.

CONCLUSIONS: The authors call for recognition of the contribution of country foods to native diets and the need to ensure the continued long-term availability of these foods.

See also Wein, E. E., Sabry, J. H., & Evers, F. T. (1989).

Oral Health

Lewis, D. W., & Thompson, G. W. (1996). A comparison of moderate and high users of Alberta's universal dental plan for the elderly. *Journal of the Canadian Dental Association, 62*(12), 938-945.

OBJECTIVES: To examine the characteristics and service utilization patterns of high and moderate users of a governmental dental plan for the elderly from 1978/79 to 1990/91 in the province of Alberta.

METHODS: Records of patients who had used the plan for either 7 or 14 years and who were aged 75+ were selected for analyses. High users of the dental plan were defined as those who used the plan for 14 consecutive years (n = 2,071); moderate users used the plan in 7 of the 14 years (n = 2,337). The higher users' mean age in 1991/92 was 81.1 years compared to 80.0 years for moderate users. Although the average age was similar for the two groups, the moderate users group had proportionately more persons in the 75 - 79 age group. Age, gender, region of residence, and dental provider type were examined. The percentage of annual total expenditures by the plan for each general category or specific type of dental service was calculated and adjusted for inflation to 1978/79 dollars.

DEFINITION OF RURAL: No definition of rural was provided. Comparisons were made between northern Alberta and the metropolitan centres of Edmonton and Calgary.

RESULTS RELATED TO RURAL AGING: Compared to high users, moderate users lived in less urbanized regions. No other rural-urban differences were examined. Overall, moderate users visited denturists more often. The mean number of complete dentures was higher for this group while the mean number of partial dentures was lower. Moderate users spent proportionally less of their total annual plan expenditures on diagnostic, preventive, periodontal, and restorative services, and more on removable prosthodontic and denturists' services. During the study period, moderate users increased their annual relative expenditures for diagnostic, preventive, and periodontal services, and decreased them for prosthodontic services. The percent of total annual expenditures for dental prophylaxis, topical fluoride applications, periodontal scaling, gingival curettage, and combinations of these were lower for the moderate group although they increased their relative expenditures for dental prophylaxis, topical fluoride, and periodontal scaling services.

CONCLUSIONS: The shift over time to using more preventive and periodontal services by both the moderate and high users was viewed as an encouraging harbinger of the 'new elderly' dental patients.

Locker, D., Ford, J., & Leake, J. L. (1996). Incidence of and risk factors for tooth loss in a population of older Canadians. *Journal of Dental Research, 75*(2), 783-789.

OBJECTIVES: To estimate the incidence of tooth loss and edentulism, and to identify clinical, social, and behavioural factors predictive of tooth loss among older adults in the province of Ontario.

METHODS: This longitudinal study involved adults aged 50+ and living independently in two metropolitan and two non-metropolitan communities. In 1989, telephone interviews were completed by 3,033 respondents. These individuals were invited to participate in a detailed personal interview and comprehensive clinical examination (n = 907). In 1992, respondents were re-contacted and asked to participant in a second personal interview and clinical examination. At the 3-year follow-up, complete data were available on 491 of the original 699 dentate respondents. Individuals lost to follow-up were more likely to live in the non-metropolitan communities.

DEFINITION OF RURAL: No definition of rural was provided.

RESULTS RELATED TO RURAL AGING: Overall, 23% lost one or more teeth between baseline and follow-up. Only six (1%) became edentulous. There was no reported association between tooth loss and community of residence. In a logistic regression analysis, five baseline factors were significantly associated with the probability of loss: gender, marital status, self-rating of oral health status, the number of decayed root surfaces, and a mean periodontal attachment loss of ≥ 4 mm. The overall predictive ability of the model was poor.

CONCLUSIONS: Tooth loss is a complex outcome which depends on decisions taken by dentists and patients. The authors call for observational studies in actual clinical setting to further understand tooth loss in this population.

See also Locker, D., Leake, J. L., Hamilton, M., Hicks, T., Lee, J., & Main, P. A. (1991).

Locker, D., Leake, J. L., Hamilton, M., Hicks, T., Lee, J., & Main, P. A. (1991). **The oral health status of older adults in four Ontario communities.** *Journal of the Canadian Dental Association, 57*(9), 727-732.

OBJECTIVES: To examine the oral health and treatment needs of current (age 65+) and future (age 50 - 64) older adults living in Toronto, North York, Simcoe County, and Sudbury and district, in the province of Ontario.

METHODS: Telephone interviews focusing on socio-demographic characteristics, oral and general health, and use of services were completed with a random sample of individuals from households identified as containing at least one person aged 50+ (n = 3,033). A subsample was selected to participate in a detailed personal interview and a clinical examination in their own home or at a public health department dental clinic (n = 907). At that time, data were collected on self-reported and clinically-defined indicators of oral health and treatment needs. Differences according to age group (50 - 64, 65 - 74, 75+), gender, and community of residence were examined.

DEFINITION OF RURAL: No definition of rural was provided.

RESULTS RELATED TO RURAL AGING: Among the individuals who completed the telephone interview, 24% reported that they were edentulous, with a range from 17% for the 50 - 64 age group to 41% for the 75+ group. Among the residents of Simcoe County, 32% of the 65 - 74 age group and 49% of the 75+ age group were edentulous. The corresponding percentages for Sudbury and district were 49% and 54%, respectively. No other age by geographical differences were reported.

CONCLUSIONS: The authors discuss the geographical inequalities in oral health and the impact of oral disorders on quality of life of current and future generations of older adults. They call for increased and appropriate levels of resources to be allocated to this emerging issue.

See also Locker, D., Ford, J., & Leake, J. L. (1996).

Sbaraglia, M., Turnbull, R. S., & Locker, D. (2002). Risk indicators for periodontal disease in a remote Canadian community—a dental practice-based study. *Journal of Public Health Dentistry, 62*(1), 51-56.

OBJECTIVES: To identify risk markers and risk indicators for periodontal attachment loss in a rural northern community in the province of Ontario.

METHODS: Data were from a convenience sample of 187 adult patients attending a rural dental office in Kirkland Lake over a 3-month period in Summer 1996. Individuals who used the dental facility regularly (at least once a year) (63%) and those who relied on it strictly for emergencies (37%) were included. Patients completed a questionnaire on the use of dental services, self-care behaviors, general health status, smoking, and personal characteristics, and also were given a periodontal examination. Periodontal health was assessed using the mean periodontal attachment loss (MPAL) measured at two sites on all remaining teeth and the proportions of sites examined with loss of ≥ 2 mm and ≥ 5 mm. Plaque scores and measures of the number of missing teeth also were obtained. Of the 187 patients, 26 were aged 61+.

DEFINITION OF RURAL: Kirkland Lake is a remote mining community with a 1991 population of 10,440. It is located 250 kilometres from the nearest city with a population of 100,000. The dental office in the study was the only private dental facility serving Kirkland Lake and outlying areas.

RESULTS RELATED TO RURAL AGING: The mean periodontal attachment loss for the 61+ age group was 5.5 mm (SD = 1.4). Based on a linear regression analysis, age had a statistically significant independent effect on the mean periodontal attachment loss as did plaque scores, the number of missing teeth, current smoking status, regularity of dental visits, and flossing frequency. Severe periodontal disease, defined as 50% or more of sites examined with loss of 5+ mm, was reported for 69% of the 61+ age group. This compared to rates of 11% for the 21 - 30 age group, 14% for those 31 - 40, 31% for the 41 - 50 age group, and 52% for those aged 51 - 60. In a logistic regression analysis, age, missing teeth, dental visiting, smoking status, and flossing frequency had significant independent effects on the severity of periodontal disease.

CONCLUSIONS: Age was one of the important risk markers for poor periodontal health in the population studied. The authors call for longitudinal studies to verify potential risk factors for the progression of periodontal disease.

Simard, P. L., Brodeur, J. M., Kandelman, D., & Lepage, Y. (1985). **Oral health status and needs of the elderly in Quebec.** *Journal of the Canadian Dental Association, 51*(1), 43-46.

OBJECTIVES: To determine the oral health and prosthetic status, and the correlation between perceived and diagnosed needs among older adults in the province of Quebec.

METHODS: Data were from a probability sample of 1,822 individuals aged 65+ who completed a questionnaire focusing on sociodemographic characteristics, dental problems, and subjective treatment needs, as well as a clinical examination to assess oral health status and need for treatment. Two-stage sampling by region (metropolitan, urban, semi-urban, and rural) and place of residence (private residence, nursing home, and institution) was used. Semi-urban and rural were combined in the analyses and represented 32% of the weighted sample.

DEFINITION OF RURAL: No definition of rural was provided.

RESULTS RELATED TO RURAL AGING: Among the 162 semi-urban and rural respondents, the average number of decayed teeth was 2.57. On average, the semi-urban and rural residents had 19.81 missing teeth and 1.57 filled teeth, which was lower than the corresponding numbers for the metropolitan residents. In terms of treatment needs, 91% of the semi-urban and rural respondents were identified as requiring periodontal treatment while 64% of denture wearers needed prosthetics.

CONCLUSIONS: The authors concluded that while the dental health of older adults in Quebec was poor, their results were quite similar to those found in other studies.

Slade, G. D., Spencer, A. J., Locker, D., Hunt, R. J., Strauss, R. P., & Beck, J. D. (1996). Variations in the social impact of oral conditions among older adults in South Australia, Ontario, and North Carolina. *Journal of Dental Research, 75*(7), 1439-1450.

OBJECTIVES: To assess variations in the social impact of oral conditions among individuals aged 65+ living in metropolitan and rural South Australia, metropolitan and non-metropolitan areas in the province of Ontario, and the Piedmont region of North Carolina.

METHODS: The Canadian data were from a study of individuals aged 50+ living in metropolitan Toronto-North York and in non-metropolitan Simcoe-Sudbury counties. In 1989/90, a random sample of Toronto-North York residents completed a telephone interview. They were then invited to take part in detailed personal interviews and comprehensive clinical examinations. In 1990/91, they were mailed the 49-item Oral Health Impact Profile Questionnaire (OHIP) on dysfunction, discomfort, and disability caused by oral conditions. In Simcoe-Sudbury counties, the telephone interviews, personal interviews, and examinations were conducted in 1991. The OHIP questionnaire was left with the participants to complete and return by mail. For comparability to the other studies, the analysis was restricted to the 65+ age group. Sample size was 164 in Toronto-North York and 115 in Simcoe-Sudbury. The median age was 70 years for both groups; 64% of the Toronto-North York and 66% of the Simcoe-Sudbury samples were female. A higher percentage of the Simcoe-Sudbury sample (33%) was edentulous than the Toronto-North York sample (17%).

DEFINITION OF RURAL: The non-metropolitan counties of Simcoe and Sudbury are in the province's central and northwest regions and had a combined population of 230,000.

RESULTS RELATED TO RURAL AGING: The percentages of dentate respondents reporting social impacts fairly often or very often on the OHIP items were virtually the same for the Toronto-North York and Simcoe-Sudbury samples. The mean number of items did not differ significantly between the dentate groups or between the edentulous groups in the two samples. Overall, among dentate people, the mean levels of social impact were greatest for blacks in North Carolina and lowest for whites in North Carolina, while respondents from South Australia and Ontario had intermediate levels of social impact. Among edentulous people, there was no statistically significant variation in social impact among the six groups.

CONCLUSIONS: The findings suggest that, while there are social and cultural factors influencing oral health and its social impact, the differences are minimal between older metropolitan and non-metropolitan residents in the Ontario study.

Westover, W. (1999). Results of a seniors' oral health survey in rural Alberta. *Probe, 33*(2), 57-62.

OBJECTIVES: To determine the oral health needs of older adults in a rural health authority in the province of Alberta.

METHODS: The study took place in the area serviced by the Minburn Vermillion Health unit. A questionnaire was completed with a random sample of 335 individuals aged 65+. Oral screening was completed with 134 respondents. The questionnaire focused on oral health status, preventive health behaviours, risk factors, health attitudes, the use of dental care and sources of dental care, and sociodemographic characteristics. The screening measured levels of edentulousness, levels of decay and fillings in remaining teeth, periodontal treatment needs, and mucosal lesions; partial and complete dentures were examined.

DEFINITION OF RURAL: The Minburn Vermillion Health unit is located in a rural area east of Edmonton near the Saskatchewan border. During the time of the study, it was part of the East Central Regional Health Authority.

RESULTS RELATED TO RURAL AGING: Both the dentate and the edentulous respondents had high levels of treatment need. Of the dentate respondents, 42% had coronal caries, with an average of .88 caries. All dentate respondents had calculus and/or pocketing as measured by the Community Periodontal Index of Treatment Needs (CPITN). Among denture wearers, 64% were found to have calculus on one or both dentures and 61% of lower dentures exhibited poor retention. In terms of self-assessed oral health, 76% rated themselves as good, very good, or excellent. Among the dentate, 84% brushed daily but 57% never flossed. Visits to a dentist/denturist within the last year were reported by 41% of the respondents but 70% visited only when they experienced pain or problems. The primary reason for not visiting was because there was nothing wrong.

CONCLUSIONS: The authors argue that lasting change in the oral health status of this group requires more than immediate treatment of their current needs. From their perspective, enduring effects can only be facilitated by educating older adults about optimal oral health, appropriate preventive behaviours, and the effective use of available professional services.

Physical/Functional Status

Brownell, M., Lix, L., Ekuma, O., Derksen, S., De Haney, S., Bond, R., Fransoo, R., MacWilliam, L., & Bodnarchuk, J. (2003). *Why is the health status of some Manitobans not improving? The widening gap in the health status of Manitobans.* **Winnipeg, MB: Manitoba Centre for Health Policy, University of Manitoba. Retrieved from:**
http://www.umanitoba.ca/centres/mchp/reports/pdfs/hlthgap.pdf

OBJECTIVES: To examine the gap in health status among residents in the province of Manitoba.

METHODS: Data were from the Manitoba Population Health Research Data Repository, including the population registry, hospital abstracts, physician visits, vital statistics, and census data, and from CancerCare Manitoba. All residents of Manitoba were included in the analyses that examined trends from the fiscal years 1985/1986 to 1999/2000. Mortality and morbidity indicators were examined.

DEFINITION OF RURAL: Separate analyses were conducted for the Winnipeg and non-Winnipeg populations. Winnipeg is the major urban centre in the province. Non-Winnipeg comparisons were made between the least healthy (Nor-Man, Burntwood, Churchill), average health (Interlake, Marquette, North Eastman, Parkland), and most healthy (South Eastman, South Westman, Brandon, and Central) regions, based on pre-mature mortality rates.

RESULTS RELATED TO RURAL AGING: Mortality for Manitobans declined significantly over the 15 year study period, with the decline occurring for all age groups except those aged 25 to 44. Among the non-Winnipeg residents, a decrease in the gap in mortality rates between the least healthy, average health, and most healthy regions was evident for the 65 - 74 age group but not for the 75+ group. Disease-specific mortality rates also were examined. For example, there was a widening gap in cancer mortality over time between the least and most healthy non-Winnipeg populations for the 75+ age group only. For heart disease mortality, widening gaps were evident for both the 65 - 74 and 75+ age groups. The gap in diabetes treatment prevalence increased for the 60 - 79 age group between the least and most healthy regions. In terms of hospital separations for the 75+ age group, there was a decrease in the areas with the least healthy population and an increase for the most healthy population.

CONCLUSIONS: No consistent pattern in the changes in health status was evident across age. The authors argue that the widening gap between the least healthy and most healthy does not seem to be driven by any particular age group. They call for further examination of factors that contribute to health status in order to determine why residents of areas with the least healthy population have not enjoyed the same improvements in health as those in other areas of the province.

See also Menec, V. H., Lix, L., & MacWilliam, L. (2005); and Roos, N. P., Shapiro, E., Bond, R., Black, C., Finlayson, G., Newburn-Cook, C., MacWilliam, L., Steinbach, C., Yogendran, M., & Walld, R. (2001).

Buckley, N. J., Denton, F. T., Robb, A. L., & Spencer, B. G. (2004). Healthy aging at older ages: Are income and education important? *Canadian Journal on Aging, 23*(Suppl.), S155-S169.

OBJECTIVES: To examine the relationship between socioeconomic status (SES) and health among Canadians aged 50+.

METHODS: Longitudinal data (1996 - 1998) from Statistic Canada's Survey of Labour and Income Dynamics (SLID) were analyzed. Self-rated health was measured by the question: *Compared to other people your age, how would you describe your state of health? Would you say it is excellent, very good, good, fair, or poor?*

DEFINITION OF RURAL: Four categories of location were considered: census metropolitan area, census agglomeration, other urban, and rural. Specific definitions of the categories were not provided.

RESULTS RELATED TO RURAL AGING: The rural-urban categories were used only as a control variable in an examination of transitions in health status over the subsequent two years. Rural-urban location did not emerge as a significant factor when the analyses focused on males only, females only, or both sexes.

CONCLUSIONS: The authors discuss the importance of longitudinal data which allows for a study of changes in health status over time.

Forbes, W. F., Hayward, L. M., & Agwani, N. (1993). Factors associated with self-reported use and non-use of assistive devices among impaired elderly residing in the community. *Canadian Journal of Public Health, 84*(1), 53-57.

OBJECTIVES: To examine the extent to which older Canadians with impairment use assistive devices.

METHODS: Data were from the 1986 Canadian Health and Activity Limitation Survey (HALS) undertaken by Statistics Canada. The sample was drawn from the 1986 Census, based on responses to a question on activity limitations. Individuals were not considered impaired if the use of a special aid such as eyeglasses, a hearing aid, or a cane eliminated the limitation, or if the limitation was < 6 months in duration. The unweighted sample aged 15+ was 132,337 of which 71,900 were classified as disabled. Data were weighted to be representative of the 1986 Census. Respondents were interviewed; proxy interviews with another household member were completed in cases where the impairment prevented this (12%). The degree of impairment, type of impairment, and sociodemographic variables were analyzed for their association with non-use of assistive devices for mobility, hearing, and vision.

DEFINITION OF RURAL: No definition of rural was provided.

RESULTS RELATED TO RURAL AGING: The use of assistive devices by individuals with an impairment varied according to type of impairment. For mobility, the percentage of older Canadians using a device increased with age, from 18% for the 65 - 74 age group to 48% for the 85+ group. The corresponding figures for hearing were 24% to 59%. Less variability was evident for vision aids, where 90% of the 65 - 74 age group and 87% of the 85+ group reported use. There was no consistent pattern of rural-urban differences in the non-use of assistive devices. Among the men, non-use of devices for hearing impairment was significantly related to residing in a rural area for the 65 - 74 age group only; among women, this relationship existed only among the 85+ group. For vision impairment, the only statistically significant association was for women aged 65 - 74. For mobility, no clear patterns were evident.

CONCLUSIONS: The authors caution that the use of devices is likely underestimated in the HALS. They advocate for greater efforts to provide information about assistive devices, and particularly about hearing aids.

See also Forbes, W. F., Sturgeon, D., Hayward, L. M., Agwani, N., & Dobbins, P. (1992).

Forbes, W. F., Sturgeon, D., Hayward, L. M., Agwani, N., & Dobbins, P. (1992). Hearing impairment in the elderly and the use of assistive listening devices: Prevalences, associations, and evaluations. *International Journal of Technology and Aging, 5*(1), 39-61.

OBJECTIVES: To examine the use of assistive listening devices among elderly Canadians with hearing impairments and to provide a preliminary evaluation of selected assistive devices.

METHODS: Data were from the 1986 Canadian Health and Activity Limitation Survey (HALS) and the 1985 General Social Survey (GSS). In HALS, the sample was drawn from the 1986 Census, based on responses to a question on activity limitations. Individuals were not considered impaired if the use of a special aid such as eyeglasses, a hearing aid, or a cane eliminated the limitation, or if the limitation was < 6 months in duration. The unweighted sample aged 15+ was 132,337 of which 71,900 were classified as disabled, and then weighted to be representative of the 1986 Census. Respondents were interviewed; proxy interviews with another household member were completed in cases where the impairment prevented this (12%). In the GSS, various sampling techniques were used. For the 65+ sample, persons who recently had rotated out of the Labour Force Survey were interviewed. The unweighted sample aged 15+ was 11,200; weights were applied to adjust for sample variability and non-response. Both studies focused on individuals living in the community but the wording of the question on hearing disabilities varied. The GSS screened a larger number of people into the hearing-disabled category. The use of hearing aids, telecommunication devices for the deaf (TDDs), telecaption decoders, special amplification systems, volume control telephones, and other aids were examined. A preliminary evaluation of three assistive listening devices (the Easylistener personal FM system, the PockeTalker, and an infrared system) also was carried out with participants in the Canadian Hearing Society Senior Outreach Program.

DEFINITION OF RURAL: No definition of rural was provided.

RESULTS RELATED TO RURAL AGING: The prevalence of hearing impairment was 18% for the 65+ and 34% for the 85+ in the HALS, with the corresponding percentages from the GSS at 26% and 39%, respectively. Based on the HALS, rural residence was significantly related to hearing impairment for males and females aged 65 - 74; no significant associations emerged for either males or females aged 75+. Hearing aids (which are publicly subsidized) were the most widely used assistive devices; volume control telephones were the second most widely used device. Among those with severe hearing impairment, residing in a rural setting was related to a greater likelihood of not using a device for males aged 65 - 74, males aged 75 - 84, females aged 65 - 74, and females aged 85+. Rural-urban differences in the use of specific devices were not examined. In the evaluation of the three assistive listening devices, the PockeTalker, which can be used for television viewing or for personal conversations, was the preferred device. The geographical location of this program was not discussed.

CONCLUSIONS: Hearing impairments are common at older ages, and rural older Canadians appear to be more likely to experience this type of impairment. The authors call for increased dissemination of information about assistive devices, particularly in rural areas.

See also Forbes, W. F., Hayward, L. M., & Agwani, N. (1993).

Gittelsohn, J., Harris, S. B., Thorne-Lyman, A. L., Hanley, A. J. G., Barnie, A., & Zinman, B. (1996). Body image concepts differ by age and sex in an Ojibway-Cree community in Canada. *Journal of Nutrition, 126*(12), 2990-3000.

OBJECTIVES: To examine body shape perception in an Ojibway-Cree community in the northern region of the province of Ontario.

METHODS: Data were from the Sandy Lake Health and Diabetes project which involved data collection with 729 respondents aged 10+ between July 1993 and March 1995. There were 20 males and 27 females aged 60+. Nine figure outline drawings ranging from very thin to very obese were used to examine perceived body shape, body shape satisfaction, and ideals of healthiness across age-sex groups. The figures were numbered incrementally from 1 to 9, with 1 representing 'thin' and 9 'heavier' shapes.

DEFINITION OF RURAL: Sandy Lake is an isolated First Nations reservation located approximately 2,000 kilometres northwest of Toronto. It had a population of about 1,600 at the time of the study, with little in- or out-migration.

RESULTS RELATED TO RURAL AGING: Respondents aged 60+ had a mean perceived current body shape of 4.46 (4.57 – males; 4.37 - females) and a mean desired future body shape of 4.49 (4.24 – males; 4.15 - females). The 50 - 59 and 60+ age groups desired a larger future body shape than all other age groups. The 60+ group also chose significantly larger healthy male and female body shapes than the other age groups. Their mean scores for a perceived healthy First Nations male and female were 4.50 and 4.52, respectively.

CONCLUSIONS: The authors conclude that the 60+ age group has a larger 'traditional' concept of body image. They argue that knowledge of age- and sex-related patterns of body image concepts in communities can assist in the design of obesity-reducing interventions targeting specific groups.

Kerr, R., & Normand, R. (1992). Independent living and psychomotor performance. *Canadian Journal on Aging, 11*(1), 92-100.

OBECJTIVES: To examine the relationship between level of independent living (single family dwelling vs. seniors' apartment building) and psychomotor performance.

METHODS: A convenience sample of 36 volunteers from regional seniors' organizations and community groups participated in the study. Individuals had to be free of any medical handicap that might limit their ability to perform a tracking task and had to have normal or corrected to normal vision. Three matched groups (independent-urban, less-independent, and independent-rural) were established based on gender and age; there were 9 females and 3 males in each group. Less–independent was defined as living in seniors' apartment blocks; independent was defined as living in one's own home. Each respondent was asked to complete a discrete (step-input) pursuit tracking task that required using a control steering wheel to align the pointer with the target light. Each person completed 8 trials that were performed successively.

DEFINITION OF RURAL: Reference was made to a "small rural community" (p. 95); no further details were provided.

RESULTS RELATED TO RURAL AGING: Significant differences in performance were found for both reaction time and speed of movement. Older adults living in their own homes, in either urban or rural areas, responded faster than those in senior's apartment buildings. No statistical comparisons of the rural and urban groups were presented.

CONCLUSIONS: The authors caution that their findings cannot be interpreted as showing a causal relationship between independent living and psychomotor performance, and call for longitudinal studies to address this issue further. The small sample size within each group limits the findings.

Menec, V. H., Lix, L., & MacWilliam, L. (2005). Trends in the health status of older Manitobans, 1985 to 1999. *Canadian Journal on Aging, 24*(Suppl. 1), 5-14.

OBJECTIVES: To examine trends from 1985 to 1999 in the health status of older adults in the province of Manitoba.

METHODS: Data were from the Manitoba Population Health Research Data Repository, including the population registry, hospital abstracts, physician visits, and vital statistics. All Manitoba residents aged 65+ were included in the analyses that examined trends from 1985/86 to 1999/2000. Mortality, hospitalizations for acute conditions, and chronic disease diagnoses were examined.

DEFINITION OF RURAL: Urban regional health authorities (RHAs) included Winnipeg and Brandon; all other RHA's were considered as rural. Rural-urban comparisons were made.

RESULTS RELATED TO RURAL AGING: Significant health gains were apparent for a number of important indicators, including acute myocardial infarction (AMI), stroke, cancer, and hip fractures, although some of these gains were restricted to urban areas. The relative risk of cancer deaths increased significantly in the rural areas although the risk of deaths due to cardiovascular disease, pneumonia, and influenza declined. Declines in AMI and stroke hospitalization rates were evident in urban regions but not in rural areas. The risk of being admitted for a hip fracture increased in rural areas but declined in urban regions. There were increases in the relative rates of chronic diseases (e.g., hypertension, diabetes, and dementia) in both rural and urban areas.

CONCLUSIONS: There were rural-urban differences in the health gains over time. The authors call for further research to understand the cause of these discrepancies.

See also Brownell, M., Lix, L., Ekuma, O., Derksen, S., De Haney, S., Bond, R., Fransoo, R., MacWilliam, L., & Bodnarchuk, J. (2003); and Roos, N. P., Shapiro, E., Bond, R., Black, C., Finlayson, G., Newburn-Cook, C., MacWilliam, L., Steinbach, C., Yogendran, M., & Walld, R. (2001).

Moore, C. D. (1985). *A cross-longitudinal analysis of aspects of physical health of Ontario dairy farmers aged fifty years and over.* **Master's thesis, University of Guelph, Guelph, ON.**

OBJECTIVES: To examine the effect of a lifetime of physical activity on physical aging among dairy farmers aged 50 to 68 in the province of Ontario.

METHODS: Letters requesting participation were sent to all dairy farmers in Wellington County, Ontario, followed up by a telephone call. Data were collected between May 1984 and January 1985 from 36 Wellington County dairy farmers aged 50 - 68. The testing protocol was the Standardized Test of Fitness (Department of National Health and Welfare, 1981). Height, weight, sums of skinfold thicknesses, and grip strength were measured. The Canadian Home Fitness Test (CHFT), a submaximal step test, was used to measure cardiorespiratory fitness (predicted VO_2 max). Changes over a 2.2 year period in a subsample of 21 farmers also were examined.

DEFINITION OF RURAL: The dairy farms were in Wellington County, located in southern Ontario. The average number of milking cows per herd was 46 cows.

RESULTS RELATED TO RURAL AGING: Comparisons to standardized scores revealed that these farmers were heavier on average. Farmers aged 50 - 69 years had significantly greater grip strength. The predicted VO_2 max values were significantly greater for those aged 50 - 59 years. Over the 2.2 years, grip strength declined significantly and mean exercise heart rates increased significantly.

CONCLUSIONS: Despite increased mechanization and concern about the health of the farming environment, older Wellington County dairy farmers show favourable levels of physical health. The authors speculate that a lifetime of physical activity promotes healthy aging.

See also Moore, C. D., & Pfeiffer, S. (1985).

Moore, C. D., & Pfeiffer, S. (1987). Cross-longitudinal study of physical fitness in Ontario dairy farmers, aged fifty years and over. *Canadian Journal on Aging,* *6*(3), 189-198.

OBJECTIVES: To examine the effects of occupational activity on age-related changes in fitness in full-time dairy farmers aged 50 to 68 in the province of Ontario.

METHODS: Letters requesting participation were sent to all dairy farmers in Wellington County, Ontario, followed up by a telephone call. Physical fitness testing was completed between May 1984 and January 1985 with 36 full-time dairy farmers aged 50 - 68. Twenty-one of the farmers had been tested 2 years earlier, allowing for longitudinal analyses. Stature, weight, four skinfold thicknesses, and hand grip strength were assessed, and maximal oxygen consumption (VO_2) was estimated from the Canadian Aerobic Fitness Test, a submaximal bench-stepping test. Stature and weight were compared to age means available from Nutrition Canada (1980); other measures were compared with the Standardized Test of Fitness reference values from the Department of National Health and Welfare (1984). Data were presented for two age categories (50 - 59, 60 - 69).

DEFINITION OF RURAL: No definition was provided and there was no information on farm size.

RESULTS RELATED TO RURAL AGING: Irrespective of age group, the 36 farmers had greater fat-free mass, higher grip strength values, and higher VO_2 values than age-matched reference groups. Over the two-year period, the 21 farmers as a group had a decrease in the mean grip strength and in VO_2, consistent with other longitudinal studies. The decline in the mean aerobic function was within the range of changes reported in the literature.

CONCLUSIONS: Initial fitness appears to be higher in this occupationally active group than the Canadian average. However, the decline in function with age is comparable in magnitude to that seen in less active older men. However, change in lifestyle (e.g., farming) is unlikely to account for the findings as all participants were full time farmers during both measurement periods.

See also Moore, C. D. (1985).

Moore, E. G., Burke, S. O., & Rosenberg, M. W. (1990). *The disabled adult residential population of Ontario.* **Kingston, ON: Queen's University.**

OBJECTIVES: To examine sociodemographic characteristics of the adult disabled population in the province of Ontario, and to establish rates of disability for the overall adult population classified by age, sex, economic status, and region.

METHODS: Data were from Statistics Canada's 1986 Health and Activity Limitation Survey (HALS). Only the adult sample (aged 15+) was included in these analyses. Disability covered mobility, agility, seeing, speaking, and hearing.

DEFINITION OF RURAL: Comparisons were made between Toronto, other urban, and rural locations. No definitions of other urban or rural were provided.

RESULTS RELATED TO RURAL AGING: The relative proportions of the disabled population in Toronto, other urban locations, and rural areas did not differ significantly for either males or females. The estimates of age-specific rates for the three regions were very similar. Irrespective of location, there was an increase in the proportion with a disability with increasing age.

CONCLUSIONS: A methodology for estimating age-sex composition of the disabled concludes the report.

MSHA-2 Research Group (1999). *Follow-up to the Manitoba Study of Health and Aging (MSHA-2): Functional Status Transitions in Later Life.* **Winnipeg, MB: Centre on Aging, University of Manitoba.**

OBJECTIVES: To examine the likelihood of being dependent in basic activities of daily living (ADLs) and instrumental activities of daily living (IADLs), to explore transitions in functional status from 1991/92 to 1996/97, and to identify characteristics associated with becoming dependent in ADLs and/or IADLS over that time period in the province of Manitoba.

METHODS: Data were from the Manitoba Study of Health and Aging (MSHA). In 1991/92, 1,751 individuals aged 65+ living in the community completed in-person interviews; in 1996/97, 1,033 were re-interviewed. ADLS included bathing/showering, dressing/undressing, eating, getting in/out of bed, walking, going to the bathroom, and taking care of appearance. IADLs included preparing meals, shopping, handling day-to-day finances, using the telephone, doing heavy housework, doing light housework, and taking medications. Place of residence was considered in an analysis of the characteristics associated with becoming dependent in ADLs and/or IADLs from 1991/92 to 1996/97.

DEFINITION OF RURAL: Comparisons were made between Winnipeg and non-Winnipeg respondents. Winnipeg is the major urban centre in the province; non-Winnipeg was defined as all areas outside of Winnipeg.

RESULTS RELATED TO RURAL AGING: Individuals were more likely to have changed from independent in 1991/92 to dependent in 1996/97 if they lived outside Winnipeg. In terms of specific ADLs, only bathing/showering was examined as it was the only ADL in which at least 10% of the respondents were dependent in 1996/97; there were no Winnipeg/non-Winnipeg differences. In terms of specific IADLs, the activities examined were shopping, preparing meals, handling day-to-day finances, and doing heavy housework. The only significant Winnipeg/non-Winnipeg difference was for shopping, with individuals living outside Winnipeg more likely to have become dependent for shopping than their Winnipeg counterparts.

CONCLUSIONS: The findings highlight different transitions in the functional status of community-dwelling older adults.

Nilson, R. A. (1991). Self-perceived disabilities and activity participation of older adults in rural environments. *Topics in Geriatric Rehabilitation, 7*(2), 60-74.

OBJECTIVES: To examine the self-perceived disabilities and level of activity participation among older rural adults in the province of Saskatchewan.

METHODS: Data were from a 1990 Saskatchewan study on leisure and aging. A mailed questionnaire was sent to 4,800 individuals aged 65+, with a return rate of 66%. Respondents were asked: *Are you limited in the kind or amount of activity you can do because of a long-term physical condition or health problem?* Individuals answering yes or no to that question (n = 2,561) comprised the sample for the analyses presented; 49% of those respondents resided in rural areas.

DEFINITION OF RURAL: Rural was defined as < 5,000 population; urban was defined as > 5,000.

RESULTS RELATED TO RURAL AGING: A high proportion of both rural (87%) and urban (90%) respondents had a self-perceived long-term physical or health limitation that restricted their participation in activities. Problems with mobility were the most commonly perceived activity limitations among rural residents. Other disabilities were lack of agility and difficulties in seeing, hearing, and speaking. Patterns in activity limitation were examined by age, gender, and level of education. Generally, rural older adults without a specific perceived disability felt themselves to be healthier and happier than other individuals their own age. In terms of activity participation, a home-based leisure participation pattern was evident. Active pursuits generally declined with each successive age cohort. There were seasonal variations in activities, with place of residence being more of a factor in the frequency of participation in summer than in winter months. Health was identified as the top constraint to leisure participation, irrespective of age and self-perceived disabilities.

CONCLUSIONS: The authors conclude that the majority of older adults in rural areas have long-term physical/health limitations that restrict their participation in activity. They call for research to investigate factors over the lifespan that influence perceptions and choices in later life. They suggest that specific programs to reduce activity constraints and enhance opportunities for participation should be developed for the population of rural older adults who may not have access to services.

Raina, P., Wong, M., Dukeshire, S., Chambers, L. W., & Lindsay, J. (2000). Prevalence, risk factors and self-reported medical causes of seeing and hearing-related disabilities among older adults. *Canadian Journal on Aging, 19*(2), 260-278.

OBJECTIVES: To examine the prevalence of, risk factors for, and medical conditions associated with seeing and hearing disabilities among older adults in Canada.

METHODS: Data from Statistics Canada's 1986 and 1991 Health and Activity Limitation Surveys (HALS) were analyzed for 60,904 non-institutionalized adults aged 55 - 64 and 16,613 non-institutionalized adults aged 65+ who were classified as disabled. Seeing disabilities were assessed by questions on difficulty seeing ordinary newsprint and clearly seeing the face of someone across the room, while hearing disabilities were determined by responses to questions about difficulty hearing what is said in a conversation with one other person and difficulty hearing what is said in a group conversation with at least three other people.

DEFINITION OF RURAL: Rural-urban comparisons were made; no definition of rural was provided.

RESULTS RELATED TO RURAL AGING: Respondents aged 65+ were 5 times more likely than those aged 55 - 64 to experience seeing and hearing difficulties. Hearing disabilities were reported by approximately 13% of respondents and seeing disabilities by 6%. Among the 65+, 23% reported seeing and/or hearing problems. Individuals living in rural areas were more likely to be hearing disabled but seeing able, and to be seeing disabled and/or hearing disabled than their urban counterparts.

CONCLUSIONS: The authors call for future studies that examine factors leading to the development of sensory disability among older adults, the effects of sensory aids on everyday tasks, and the impact of sensory impairment on the quality of life among older Canadians.

Raiwet, C. (1990). *As long as we have health: The experience of age-related physical change for rural elderly couples.* **Master's thesis, University of Alberta, Edmonton, AB.**

OBJECTIVES: To understand the meaning of physical changes to elderly couples living in a remote, northern area in the province of Alberta.

METHODS: Unstructured, open-ended, face-to-face interviews were conducted with 11 couples aged 65+. The couples were located through the local Home Care Co-ordinator and the Community Health nurse. All couples were married, lived in the community and not in any type of institutional setting, and had farmed or were farming. Neither partner was confused or had dementia. Grounded theory methodology, focusing on the lived experience, facilitated the development of a model for maintaining health.

DEFINITION OF RURAL: The setting was considered remote as the majority of the residents lived ≥ 1 hour from the nearest service (e.g., hospital, police, pharmacy).

RESULTS RELATED TO RURAL AGING: Maintaining health was a goal of these couples. Physical changes such as arthritis, environmental factors such as mechanization, and human resources such as a spouse, children, and neighbours influenced what people were able to do. Individuals used strategies such as minimizing and altering expectations and priorities in order to match what they were able to do with what they wanted to do. If the matching was successful, people perceived themselves as healthy. If it was unsuccessful, they saw themselves as unhealthy.

CONCLUSIONS: The author calls for additional research on how individuals match what they are able to do with what they want to do.

Reeder, B. A., Chen, Y., Macdonald, S. M., Angel, A., Sweet, L., & Canadian Heart Health Surveys Research Group. (1997). Regional and rural-urban differences in obesity in Canada. *Canadian Medical Association Journal, 157*(Suppl.1), S10-S16.

OBJECTIVES: To describe regional and rural-urban differences in weight and weight loss patterns in Canadian adults.

METHODS: Data were from the population-based, cross-sectional Canadian Heart Health Surveys conducted in Canadian provinces from 1986 to 1992. A probability sample of 27,120 individuals aged 18 to 74 years was selected using the health insurance registration files in each province. Household interviews that included a standard questionnaire and two blood pressure measurements were completed with 21,021 (71%) participants. A total of 18,043 (67%) completed the household interview and attended a clinic where anthropometric tests were performed. Data on rural-urban residence were not available for the Nova Scotia sample, resulting in a sample size of 18,043 (38% rural).

DEFINITION OF RURAL: Rural was defined as residing in a community whose population was < 10,000; urban was defined as ≥ 10,000 population.

RESULTS RELATED TO RURAL AGING: Overall, mean body mass index (BMI) values and the prevalence of obesity in rural men and women were not significantly different from those for their urban counterparts. Among rural males, the mean BMI was highest for 55 - 64 age group and dropped slightly in the 65 - 74 age group. Among rural females, the 65 - 74 age group had the highest mean BMI. A difference in overall rates was observed in western Canada where 41% of rural and 34% of urban males were obese as were 35% of rural and 25% of urban females (adjusted for age and education). Among men in western Canada, the rural-urban differences were greatest in the 25 - 64 year age group, whereas in women the differences were present at all ages.

CONCLUSIONS: Considerable regional and rural-urban differences were seen in the patterns of weight and weight loss in Canada. The authors call for future research to more fully understand the underlying behavioural determinants of these differences and subsequent development of programs to promote healthy weights for individuals and communities in these areas.

Roos, N. P., Shapiro, E., Bond, R., Black, C., Finlayson, G., Newburn-Cook, C., MacWilliam, L., Steinbach, C., Yogendran, M., & Walld, R. (2001). *Changes in health and health care use of Manitobans: 1985 - 1998.* **Winnipeg, MB: Manitoba Centre for Health Policy and Evaluation, University of Manitoba. Retrieved from:** http://www.umanitoba.ca/centres/mchp/reports/pdfs/14year.pdf

OBJECTIVES: To examine the health of the population, the supply of health care resources, access to care, and use of the system from 1985 to 1998 in the province of Manitoba.

METHODS: Data were from the Manitoba Population Health Research Data Repository. Expenditure data were obtained from published Manitoba Health Annual Reports and from the Canadian Institute of Health Information (CIHI). Data on physician supply was obtained from CIHI. Health indicators (premature mortality, life expectancy) and characteristics of sectors of the health care system (hospital, physician, nursing homes, and pharmaceuticals) were examined. Changes in access, rate of contact, expenditure, and the number of beds and physicians were tracked. Separate analyses were presented for the 75+ age group.

DEFINITION OF RURAL: Winnipeg and non-Winnipeg comparisons were made. Winnipeg is the major urban centre in the province. Non-Winnipeg comparisons were made between the least healthy (Nor-Man, Burntwood, Churchill), average health (Central, Interlake, Marquette, North Eastman, Parkland), and most healthy (South Eastman, South Westman, and Brandon) regions, based on pre-mature mortality rates.

RESULTS RELATED TO RURAL AGING: Among the 75+, the mortality rate fell 7.9% over the 14-year period, with the fall somewhat greater in Winnipeg (8.9%) than outside Winnipeg (6.6%). Winnipeg residents in this age group were admitted to hospital at a considerably lower rate than non-Winnipeg residents. There was an increase in the rate at which the Winnipeg residents were hospitalized while the high rate for rural residents was consistent over the 14 year period. There was a higher rate of admission to nursing homes among the 75+ age group at the end of the period than at the beginning, with a higher rate among the non-Winnipeg residents. There was a Winnipeg/non-Winnipeg difference in the frequency of contacting physicians, with non-Winnipeg older residents having less frequent contact than their Winnipeg counterparts.

CONCLUSIONS: The authors argue that the challenge for the next 14 years will be to ensure that individuals in the most disadvantaged circumstances achieve the health benefits that the majority has achieved.

See also Brownell, M., Lix, L., Ekuma, O., Derksen, S., De Haney, S., Bond, R., Fransoo, R., MacWilliam, L., & Bodnarchuk, J. (2003); De Coster, C., Bruce, S., & Kozyrskyj, A. (2005); DeCoster, C., Roos, N., & Shapiro, E. (1995); Fakhoury, W. K. H., & Roos, L. (1996); Finlayson, M., Lix, L., Finlayson, G. S., & Fong, T. (2005); Frohlich, N., Markesteyn, T., Roos, N., Carriere, K. C., Black, C., DeCoster, C., Burchill, C. A., & MacWilliam, L. (1994); Kozyrskyj, A. L., Black, C., Chateau, D., & Steinbach, C. (2005); Menec, V. H., Lix, L., & MacWilliam, L. (2005); Mustard, C., Finlayson, M., Derksen, S., & Berthelot, J.-M. (1999); Tataryn, D. J., Roos, N. P., & Black, C. D. (1995); and Tomiak, M., Berthelot, J.-M., Guimond, E., & Mustard, C. A. (2000).

Self, R. B., Birmingham, C. L., Elliott, R., Zhang, W., & Thommasen, H. V. (2005). The prevalence of overweight adults living in a rural and remote community. The Bella Coola Valley. *Eating and Weight Disorders, 10*(2), 133-138.

OBJECTIVES: To determine the prevalence of overweight adults living in the Bella Coola Valley in the province of British Columbia.

METHODS: In 2002, a retrospective review of all charts of individuals attending the Bella Coola Medical Clinic and residing in the Bella Coola Valley was undertaken. Information was extracted on aboriginal status, chronic diseases, age, gender, height, and weight. Body mass index (BMI) was calculated for 65% of the clinic population. Of the 1,119 charts reviewed, 176 were for the 65+ age group.

DEFINITION OF RURAL: Bella Coola Valley is a geographically isolated community in the central coast region of British Columbia. In 2001, there were 2,285 people living in the Valley; 46% were of aboriginal descent.

RESULTS RELATED TO RURAL AGING: Among the 65+ age group, 66% were considered overweight (BMI > 27, the Health Canada definition) and 17% had excess weight (BMI 25.0 - 27.9). Only 13% had a BMI within the acceptable range (20.0 - 24.9) while 5% were underweight (< 20). No aboriginal/non-aboriginal comparisons were provided for the 65+ age group.

CONCLUSIONS: The authors call for studies to determine whether there are aboriginal/ non-aboriginal differences in attitudes and behaviours that indicate a need for an individualized approach to prevention and treatment of obesity.

St. John, P. D., Havens, B., van Ineveld, C. H. M., & Finlayson, M. (2002). Rural-urban differences in health status of elderly Manitobans. *Canadian Journal of Rural Medicine, 7*(2), 89-93.

OBJECTIVES: To examine rural and urban differences in health status of older adults in the province of Manitoba.

METHODS: Data were from the 1991/92 Manitoba Study of Health and Aging (MSHA) conducted in conjunction with the Canadian Study of Health and Aging (CSHA). A random sample of individuals aged 65+ was obtained from the Manitoba Health registry. A total of 1,763 individuals living in the community were interviewed in-person between February 1991 and November 1992. The rural/urban split in the sample was not provided. The rural sample had a mean age of 76.5 years and 46% were females; the urban sample had a mean age of 76.1 years and 39% were females. The mean years of education were lower for the rural sample (8.3) than for the urban sample (10.0). Measures of health included a single-item question on self-rated health, the health satisfaction item from the Terrible-Delightful scale, and 16 items relating to functional status.

DEFINITION OF RURAL: Rural was defined as all small towns and farms in Manitoba; urban included the cities of Winnipeg and Brandon.

RESULTS RELATED TO RURAL AGING: There was no rural-urban difference in self-rated health; 76% of the rural and 75% of the urban respondents rated their health as good or very good. Rural residents (92%) were more likely than their urban counterparts (85%) to be satisfied with their health, even after controlling for age, gender, cognitive status, and education. There was no statistically significant rural-urban difference in functional status.

CONCLUSIONS: While rural and urban older adults did not differ in the self-rated health or functional status, they did differ in their rating of satisfaction with their health. The authors advocate for further research to explore rural-urban differences in health attitudes and beliefs, social networks, and depression symptoms as well as longitudinal research to study rural-urban differences over time.

Wanless, D. (2005). *Health differentials among elderly women: A rural-urban analysis.* **Master's thesis, Simon Fraser University, Vancouver, BC. Retrieved from:**
http://proquest.umi.com/pqdweb?index=0&did=1130586971&SrchMode=1&si
d=5&Fmt=13&VInst=PROD&VType=PQD&RQT=309&VName=PQD&TS=117260
5520&clientId=12301

OBJECTIVES: To examine the influence and interrelations of socioeconomic, regional, and social factors on the health of older female Canadians.

METHODS: A sample of 8,684 females aged 65+ was drawn from the master files of Statistics Canada's 2001 Canadian Community Health Survey. Variables examined included self-rated health, chronic conditions, sociodemographic characteristics (age, marital status, and visible minority status), rural-urban residence, socioeconomic status (household income, educational level, and food insecurity), social/community support (affection, emotional/informational, positive social interaction, and a sense of belonging to local community), and lifestyle factors (physical activity index and smoking status).

DEFINITION OF RURAL: Rural-urban residence was measured on a 5-category continuum, based on 1996 Census data and Statistics Canada definitions. These categories were urban core (large area around a census metropolitan area [CMA] or census agglomeration [CA] with a population of > 10,000); urban fringe (area with population 1,000 to 9,999 in the CMA/CA boundary but not adjacent to the urban core); urban outside of a CMA/CA (not within boundaries of CMA/CA but has a population 1,000 to 9,999); rural fringe (within a CMA/CA that is not classified as urban core or urban fringe and has a population < 1,000); and rural outside a CMA/CA (all remaining areas).

RESULTS RELATED TO RURAL AGING: Rural females were more likely to report having any chronic condition, hypertension, diabetes, and heart disease, compared to their urban counterparts, after controlling for socioeconomic status, social capital, and lifestyle. However, while community integration (a form of social capital associated with better health) was often stronger in rural communities, no rural advantage for subjective health was observed. Separate analyses of the rural and urban sub-samples revealed a number of differences in the factors associated with subjective and objective health outcomes.

CONCLUSIONS: Findings are discussed with regard to implications for policy and future research.

Wood, D. W., & Turner, R. J. (1985). The prevalence of physical disability in southwestern Ontario. *Canadian Journal of Public Health, 76*(4), 262-265.

OBJECTIVES: To determine the extent of physical disability between 1980 and 1982 in 10 southwestern counties in the province of Ontario.

METHODS: A two-stage cluster sampling was used to identify the sample. The first stage was the random selection of 200 enumeration areas in southwestern Ontario and the second was a random selection of households. Rural households were over-sampled; the results were adjusted for this oversampling. Screening interviews that included questions on demographic characteristics and the nature of any disabilities were completed with 10,972 households (22,680 adults aged 18+). Long-term disability was defined as a disability of 3+ months.

DEFINITION OF RURAL: No definition of rural was provided.

RESULTS RELATED TO RURAL AGING: An overall prevalence rate of disabling conditions was 66.78 per 1,000 population. For the 65 - 69 and the 70+ age groups, prevalence rates were higher for urban residents than for rural residents (65 - 69: 182.71 urban, 149.78 rural; 70+: 226.61 urban, 175.68 rural). In the rural areas, the rates for males were higher in the 65 - 69 age group than for females; among the 70+, the rates for males and females were similar. In the urban areas, females in both age groups had higher rates than their male counterparts. The population estimate of the number of disabled females aged 70+ (13,753) was almost double that of the estimate for males in that age group (7,613).

CONCLUSIONS: The authors argue that, for the 65+ group, differences in the population estimates by gender are important to take into account when planning services. They also discuss the inadequacy of total prevalence rates for health service planning and call for consideration of age, sex, and area of residence specific information.

Zimmer, Z., & Chappell, N. L. (1994). Mobility restriction and the use of devices among seniors. *Journal of Aging and Health, 6*(2), 185-208.

OBJECTIVES: To examine the use of assistive devices among community-dwelling older adults with varying levels of physical mobility restrictions in the province of Manitoba.

METHODS: Data were from the 1991/92 Canadian Aging Research Network (Group A) needs assessment conducted in Manitoba. The random sample was comprised of 1,406 individuals aged 65+ living in the community, with 50% residing in Winnipeg and 50% equally split between 8 smaller communities in Manitoba. In-person interviews included questions on demographic characteristics, health status, and mobility restrictions and device use.

DEFINITION OF RURAL: The rural communities ranged in size from 2,000 to 10,000. Winnipeg is the major urban centre in the province.

RESULTS RELATED TO RURAL AGING: Some difficulty with at least one of four mobility tasks was reported by 607 respondents, including getting up and down stairs (31%), walking a city block (29%), getting in and out of the bath (24%), and getting in and out of the car (20%). Among these 607 respondents, 62% used a device for at least one mobility task. Rural residence was associated with a greater likelihood of device use. In general, the number of problems encountered was the most significant factor related to device use.

CONCLUSIONS: The authors conclude that it is the sheer number of mobility restrictions, and not necessarily the severity of those problems, that determine device use. They identify various questions for future research, including an examination of environmental and attitudinal reasons for increased use of devices in rural areas.

HEALTH AND SOCIAL SERVICES

Day Programs

Adult Day Care Research Group. (1997). *An Evaluation of Adult Day Care in Manitoba: Final Report.* **Winnipeg, MB: Centre on Aging, University of Manitoba.**

OBJECTIVES: To describe the nature and scope of services offered through the Adult Day Care (ADC) program and its current target population, to assess the impact of program attendance on meeting the needs of ADC clients and their caregivers, to evaluate the impact of attendance on use of other services in the health care system, and to examine the role of the ADC program within the Provincial Home Care program, in the province of Manitoba.

METHODS: In 1995/96, mailed questionnaires were completed by 68 ADC coordinators who were responsible for the planning and implementation of the provincially-funded ADC program in their communities and by 126 Manitoba Health's Home Care Case (HCC) coordinators who referred Home Care clients to ADC. In-person interviews were completed with a sample of 633 ADC clients who had attended the program for a minimum of 3 months and with 517 informal caregivers. Key informant interviews were conducted with 16 Manitoba Health representatives and a review/analysis of Manitoba Health administrative data relevant to the project was undertaken.

DEFINITION OF RURAL: Winnipeg/non-Winnipeg comparisons were made as well as regional breakdowns. Winnipeg is the major urban centre in the province; non-Winnipeg was defined as all areas outside of Winnipeg.

RESULTS RELATED TO RURAL AGING: This report provides a profile of the ADC program in Manitoba. It begins with structural characteristics and then turns to staffing, relationships between ADC and HCC coordinators, and reasons for referral. An in-depth examination of the services, including the identification of service clusters, and a discussion of program costs, are included. Winnipeg/non-Winnipeg differences were examined throughout the report. For example, differences were evident in the number of days open per week, average number of visits per week per client, frequency of attendance, allocated spaces per week, total used spaces per week, number on the waiting list, number of clients referred but not yet attending, approved staffing levels, number of staff employed, percent of programs having at least one staff as an ADC assistant/activity aide, number of clients on the HCC coordinators case load who were enrolled in ADC, frequency of in-person contact between the ADC and HCC coordinators, working relationship between ADC and HCC coordinators, reasons for referral to ADC, reasons clients decline ADC, reasons for leaving ADC, and the provision of certain services.

CONCLUSIONS: The ADC program appeared to be meeting the goals of increased socialization and provision of respite for caregivers. Variations across individual ADC sites were evident. As not all communities are the same, the authors argue that this can be considered as a strength if ADC is able to meet the needs of its community.

Gutman, G. M., Milstein, S., Killam, J., & Lewis, D. (1991). *Urban-rural comparison of adult day care centres in British Columbia.* **Vancouver, BC: Gerontology Research Centre, Simon Fraser University.**

OBJECTIVES: To compare and contrast the characteristics of clients of Adult Day Care Centres (ADCs) in rural and urban communities in the province of British Columbia.

METHODS: This report included data from the first 2 phases of a 3-phase study. Phase I was conducted in August 1989 and involved the collection of information regarding organizational structure/operating characteristics, staffing, and activities/services from all 38 urban and 11 rural ADCs. A stratified random sample of 18 urban and 4 rural centres participated in Phase II; stratification was based first on region of the province (n = 4) and then on size of ADC (1 - 29, 30 - 69, 70+ clients). Data were collected from the B.C. Long Term Care Program's standard client assessment form for 479 new admissions to ADC from December 1988 to November 1989.

DEFINITION OF RURAL: Rural communities were defined as those with a 1986 population of < 10,000.

RESULTS RELATED TO RURAL AGING: Rural ADCs tended to be affiliated with long-term care facilities, with which they shared space (90%), staffing (100%), programs (100%), and other resources (82%). They averaged 9.7 clients/day, with 73% of the centres serving fewer than 10 clients per day. Rural clients attended less frequently than their urban counterparts; 55% attended only one day per week. While 73% of the rural ADCs employed a program worker, only 64% had a designated administrator/coordinator. Use of volunteers was not as common in rural (36%) as urban (79%) ADCs. In terms of activities, there were no differences in the recreational and social activities or meals offered by the rural and urban ADCs. Compared to urban centres, more rural centres provided traditional hands-on services such as changing medical dressings and performing skin care; baths; transportation for social/recreational events; training/re-training in activities of daily living; whirlpool therapy; art therapy; and had clients watch TV as a quiet time activity. The rural ADCs appeared to be accepting an increasingly physically frail clientele. Rural-urban differences in client characteristics also were presented. However, no statistical tests of significance were conducted to assess these differences and data for several key characteristics were incomplete.

CONCLUSIONS: The authors identify a number of policy questions, including whether rural settings should be encouraged to develop free-standing ADCs, whether there should be minimum/maximum size requirements for ADCs, and whether separate criteria and standards should be developed for urban and for rural ADCs. The changing type of clientele in rural areas suggests a need to develop services for a heavier case load.

Ritchie, L. (2003). Adult day care: Northern perspectives. *Public Health Nursing,* **20(2), 120-131.**

OBJECTIVES: To explore older adults', caregivers', and nurses' perceptions regarding adult day care (ADC) in the northern interior region in the province of British Columbia.

METHODS: This qualitative study occurred in two small towns and one small city in the northern interior region of British Columbia. Focus groups and interviews were conducted with 32 participants, including 21 seniors (aged 58 - 93), 7 caregivers (aged 59 - 79), and 4 nurses (aged 28 - 56).

DEFINITION OF RURAL: The specific communities were not identified and population sizes were not provided. The population density of the northern region of British Columbia was reported to be approximately 4 persons per square kilometre.

RESULTS RELATED TO RURAL AGING: Six key themes emerged related to ADC programming, including: the need for respite; aging in place; ADC program components; program characteristics; staff knowledge, skills, and attitudes; and northern perspectives. Identified reasons for the underuse of the ADC program included community awareness, stigma, client participation, bureaucratic processes, and geographical isolation.

CONCLUSIONS: The author argues that the findings can be used to facilitate the grounding of ADC policy within the clients' perspectives and a northern context.

Home Care

Alcock, D., Angus, D., Diem, E., Gallagher, E., & Medves, J. (2002). Home care or long-term care facility: Factors that influence the decision. *Home Health Care Services Quarterly, 21*(2), 35-48.

OBJECTIVES: To identify factors that determine if a long-term care client will be cared for at home or in a long-term care facility across Canada.

METHODS: Data were collected in five provinces in western, central, and eastern Canada. Three to eight Community Care Coordinators were selected by each agency based on availability and seniority. A total of 89 participants answered a demographic questionnaire and participated in a focus group. The questionnaire covered age, gender, discipline, education, experience, case load, whether direct care was provided by the Coordinator, and the category of clients who received care (palliative, acute care, etc.). All tape-recorded focus groups followed the same set of guiding questions. Participants included nurses (74%), social workers (3%), physiotherapists (2%), occupational therapists (2%), teachers (2%), home support worker (1%), and unidentified disciplines (3%). Most were aged 40+; 87% were females. No information was provided on the rural-urban distribution of the participants.

DEFINITION OF RURAL: No definition of rural was provided.

RESULTS RELATED TO RURAL AGING: The factors that influence the choice between home care and facility care were grouped under organizational, system, client, informal provider, formal provider, and case manager factors. Reference to rural settings was made with regard to system, informal provider, and formal provider factors. Transportation was identified as particularly problematic for rural and remote areas. Solutions such as mobile laboratories and health screening, assessment and treatment units, and community design ideas to enhance quality of life and independence were offered. Coordinators serving rural clients discussed the mindset of farming communities that elderly family members will be cared for at home and expressed the view that this was becoming increasingly difficult with younger family members seeking employment elsewhere and a volunteer shortage in rural areas. The rural home care teams were perceived to have better communication and long standing partnerships between professionals and home support workers. The familiarity of the rural nurses to the clients was discussed as was the 24-hour on-call nature of their position in the community.

CONCLUSIONS: Discussion focused on changes needed to foster more long-term care in the home. Community characteristics such as access to seniors' housing, volunteer programs such as meals-on-wheels, public transportation, day and evening programs, and inexpensive home maintenance programs were identified as critical to the ability of long-term care clients to remain in their homes. The authors call for future research to include all community care agencies within each province and to elicit the perspectives of both clients and informal providers.

Browne, A., & Shultis, J. (1995). Adult home care services: A comparison of First Nations and non-First Nations communities in Ontario. In B. Minore & C. Hartviksen (Eds.), *Redressing the imbalance: Health human resources in rural and northern communities* **(pp. 553-568). Thunder Bay, ON: Lakehead University.**

OBJECTIVES: To identify and describe basic demographic characteristics of First Nations and non-First Nations chronically ill and disabled persons in the province of Ontario, to describe and compare the range of home care and health services provided in these communities, to compare training requirements and the provision of training, and to compare the actual needs of the First Nation clients to the type and amount of services offered.

METHODS: Data on adult care services and chronically ill/disabled persons were collected in both First Nations and non-First Nations communities, matched with respect to geographical isolation. Communities were contacted and asked if they would be willing to participate; all but 2 of the 17 agreed. Questionnaires were sent to each community; health and home care administrators were involved in their completion.

DEFINITION OF RURAL: Communities were divided into non-isolated (2 First Nations, 1 non-First Nations), semi-isolated (2 First Nations, 2 non-First Nations), isolated (2 First Nations, 3 non-First Nations) and remote isolated (3 First Nations), based on the levels of air and road access, telephone service, and access to physician services. Population size ranged from 132 to 4,100 for the First Nations communities and from 167 to 4,100 for the non-First Nations communities.

RESULTS RELATED TO RURAL AGING: The age distribution of adult care services clients differed between the First Nations and non-First Nations communities. The non-First Nations clients were much more likely to be aged 61+, with females aged 80+ being the most prevalent age group. Among the First Nations clients, there was a much higher prevalence in the 41 - 50 and 51 - 60 age groups, reflecting in part the health status, socioeconomic conditions, and morbidity patterns of this group. The provision of personal care to clients and access to a range of health care services also varied between First Nations and non-First Nations; no age differences were presented.

CONCLUSIONS: The authors call for more homemaking and personal care services, more trained homemakers, and a wider range of homemaking services for First Nation communities as well as running water, plumbing, and improved housing. Recommendations relating to service delivery, homemaking and support services, personal care services, community support services, and training for service providers were outlined.

Note: For the full report, see Browne, A. & Shultis, J. D. (1993). Adult care/disabilities initiative: Ontario region. Thunder Bay, ON: Nishnawbe-Aski Nation.

Ducharme, F., Pérodeau, G. , Paquet, M., Legault, A., & Trudeau, D. (2004). Virage ambulatoire et soins familiaux à domicile. Un enjeu de santé publique. (Ambulatory turning point and family home care: A gamble in public health). *Canadian Journal of Public Health, 95*(1), 64-68.

OBJECTIVES: To explore the perceptions and expectations of caregivers, health professionals and social workers, members of community organizations, and hospital and community services managers regarding services to be offered to family caregivers in the context of an 'ambulatory turning point', in the province of Quebec.

METHODS: Using a qualitative ethnographic approach, data were collected in two phases. Both phases included urban and rural areas, specifically the socio-sanitary regions of Montreal and Lanaudiere. Phase I comprised 11 focus groups (26 urban and 23 rural participants). Phase II involved semi-structured individual interviews with 29 key informants (16 urban, 13 rural). Verbatim transcripts were analyzed thematically in order to identify themes and recurrent patterns.

DEFINITION OF RURAL: The socio-sanitary region of Lanaudiere was considered rural.

RESULTS RELATED TO RURAL AGING: Differences between rural and urban contexts were discussed. In the rural context, difficulties with transportation and geographical distances limited the accessibility of services and specialized care; however, communitarian life, informal help, better organized partnerships, and more flexibility/better coordination of services were identified. In the urban context, two issues emerged, namely a more cumbersome bureaucracy and an urgent need to develop the role of case managers in order to assure service coordination.

CONCLUSIONS: This study pointed out the precariousness and the limitations of services offered to families as well as certain specificities of rural and urban contexts that need to be taken into account when planning services. The importance of considering caregivers as clients of the health care system, the need for the development of preventive interventions in terms of services available for caregivers, and the need for a more systemic approach for building an integrative service system were discussed.

Elgar, F. J., Worrall, G., & Knight, J. C. (2002). Functional assessment of elderly clients of a rural community-based long-term care program: A 10-year cohort study. *Canadian Journal on Aging, 21*(3), 455-463.

OBJECTIVES: To assess activities of daily living (ADL), and cognitive and affective functioning among elderly clients in a rural community-based long-term care (CBLTC) program in the province of Newfoundland, to describe attrition trends and reasons why clients left the program, and to determine whether demographic factors and functional assessments at entry predicted rates of mortality and institutionalization over a 10-year period.

METHODS: The study enrolled 237 consecutive new clients of a CBLTC program in eastern Newfoundland, from January to May 1990. A home care nurse assessed each client's medical, social, financial, and functional status at baseline. The status of the patient was recorded annually for a 10-year period. Most participants were female (59%).

DEFINITION OF RURAL: The CBLTC program serviced a total population of 61,766 and a 65+ population of 6,420. The authors write the region is "indisputably rural" (p. 456).

RESULTS RELATED TO RURAL AGING: At baseline, 8% of the clients had marked dependence on ADLs, 8% showed moderate or severe cognitive impairment, and 54% were reported to have moderate or severe affective impairment. By the 2-year follow-up, 59% of clients had left the program and only 2% were still clients after 10 years. Among the clients who left, 32% were discharged due to improvement, 22% were institutionalized, and 47% had died. Poorer ADL functioning at baseline increased the risk of death and institutionalization by 2% each year. Poor cognitive functioning at baseline increased the risk of death by 9% over the 10-year period, while the likelihood of leaving the program due to improvement decreased the risk of death by 18%. Reduced affective functioning at baseline increased the risk of institutionalization by 3%.

CONCLUSIONS: The authors conclude that routine functional assessments with older adults may help in the management of similar home care programs. They note, however, that predicting attrition rates for CBLTC clients remains elusive. Data from the current study indicate that routine functional assessment on admission to a CBLTC program can be used to predict total drop-out, but no single functional assessment is predictive at the individual level.

See also Worrall, G., Elgar, F. J., & Knight, J. C. (2001). The study population and methods are identical; the current article has one additional year of data collection.

Forbes, D. A., & Janzen, B. L. (2004). Comparison of rural and urban users and non-users of home care in Canada. *Canadian Journal of Rural Medicine, 9*(4), 227-235.

OBJECTIVES: To examine the demographic, economic, psychosocial, and physical characteristics associated with the use of publicly funded home care services among rural and urban Canadians aged 18+ in all provinces of Canada.

METHODS: The data were from the 1996/97 and 1998/99 cross-sectional cycles of Statistics Canada's National Population Health Surveys. Sample sizes were 13,070 in 1996/97 and 14,148 in 1998/99. Household residents in all provinces excluding populations on Indian Reserves, Canadian Forces Bases, and some remote areas of Ontario and Quebec were selected through a multistage stratified sampling design. Home care was defined as "health care or homemaker services received at home, with the cost being entirely or partially covered by government (e.g., nursing care, help with bathing, help around the home, physiotherapy, counseling and meal delivery)" (p. 229).

DEFINITION OF RURAL: The Census definition of rural was used, more specifically the population living outside places of 1,000 people or more *(i.e., living in places of < 1000)*, or a population living outside places with densities of 400 or more people per square kilometre *(i.e., living in places with densities < 400 people per square kilometre)*, based on the previous Census.

RESULTS RELATED TO RURAL AGING: Home care use increased with age in rural and urban areas. Individuals aged 65+ were 5 times more likely than those aged < 65 to use these services. Among the 65+ age group, 11% of rural sample and 12% of the urban sample reported using home care services. In rural areas, those who used home care had higher levels of education and a higher sense of coherence (the extent to which respondents perceive events as comprehensible, manageable, and meaningful). In terms of specific services, rural home care users were more likely than their urban counterparts to receive housework services and less likely to receive personal care assistance.

CONCLUSIONS: The authors argue that rural health care practitioners are ideally positioned to ensure that rural residents who need services are encouraged to use such services.

Hawranik, P. (1998). The role of cognitive status in the use of inhome services: Implications for nursing assessment. *Canadian Journal of Nursing Research, 30*(2), 45-65.

OBJECTIVES: To examine the association between cognitive status and in-home service use by older adults and their informal caregivers in the province of Manitoba.

METHODS: Data were from the 1991/92 Manitoba Study of Health and Aging (MSHA). The study involved in-person interviews with a random sample of older adults aged 65+ in the community and clinical assessments with those whose screening assessment indicated possible cognitive impairment. A subsample of caregivers also was interviewed in-person. Data from 380 elder-caregiver dyads were included in these analyses. Four in-home services were examined, including homemaking, in-home nursing, personal care, and home-delivered meals. Three types of cognitive status (dementia, cognitive loss without dementia, and no cognitive impairment) were considered. The Andersen-Newman model was used to guide the research; elder mental status needs, elder functional needs, caregiver needs, enabling characteristics, and predisposing characteristics were examined in the regression analyses.

DEFINITION OF RURAL: Rural-urban comparisons were made. No definition of rural was provided.

RESULTS RELATED TO RURAL AGING: There were no statistically significant rural-urban differences for the use of in-home nursing or home-delivered meals. In addition, the rural-urban variable did not meet the inclusion criteria for logistic modeling for homemaking or for personal care.

CONCLUSIONS: Overall, the cognitive status of the older adult was not a predictor of homemaking, in-home nursing, and home-delivered meals but it was significant for personal care services. There was no discussion of the lack of rural-urban differences.

See also Hawranik, P. (2002).

Hawranik, P. (2002). Inhome service use by caregivers and their elders: Does cognitive status make a difference? *Canadian Journal on Aging, 21*(2), 257-271.

OBJECTIVES: To examine the effect of cognitive status on the use of in-home services by caregivers and care receivers in the province of Manitoba.

METHODS: Secondary analysis of data from the 1991/92 Manitoba Study on Health and Aging (MSHA) for 380 caregivers (mean age 58) and their care receivers (mean age 77) was conducted. A modified Anderson-Newman model was used to examine predisposing, enabling, and need factors associated with use. In-home service use (homemaking, nursing, personal care, and home delivered meals) was reported by caregivers.

DEFINITION OF RURAL: No definition of rural was provided; rural-urban comparisons were made.

RESULTS RELATED TO RURAL AGING: There were no rural-urban differences in the likelihood of in-home service use. No separate analyses of the rural sample only were presented. Overall, cognitive status was not a major factor related to in-home service use although it was significantly associated with use of personal care and the use of 2+ in-home services. There were no differences in service use by caregivers of elders with cognitive impairment but not dementia and caregivers of elders with no cognitive impairment.

CONCLUSIONS: The author speculates that lack of perceived need, lack of knowledge of available resources, and lack of relevancy of services to those with cognitive problems may explain non-use of services by caregivers and their elders. She calls for further study on the role of specific functional limitations related to service use.

See also Hawranik, P. (1998).

Hayward, L., Davies, S., Robb, R., Denton, M., & Auton, G. (2004). Publicly funded and family-friend care in the case of long-term illness: The role of the spouse. *Canadian Journal on Aging, 23*(Suppl. 1), S39-S48.

OBJECTIVES: To examine the impact of the presence of a spouse on the amount of publicly funded care used by seniors aged 55+ with a long term illness, and to estimate the value of time spent caring for spouses and the savings generated by caregiving spouses for the publicly funded care system across Canada.

METHODS: Data were from Statistics Canada's 1996 General Social Survey that included 1,502 individuals aged 55+ who were receiving some type of help or care because of a long-term health problem or physical limitation. The types of care included meal preparation, house cleaning, house maintenance, grocery shopping, transportation, banking-bill paying, and personal care. The caregiver could be a spouse, child, another family member, friend, neighbour, co-worker, non-governmental organization, a paid employee, or a government organization. The total minutes per year for help from non-governmental organizations, government, a combination of individual and non-governmental organizations, or a combination of individual and government were examined. The total minutes of care per year provided by the spouse and the number of spouses providing care were used to value the unpaid contribution of the spouse. Less than one-quarter (23%) of the sample lived in a rural area.

DEFINITION OF RURAL: Rural respondents and those from Prince Edward Island were compared to urban respondents. No definition of rural was provided.

RESULTS RELATED TO RURAL AGING: Living in rural areas was not significantly associated with the minutes of publicly funded care per year. Residents of Nova Scotia, New Brunswick, and British Columbia were estimated to obtain significantly more publicly funded care than those in Ontario. The presence of a spouse significantly reduced the amount of publicly funded care used. Spousal care represented a total of 182,547,204 hours a year of care time and was estimated to be worth approximately $1.88 billion (Canadian) per year. This was considered to be the lower limit of the value of spousal care in Canada since this figure was based on an underestimate of the spousal care actually received. The rural-urban difference in the value of spousal care was not examined.

CONCLUSIONS: The authors argue that their findings clearly indicate the importance of spousal caregiving in Canada. Policy implications are explored.

Joseph, A. E. (1992). Issues in the provision of in-home health services to the rural elderly. In W. M. Gesler, & T. C. Ricketts (Eds.), *Health in rural North America: The geography of health care services and delivery* (pp. 89-110). New Brunswick, NJ: Rutgers University Press.

OBJECTIVES: To address the impact of elderly migration on service demands and the issue of service coordination in the province of Ontario.

METHODS: This chapter included a review of relevant literature and the presentation of two case studies (Grey County and Huron County). One case study was conducted in Grey County and dealt with the role of migration in the aging of the county and with differential use of in-home services. Interviews were conducted with 202 randomly selected individuals aged 65+ in the town of Meaford and the village of Markdale. The Huron County case study focused on the development of a pilot model of One-Stop Access (a service co-ordination strategy) for a rural county. The location of case management was conceptualized along a centralized-decentralized continuum. Four factors believed to be critical to successful implementation were considered: community visibility and communication; ease of contact among case managers, clients, and providers; peer interaction; and cost from the perspectives of clients/consumers, case managers, service providers, and the system as a whole.

DEFINITION OF RURAL: No definition of rural was provided.

RESULTS RELATED TO RURAL AGING: Based on published Census data for 1976 to 1981, Grey County experienced a net out-migration of younger people and a net in-migration of older adults in this period. A considerable amount of age-specific population redistribution occurred within the county; towns and villages gained at a higher rate than the county as a whole. Based on interview data, four categories of movers were identified: non-movers [i.e., residents of same location for 15+ years] (49%), local movers (15%), county movers (22%), and distance movers (14%). Movers were described as being more service-dependent. However, irrespective of type of move, few individuals reported the use of either homemaker or home nursing which "forces a guarded, noninferential interpretation of results" (p. 101). The Huron County case study illustrated the complex trade-offs between centralized and decentralized scenarios. It was decided that the client perspective should take precedence over all other perspectives. The recommendation was for a partially decentralized system, in recognition of the importance of local visibility while acknowledging increased costs associated with decentralization.

CONCLUSIONS: The complex variety of geographical and organizational constraints on efficient long-term, in-home service delivery to rural older adults was highlighted. The author argues that variety in rural conditions and migration history need to be taken into account. Calls for a broad approach in future research in the area of in-home services are made.

See also Joseph, A. E., & Cloutier, D. S. (1990) (2 abstracts); and Joseph, A. E., & Cloutier, D. S. (1991).

Keefe, J. M., & Fancey, P. (1997). Financial compensation or home help services: Examining differences among program recipients. *Canadian Journal on Aging, 16*(2), 254-278.

OBJECTIVES: To explore the experiences of caregivers who received different combinations of formal services including financial compensation in the province of Nova Scotia.

METHODS: Data were from in-person interviews with 136 caregivers who participated in the Shared Care: The Organization of Home Care and Family Caregiving project in 1989 and 1990. Municipal social service workers identified all clients aged 60+. Comparisons were made between caregivers who received financial compensation (30%), home help services (38%), or a combination of both (32%) under Nova Scotia's Home Life Support and In-Home Support programs.

DEFINITION OF RURAL: Urban included the area served by the Halifax and Dartmouth municipal social services units; non-urban included six other municipal units.

RESULTS RELATED TO RURAL AGING: Caregivers receiving financial compensation only or a combination of finances and home help services were more likely to be living in non-urban areas. In addition, paid caregivers were more likely to be female, younger, and living with the care receiver while caregivers receiving services only were more likely to be sons or spouses. No other urban/non-urban differences were provided.

CONCLUSIONS: The authors speculate that the greater proportion of financially compensated caregivers in non-urban areas was likely influenced by the limited availability of home help services in these areas, the high level of unemployment and underemployment in the non-urban areas, and the prevalent view of the traditional role of women in the home in rural areas. The independent spirit of the current older generation and the perception that assistance is 'welfare' and should be avoided also are identified as issues that may influence the findings.

Kelley, M. L., & MacLean, M. J. (1997). I want to live here for rest of my life: The challenge of case management for rural seniors. *Journal of Case Management, 6*(4), 174-182.

OBJECTIVES: To address the complexity of providing health care and social services for older adults living in small northwestern rural communities in the province of Ontario.

METHODS: The study was completed in six small communities in the District of Thunder Bay in northwestern Ontario. The communities were purposively sampled based on population size, percentage of seniors, number of community health and social services resources, and distance from Thunder Bay. Telephone interviews were conducted with 460 older individuals aged 65+. A focus group was held with seniors in each of the six communities.

DEFINITION OF RURAL: The communities were Beardmore, Geraldton, Longlac, Manitouwadge, Marathon, and Nakina. All had populations of ≤ 6,000. The distance to Thunder Bay, the major urban centre in the district, ranged from 120 to 250 miles.

RESULTS RELATED TO RURAL AGING: The service priorities identified by the older adults tended not to be those normally provided by the Canadian health care system, such as assistance with home maintenance, prescription delivery to rural communities, assistance with spring cleaning, and transportation. The authors called for new approaches to case management that are flexible to meet the needs of rural older adults. Four intervention roles of a rural case manager were discussed, including arranging and coordinating services and advocacy, providing direct service, consulting with specialists outside the community, and constructing and supporting informal helping networks. The authors proposed that a core job function of a locally-based rural case manager needs to be the stimulation of the development of new services for older adults. In rural areas, the case manager needs to have a role with both individual clients and the entire community.

CONCLUSIONS: The authors present a specialized rural case management approach to provide health and social supports to rural older adults and their families. They contend that rural case management differs from urban case management by requiring specialized knowledge, skills, and educational programs.

McWilliam, C. L., & Sangster, J. F. (1994). **Managing patient discharge to home: The challenges of achieving quality of care.** *International Journal for Quality in Health Care, 6*(2), 147-161.

OBJECTIVES: To explore and describe factors other than medical conditions and treatment which shaped the quality of the hospital discharge experiences of older patients in the province of Ontario.

METHODS: A qualitative research methodology was used to document the discharge process from the perspective of older patients, family caregivers, and professional caregivers. Phase 1 focused on a review of patients' charts/kardexes for 12 rural patients aged 65+, and interviews with 10 of these patients as well as with a purposeful sample of 12 family caregivers and 62 professional caregivers. Phase 2 involved an urban sample. Data were collected over a 6-week period in the rural study and over a 12-week period in the urban study.

DEFINITION OF RURAL: Phase 1 took place in a city of 30,000, situated within a rural, agricultural county. Health care services were provided by a 200-bed acute care non-teaching hospital and a county-wide home care program.

RESULTS RELATED TO RURAL AGING: In the rural community, patients' care both in and out of the hospital was managed by family physicians, with involvement from other professionals to a lesser degree. At home, patients received home care services and 9 individuals received additional care from family members. The rural professionals developed a division of labour and a 'professionally democratized order'. Quality management of the discharge process was undermined by role confusion and compromised efficiency. Problems with communication and coordination effects, and with a lack of information related to medications, supplies, specific treatment protocols, diet, and home care services were evident.

CONCLUSIONS: The challenges of managing patient discharge from hospital to care at home are highlighted. Strategies to address these challenges are presented. Similar problems with communication and coordination efforts are evident across both rural and urban settings.

Penning, M. J. (1995). Cognitive impairment, caregiver burden, and the utilization of home health services. *Journal of Aging and Health, 7*(2), 233-253.

OBJECTIVES: To examine the relationship between caregiver burden and the use of home health services among older adults with cognitive impairment in Canada.

METHODS: Data were from the 1991/92 Canadian Study of Health and Aging (CSHA). A sample of older adults was interviewed and those who screened positive for possible cognitive impairment were invited to complete a clinical assessment. A sample of caregivers to individuals with and without dementia also was identified and interviewed. The sample size for the community-based primary caregivers was 833, of whom 327 were caring for those diagnosed with dementia. Caregiver burden was measured by the Zarit Burden Interview and was administered only to caregivers of older adults with dementia. Information on in-home services was obtained from the caregiver. Services included homemaking/cleaning services; personal care; in-home nursing care; and physiotherapy, occupational therapy, podiatry, or chiropractic treatments. The total number of formal services also was calculated. The Andersen-Newman model guided the analysis, with predisposing, enabling, care receiver need, and caregiver need variables included in the model.

DEFINITION OF RURAL: Urban/non-urban comparisons were made; no definition of non-urban was provided.

RESULTS RELATED TO RURAL AGING: Living in a less urban setting was found to be statistically significant and associated with more extensive home health service use and the receipt of personal care services. There were no urban/non-urban differences in homemaker, nursing, or therapy services. When interaction terms with burden were added to the models, living in less urban areas was associated with therapy services. Higher levels of burden on the part of the primary caregiver and residence in a less urbanized area were associated with somewhat lower therapy service use.

CONCLUSIONS: Caregiver burden and formal home health services use were only weakly related. The author offers possible explanations for this finding.

Peterson, S., Shapiro, E., & Roos, N. P. (2005). Regional variation in home care use in Manitoba. *Canadian Journal on Aging, 24*(Suppl. 1), 69-80.

OBJECTIVES: To measure and assess variation in the use of home care across the 12 regional health authorities (RHAs) in the province of Manitoba.

METHODS: Data on home care use for all Manitoba residents in the fiscal year 1998/99 were obtained from the Manitoba Support Service Payroll (MSSP) system, an administrative database developed by Manitoba Health, and updated where necessary using the Long Term Care files and Vital Statistics. The population's use of home care, home care use after hospitalization, home care use before long term care (LTC) facility entry, and home care use before death (all age- and sex-adjusted) were examined across RHAs. In Manitoba, home care is a core service that RHAs are obligated to deliver.

DEFINITION OF RURAL: Comparisons were made between the Winnipeg RHA (urban) and the 11 non-Winnipeg RHAs (rural). Winnipeg is the major urban centre in the province.

RESULTS RELATED TO RURAL AGING: Overall, 15.7 individuals per 100 residents aged 65+ were clients of the Home Care Program in Manitoba for at least one day during 1998/99 (Winnipeg - 16.6, non-Winnipeg - 14.6). Only 7% of Manitobans aged 65+ were new clients (Winnipeg – 7%, non-Winnipeg – 6%). Winnipeg residents had 3,593 days in the Home Care program per 100 residents aged 65+ compared to 3,344 days for their non-Winnipeg counterparts. In terms of post-hospitalization use, Winnipeg (5.1 per 100 discharged patients) had a significantly higher proportion of clients than non-Winnipeg clients (3.2). There was little variation in the average number of days spent as a home care client in the year before entry to a LTC facility. One non-Winnipeg RHA (Brandon) emerged as distinctive in that clients in this region had a greater average number of hospital days for their home care clients compared to other RHAs. Home care use before death was similar across RHAs.

CONCLUSIONS: The authors conclude that, while some important differences emerged, overall there was comparable use of home care across Manitoba. Limitations of the data source are discussed.

See also Roos, N., Stranc, L., Peterson, S., Mitchell, L., Bogdanovic, B., & Shapiro, E. (2001).

Roos, N., Stranc, L., Peterson, S., Mitchell, L., Bogdanovic, B., & Shapiro, E. (2001). *A look at home care in Manitoba.* **Winnipeg, MB: Manitoba Centre for Health Policy and Evaluation, University of Manitoba. Retrieved from:** http://umanitoba.ca/centres/mchp/reports/pdfs/homecare.pdf

OBJECTIVES: To evaluate the strengths and weaknesses of using the Manitoba Support Services Payroll (MSSP) data to assess trends in access to and use of home care, and to review the use of home care in the fiscal year of 1998/99 and trends in use from the fiscal years 1995/96 to 1998/99 across the province of Manitoba.

METHODS: Data on home care use for all Manitoba residents between 1995/96 and 1998/99 were obtained from the MSSP, an administrative database that contained data on clients, employees (direct service workers employed by the Department of Health), and services (time sheets). Access was measured by the percent of the population who were registered with the Home Care Program for at least one day during the fiscal year, the number of new clients per 100 home care clients per year, and the number of new clients per 100 residents per year. Use was the number of days 'open' to Home Care during a given year.

DEFINITION OF RURAL: Winnipeg and Brandon Regional Health Authorities (RHAs) were considered urban (referred to as Winnipeg in the Tables); the other 10 RHAs were defined as rural. Distinctions were made between northern Manitoba (Churchill, Burntwood, and Nor-Man RHAs) and the rural south (Parkland, Marquette, South Westman, Central, Interlake, North Eastman, and South Eastman RHAs).

RESULTS RELATED TO RURAL AGING: In 1998/99, 16% of Manitoba's population aged 65+ was home care users (Winnipeg/Brandon - 17%; rural south - 15%; northern Manitoba - 14%). In total, 31,298 individuals were home care clients in 1998/99, including 11,355 in the rural south and 828 in northern Manitoba. In the rural south RHAs, 83% were aged 65+, compared to 79% in Winnipeg/Brandon and 53% in northern Manitoba. The median duration of days open to home care for clients aged 65+ in 1998/99 was 243, 267, and 252 days for Winnipeg/Brandon, rural south, and northern RHAs, respectively. Changes in access rates across the RHAs from 1995/96 to 1998/99 showed small increases in the proportion of those using home care in almost every region. The report includes an appendix outlining the completeness and reliability of the data by region.

CONCLUSIONS: The authors conclude that despite the challenges of delivering home care in urban versus rural settings, similar access to home care services appears to have been achieved across the province. They argue that the MSSP client registry is a useful source of data although there are limitations to its use.

See also Peterson, S., Shapiro, E., & Roos, N. P. (2005).

Shapiro, E. (1986). Patterns and predictors of home care use by the elderly when need is the sole basis for admission. *Home Health Care Services Quarterly, 7*(1), 29-44.

OBJECTIVES: To describe home care utilization from 1975 to 1978 by older adults in the province of Manitoba.

METHODS: Data were from the Manitoba Longitudinal Study on Aging (MLSA). Data from a large probability sample of Manitoba residents aged 65+ interviewed in 1971 were merged with administrative data on universally insured medical and hospital services from 1970 to 1978 and home care services from 1975 to 1978. Predictors of home care use were obtained from the interview data and examined in a multiple logistic regression analysis.

DEFINITION OF RURAL: No definition of rural was provided; rural/remote and urban comparisons were made.

RESULTS RELATED TO RURAL AGING: Between April 1975 and September 1978, 484 older adults received home care services. The multivariate analysis revealed a significant rural/urban difference; urban residents were 1.3 times more likely than rural/remote residents to be home care users. Overall, age and difficulty in coping with instrumental activities of daily living were the strongest predictors of subsequent home care use. No rural-specific analyses were presented.

CONCLUSIONS: The author concludes that a home care program based solely on professionally assessed need admits only a small minority of older adults. Policy implications of the findings are discussed.

Strain, L. A., & Greenslade, L. (1996). *An Evaluation of Manitoba Health's Support Services to Seniors Program.* **Winnipeg, MB: Centre on Aging, University of Manitoba.**

OBJECTIVES: To describe the current target population of Support Services to Seniors and to evaluate the impact of Support Services on the use of home care services and nursing homes in the province of Manitoba. The Support Services to Seniors program was introduced in Manitoba in 1984/85 to assist communities in the development of services that will support seniors in maintaining their independence in the community such as congregate meals, grocery shopping, transportation, and home maintenance.

METHODS: Data were from four sources: 195 questionnaires completed in August to September 1996 regarding the Support Services to Seniors program and a description of clients, 17 key informant interviews with Manitoba Health representatives, a file review of 1995/96 annual statistics provided by the Supportive Services to Seniors program to Manitoba Health, and the annual reports provided by Seniors' Specialists.

DEFINITION OF RURAL: Regional comparisons were made. With the exception of Winnipeg, the major urban centre in the province, the regions were considered as rural.

RESULTS RELATED TO RURAL AGING: Congregate meal programs were provided throughout the province, with the exception of the two northern regions. The number of programs in the rural regions ranged from 11 to 28 while there were 20 programs in Winnipeg. The number of clients served by non-Winnipeg programs ranged from 323 to 795 compared to 673 in Winnipeg. The age distribution of clients was generally similar across regions while the percentage of females ranged from 58% in Interlake to 78% in Winnipeg. The percentage of individuals living alone was highest in Winnipeg as was the percentage that required assistance getting to the meal program. The number of community/tenant resource councils ranged from 4 to 36 in the rural regions compared to 16 in Winnipeg. Regional differences in specific services provided by these councils also were discussed (see Appendices D and E). The report concluded with an examination of issues and challenges that face Support Services to Seniors such as funding, the expansion and administration of the program, staff and board development, relationships with Home Care and with the Regional Health Authorities, and anticipated future demand.

CONCLUSIONS: Overall, the Support Services to Seniors program was viewed as a cost-effective, quality service that serves a population at risk.

Williams, A. M. (1996). The development of Ontario's home care program: A critical geographical analysis. *Social Science & Medicine, 42*(6), 937-948.

OBJECTIVES: To provide an historical analysis of home care programs in order to identify how long-term care policy has contributed to the medically underserviced northern region of the province of Ontario.

METHODS: This historical analysis involved a review of policy documents and reports.

DEFINITION OF RURAL: The focus was on the northern region of Ontario, which consists of rural, sparsely populated areas.

RESULTS RELATED TO RURAL AGING: Issues such as the importing of programs developed in southern Ontario, being the last to introduce services, the differential fit of home care in the continuum of care in northern Ontario as compared to southern Ontario, the limited informal care networks, and the need for culturally appropriate services were examined.

CONCLUSIONS: The author argues that the geographical bias in the testing, planning, and implementation of home care programs has influenced their availability, accessibility, and quality in the underserviced regions of northern Ontario.

Worrall, G., Elgar, F. J., & Knight, J. C. (2001). Predictive value of support systems in a long-term care program. *Home Care Provider, 6*(1), 32-36.

OBJECTIVES: To describe the rates of and reasons for dropout of a cohort of clients enrolled in a community-based long-term care (CBLTC) program in the province of Newfoundland.

METHODS: This 9-year prospective study involved 237 clients of the Gander and District Continuing Care Program. From January to May 1990, a home care nurse assessed each client's medical, social, financial, and functional status at baseline. The status of the patient was recorded annually for a 9-year period.

DEFINITION OF RURAL: The CBLTC program serviced a total population of 61,766 and a 65+ population of 6,420 in rural areas of eastern and central Newfoundland.

RESULTS RELATED TO RURAL AGING: Within the first two years, 59% of the clients dropped out. Attrition was rapid at first but then leveled off. Almost one-half (47%) died while in the program, 32% were discharged because of improvement, and 21% were institutionalized.

CONCLUSIONS: The authors argue that CBLTC programs give many clients the option of living out their lives at home.

See also Elgar, F. J., Worrall, G., & Knight, J. C. (2002). The study population and methods are identical: the 2002 article covers a 10-year data collection period, whereas the current article covers a 9-year period.

Hospitalizations/Emergency Room

Carriere, K. C., Jin, Y., Marrie, T. J., Predy, G., & Johnson, D. H. (2004). **Outcomes and costs among seniors requiring hospitalization for community-acquired pneumonia in Alberta.** *Journal of the American Geriatrics Society, 52*, 31-38.

OBJECTIVES: To examine age-specific rates of hospital discharge, cost per day, and overall in-hospital, 1-year, and 4-year mortality for older adults requiring hospitalization for community-acquired pneumonia (CAP) in the province of Alberta.

METHODS: Data were from the Canadian Institute of Health's Inpatient Discharge Abstract Database for Alberta for 1994/95 to 1998/99, and from the Alberta Health Insurance Plan Registry File for 1994 to 2000. Daily hospital cost per hospital discharge, incidence of special medical care per hospital discharge, in-hospital mortality per patient or per discharge, and one-year mortality per patient or per discharge were outcomes used in the regression analysis. Urban or non-urban region of residence was a covariate.

DEFINITION OF RURAL: Five groups were identified based on the average number of discharges over the 5-year study period, geographic location, and medical school proximity. These were: rural towns with primary care facilities (< 50 cases/y); rural towns with primary care facilities (50 - 108 cases/y); regional cities with secondary care facilities (5 located in one of 5 non-metropolitan regional healthcare cities [67 - 251 cases/y]), and one high-volume rural hospital (221 cases/y); metropolitan cities with tertiary care facilities (Calgary and Edmonton); and metropolitan cities with tertiary care facilities located adjacent to medical schools.

RESULTS RELATED TO RURAL AGING: There were approximately 8,500 annual hospitalizations for CAP, costing $40 million per year. There were no rural-urban differences in the age-specific hospitalization rates for the 65 - 74, 75 - 84 and 85+ groups although patients aged < 65 were less likely to reside in one of the two Alberta metropolitan cities.

CONCLUSIONS: CAP was a common cause for hospital admission in Alberta. No specific urban/non-urban conclusions were made.

Cujec, B., Quan, H., Jin, Y., & Johnson, D. (2004). The effect of age upon care and outcomes in patients hospitalized for congestive heart failure in Alberta, Canada. *Canadian Journal on Aging, 23*(3), 255-267.

OBJECTIVES: To investigate the age-specific outcomes for patients hospitalized with newly diagnosed congestive heart failure in the province of Alberta.

METHODS: Data were from the Canadian Institute of Health's Discharge Abstract Database for Alberta for 1992/93 to 1999/2000, the Alberta Health Insurance Plan Registry File for 1994/95 to 1999/2000, the Alberta Physician Claims Assessment System Database for 1992/93 to 1999/2000, and the Alberta Blue Cross Insurance plan for 1994/95 to 1999/2000. Congestive heart failure was defined using the ICD9_CM.

DEFINITION OF RURAL: For patient characteristics, the 17 health regions in Alberta were grouped into two metropolitan regions (Calgary and Edmonton) and one non-metropolitan region.

RESULTS RELATED TO RURAL AGING: A total of 16,162 patients aged 20+ were hospitalized for newly diagnosed congestive heart failure during the 6-year study period. Approximately 85% were aged 65+. The percentage of non-metropolitan residents with heart failure increased with age.

CONCLUSIONS: Co-morbidity and mortality for congestive heart failure increased with age while the use of specialized medical services and hospital costs decreased with age (especially among those 85+). No rural-specific conclusions were presented.

De Coster, C., Bruce, S., & Kozyrskyj, A. (2005). Use of acute care hospitals by long-stay patients: Who, how much, and why? *Canadian Journal on Aging, 24*(Suppl. 1), 97-106.

OBJECTIVES: To examine trends in long-stay hospital use over time and factors that contributed to long stays in the province of Manitoba.

METHODS: Data were from the medical records of patients hospitalized in Winnipeg in 1998/99 and administrative data from the Manitoba Population Health Research Data Repository of all patient contacts with hospitals, physicians, and nursing homes. A long hospital stay was defined as lasting longer than 30 days. Historical trends were examined for the period 1991/92 to 1999/2000. The medical record review did not consider place of residence.

DEFINITION OF RURAL: Winnipeg/non-Winnipeg comparisons were made. Winnipeg is the major urban centre in the province; non-Winnipeg was defined as all areas outside of Winnipeg.

RESULTS RELATED TO RURAL AGING: Between 1991/92 and 1999/2000, 40% of acute care hospital days were used by the 5% of patients who had long stays. The distribution of days used by medical and surgical patients differed. In Winnipeg hospitals, 58% of the long-stay cases were aged 75+, and this group consumed 64% of the long-stay days. Outside Winnipeg, 70% of the long-stay patients were aged 75+, consuming 73% of the long-stay days.

CONCLUSIONS: The authors argue that unnecessarily long stays place older patients at greater risk of deterioration, functional decline, or adverse hospital events. They suggest that hospital information systems and early discharge planning may help to alleviate lengthy discharge delays and result in better care for these patients.

See also Finlayson, M., Lix, L., Finlayson, G. S., & Fong, T. (2005); Kozyrskyj, A. L., Black, C., Chateau, D., & Steinbach, C. (2005); and Roos, N. P., Shapiro, E., Bond, R., Black, C., Finlayson, G., Newburn-Cook, C., MacWilliam, L., Steinbach, C., Yogendran, M., & Walld, R. (2001).

De Freitas, T. L., Spooner, G. R., & Szafran, O. (1998). Admissions and transfers from a rural emergency department. *Canadian Family Physician, 44*, 789-795.

OBJECTIVES: To compare the characteristics of patients transferred from a rural Alberta hospital emergency department and patients admitted to the hospital on an emergency basis in the province of Alberta.

METHODS: Records of the emergency department at Bonnyville Health Centre (BHC) from January 1, 1991 to June 30, 1992 were reviewed. Transferred patients were patients who were assessed in the emergency department and transferred directly to another hospital; admitted patients visited the emergency and were then admitted to BHC.

DEFINITION OF RURAL: This rural, acute care hospital, located 240 km northeast of Edmonton, serves the town of Bonnyville (population 5,150) and a catchment area of approximately 10,000. At the time of the study, it had 67 acute care beds, 2 operating rooms with 24-hour nursing, and a general practitioner anesthesia on call.

RESULTS RELATED TO RURAL AGING: A total of 1,055 patients seen in the emergency department were either transferred to another centre (11%) or admitted to the BHC on an emergency basis (89%). The 60 - 69 age group accounted for 15% of the transferred patients and 8% of the admitted patients, while the corresponding percentages for the 70+ group were 18% and 29%, respectively. Differences between transferred patients and admitted patients based on age were significant for the very young (11% transferred vs. 5% admitted) and the old (60 – 69 age group: 15% transferred vs. 8% admitted; 70+ age group: 18% transferred vs. 29% admitted). Patients with orthopedic or neurological problems were more likely to be transferred.

CONCLUSIONS: The study highlights the importance of care of the elderly in the context of rural emergency care. The authors argue that family physicians in rural practice need to be well grounded in geriatric medicine.

Harris, L., Bombin, M., Chi, F., deBortoli, T., & Long, J. (2004). Use of the emergency room in Elliot Lake, a rural community of northern Ontario, Canada. *Rural and Remote Health, 4*(1, No. 240), 1-12.

OBJECTIVES: To examine the demographics of emergency room (ER) clients, the nature of ER use, and the level of urgency as perceived by clients versus health professionals in the northern region of the province of Ontario.

METHODS: Conducted in July 2001, this prospective survey involved patients and attending clinicians at the time of a patient's presentation to the ER of St. Joseph's General Hospital in Elliott Lake, Ontario. In-person interviews were conducted with ER patients; written questionnaires were completed by attending health professionals. Sample sizes were 1,096 patients, 1,290 attending nurses, and 1,013 physicians/nurse practitioners.

DEFINITION OF RURAL: Elliot Lake is a rural northern Ontario community. At the time of the study, its population was 12,000 and the proportion of seniors (25%) was double that of the Canadian average (12%). The 57-bed acute care hospital was staffed by family physicians, a nurse practitioner, and registered nurses (RNs), and had a catchment area of approximately 18,000 (town plus surrounding areas).

RESULTS RELATED TO RURAL AGING: Older patients accounted for 31% of the ER visits, with 14% of the visits made by the 61 - 70 age group, 12% by the 71 - 80 age group, and 5% by the 81+ group. This was roughly proportional to the population distribution for these cohorts in the catchment area. No other results were specific to older adults.

CONCLUSIONS: The authors conclude that elderly persons in Elliott Lake generally do not misuse emergency room services more than other age cohorts.

Iglesias, S., Saunders, L. D., Tracy, S., Thangisalam, N., & Jones, L. (2003). Appendectomies in rural hospitals: Safe whether performed by specialist or GP surgeons. *Canadian Family Physician, 49*, 328-333.

OBJECTIVES: To compare outcomes of appendectomies performed in rural hospitals by specialist surgeons and GP surgeons in the provinces of Ontario, Saskatchewan, Alberta, and British Columbia.

METHODS: Data were from the Canadian Institute for Health Information's (CIHI) Discharge Abstract Database (DAD) from 1996 to 1999. Data were extracted for the 4,587 admissions for appendectomies in the selected rural hospitals.

DEFINITION OF RURAL: Rural hospitals were those hospitals where most or all specialist services provided locally were carried out by non-specialist medical staff.

RESULTS RELATED TO RURAL AGING: The average age of patients having an appendectomy was 27.7 years. Being aged 75+ was associated with an increased likelihood of perforations. Older adults were no more likely to have second intra-abdominal or pelvic procedures than their younger counterparts.

CONCLUSIONS: The authors concluded that appendectomy is generally a safe procedure in rural hospitals, whether performed by specialist surgeons or family physician surgeons.

COMMENTS: **Reid, T. (2003). City mouse, country mouse: Different but the same.** *Canadian Family Physician, 49,* **277-278.** The author states that the study by Igleisas et al. (2003) confirms that "family physician surgeons perform appendectomies safely and seem to be able to triage the more difficult cases to specialist surgeons" (p. 278). The author also notes that these family physicians provide valuable medical and non-medical services to remote communities.

Kozyrskyj, A. L., Black, C., Chateau, D., & Steinbach, C. (2005). Discharge outcomes in seniors hospitalized for more than 30 days. *Canadian Journal on Aging, 24* (Suppl. 1), 107-119.

OBJECTIVES: To determine risk factors for discharge to a nursing home, death in hospital, or transfer to another institution versus discharge home in a population of older adults who stayed in Winnipeg acute care hospitals for more than 30 days; to describe the characteristics of seniors with risk factors who were discharged home; and to describe one year outcomes following home discharge in the province of Manitoba.

METHODS: Data were from the Manitoba Population Health Research Data Repository of all patient contacts with hospitals, physicians, and nursing homes. The study population was individuals with long-stay hospitalizations (more than 30 days) in Winnipeg's acute hospitals from 1993/94 to 1999/2000. Four discharge outcome variables were examined, including discharge home, discharge to a nursing home, death in hospital, and transfer to another hospital in and outside Winnipeg. Sociodemographic characteristics, health status, and hospital factors were studied, including location of residence prior to admission based on postal codes.

DEFINITION OF RURAL: Winnipeg/non-Winnipeg comparisons were made. Winnipeg is the major urban centre in the province; non-Winnipeg was defined as all areas outside of Winnipeg.

RESULTS RELATED TO RURAL AGING: Of the 17,984 long-stay hospitalizations during 1993 - 2000, 45% were discharged home, 20% died, and 30% were discharged to a nursing home or another hospital. Within one year of home discharge, 20% died, 5% - 15% were admitted to a nursing home or long-term care institution, and 26% - 35% were re-hospitalized from home while 37% experienced none of these outcomes. Winnipeg/non-Winnipeg differences were not consistent across the 65 - 74, 75 - 84, and 85+ age groups (data not provided).

CONCLUSIONS: The authors argue that their findings point to opportunities to improve discharge outcomes and plan support services for seniors and call for a more thorough understanding of the transitions from independent living to institutional care.

See also De Coster, C., Bruce, S., & Kozyrskyj, A. (2005); DeCoster, C., Roos, N., & Shapiro, E. (1995); Finlayson, M., Lix, L., Finlayson, G. S., & Fong, T. (2005); and Roos, N. P., Shapiro, E., Bond, R., Black, C., Finlayson, G., Newburn-Cook, C., MacWilliam, L., Steinbach, C., Yogendran, M., & Walld, R. (2001).

Roos, N. P., & Lyttle, D. (1985). The centralization of operations and access to treatment: Total hip replacement in Manitoba. *American Journal of Public Health, 75*(2), 130-133.

OBJECTIVES: To examine the impact of centralization on access to hip replacement surgery in the province of Manitoba.

METHODS: Data were from the Manitoba Health Services Commission that insured costs of all medical services in Manitoba. All 1,889 total hip replacements performed on patients aged 25+ for the period 1973 to 1978 were analyzed.

DEFINITION OF RURAL: Eight regions approximating those used by Manitoba Department of Health for health services purposes were studied: Winnipeg (population of 500,000), Brandon (population 36,000), Western Manitoba, Central Manitoba, Eastern Manitoba, Interlake, Parkland, and North. Surgeries were performed in Winnipeg and Brandon; the remaining regions were considered as rural regions.

RESULTS RELATED TO RURAL AGING: No consistent patterns in the age- and sex-adjusted rates per 100,000 residents were evident across the regions. Age-specific surgical rates adjusted for sex for the 75+ age group and the < 50 age group were, in general, no higher in the referral centres of Winnipeg and Brandon than those in the six rural regions. However, there was a pattern of lower rates for hip replacement in the rural regions compared to the referral regions for the 65 to 74 age group.

CONCLUSIONS: Although Manitoba's population is geographically dispersed, specialized orthopedic services were concentrated in two urban centres. No important difference in access to care for hip replacement was evident between urban centre residents and residents distant from the surgical facilities. Results also suggest that centralization probably has not restricted the overall rate of hip replacement surgery.

Scott, P. A., Temovsky, C. J., Lawrence, K., Gudaitis, E., & Lowell, M. J. (1998). **Analysis of Canadian population with potential geographic access to intravenous thrombolysis for acute ischemic stroke.** *Stroke, 29*, 2304-2310.

OBJECTIVES: To identify the Canadian population with potential access to intravenous tissue plasminogen activator within 3 hours of onset of acute ischemic stroke.

METHODS: Ambulance databases were analyzed for transport times of 60, 90, and 120 minutes and were found to correspond to transport distances of 32, 64, and 105 kilometres, respectively. Using Geographical Information System (GIS) software, these radii were overlaid on thematic maps of Canadian hospitals identified as having a third- or fourth-generation CT scanner and with a neurologist and an emergency physician on staff. Analysis was then performed on the complete Canadian Census data from 1991 and the interim 1996 Census count.

DEFINITION OF RURAL: No definition of rural was provided.

RESULTS RELATED TO RURAL AGING: In Canada, 67%, 78%, and 85% of the population were within 32, 64, and 105 kilometres, respectively, of an identified hospital. For individuals aged 65+, 64%, 77%, and 86% were within the respective radii. Additional information for the 65 - 74, 74 – 84, and 85+ age groups was provided in a graph.

CONCLUSIONS: A substantial percentage of the Canadian population, including those aged 65+, has geographic access to a hospital potentially capable of delivering intravenous thrombolysis for acute ischemic stroke. Groups identified as having limited access are located in rural regions remote from urban and suburban facilities. The absence of a neurologist in smaller hospitals/treatment centres is one of the main barriers to the provision of this type of therapy.

Seaborn Moyse, H., & Osmun, W. E. (2004). Discharges against medical advice: A community hospital's experience. *Canadian Journal of Rural Medicine, 9*(3), **148-153.**

OBJECTIVES: To identify characteristics of patients who leave hospital against medical advice (known as 'discharges against medical advice' [DAMA]) in a small community hospital in the province of Ontario.

METHODS: A retrospective chart audit was performed for patients who had discharged themselves against medical advice between April 1, 2000 and March 31, 2002 from the Strathroy Middlesex General Hospital (SMGH) in rural southwestern Ontario (n = 6,186 discharges).

DEFINITION OF RURAL: SMGH is an 87-bed, rural community hospital with a catchment area of approximately 35,000.

RESULTS RELATED TO RURAL AGING: The rate of DAMA was found to be 0.57% (35 discharges), and the average length of stay was 2.8 days, compared to 5.2 days for the remaining hospital admissions. Patients aged 65+ accounted for proportionally fewer DAMA than non-DAMA. Individuals aged 35 to 49 had the highest rate of DAMA.

CONCLUSIONS: Patients who leave hospital against medical advice represent a high-risk population. Older adults are not the highest risk group for these types of discharge.

Note: The erratum that appears in the Canadian Journal of Rural Medicine (2004) 9(4):265 relates to an error in referencing.

Thompson, J. M., & Ratcliff, M. J. (1992). Use of emergency outpatient services in a small rural hospital. *Canadian Family Physician, 38*, 2322-2331.

OBJECTIVES: To describe the use of emergency outpatient services in a 34-bed rural hospital in the province of Alberta.

METHODS: A form was completed for all emergency and elective outpatients between March 1989 and February 1990. Information was gathered on the nature of the visit, demographic characteristics, time of the visit, and post-hospital care.

DEFINITION OF RURAL: Sundre General Hospital is a 34-bed, acute care facility providing general medical, pediatric, obstetric, and emergency services. Located 115 kilometres northwest of Calgary, the hospital district area is 600 square kilometres with a 1990 population of 4,950. The geographical area served is larger.

RESULTS RELATED TO RURAL AGING: One in 10 outpatients was classified as having serious and extreme emergencies. Less than 3% were transferred to higher level of care; 10% were admitted to the local hospital. The overall trend was for a higher number of visits at the younger age ranges (e.g., ≤ 30) compared to the upper age ranges (≥ 40). A breakdown by age, including 60 – 69, 70 – 79, 80 – 89, and 90+ age groups, was presented in a graph. The statistical significance of these differences was not provided.

CONCLUSIONS: Recommendations are made for staffing, training, inventory, and funding of small rural hospital emergency departments.

Weller, I., Wai, E. K., Jaglal, S., & Kreder, H. J. (2005). The effect of hospital type and surgical delay on mortality after surgery for hip fracture. *Journal of Bone and Joint Surgery (British), 87B*(3), 361-366.

OBJECTIVES: To determine whether mortality after a hip fracture is related to the type of hospital in which the patient is treated, to examine the relationship between surgical delay and mortality after a hip fracture, and to determine whether surgical delay contributes to the differences in outcome between the hospital types, in the province of Ontario.

METHODS: Data were from the Canadian Institute for Health Information's (CIHI) Discharge Abstracts Database. Records were examined for patients aged 50+ who were admitted to hospital in Ontario between 1993 and 1999 for surgical treatment of a hip fracture (n = 57,315). Data for this cohort was linked to the Registered Persons Database which contains information about all deaths in Ontario. Hospitals were classified as teaching or non-teaching. The non-teaching hospitals were further classified as urban or rural. Females accounted for 75% of the hip fracture patients; the mean age was 77.7 years for males and 81.4 for females.

DEFINITION OF RURAL: Rural was defined as communities with a population of < 10,000.

RESULTS RELATED TO RURAL AGING: The time to surgery and the length of hospital stay for these patients aged 50+ varied among the three types of hospitals. The urban teaching hospitals had the longest surgical delay while the rural hospitals had significantly longer lengths of stay. Patients treated in urban teaching hospitals had a decreased risk of in-hospital mortality compared with those treated in urban community institutions. There was a trend toward increased mortality in rural rather than urban community hospitals.

CONCLUSIONS: The authors call for future research to understand the factors associated with hospital teaching status that lead to differences in outcomes after surgery for patients with a hip fracture.

Nursing Homes: Factors Associated with Institutionalization/Prevalence

Longhofer, J. (1994). Nursing home utilization: A comparative study of the Hutterian Brethren, the Old Order Amish, and the Mennonites. *Journal of Aging Studies, 8*(1), 95-120.

OBJECTIVES: To explain the presence/absence of nursing homes among three religious communities (Old Order Amish, Hutterian Brethren, and Alexanderwohl Mennonite) in the Great Plains region of the United States and in the Canadian province of Manitoba.

METHODS: This study used historical research, life-history interviews, nursing home registries, data from fieldwork, and census records to describe the experiences of these three rural religious communities from early times to the present. The Hutterian Brethen reside in the Pembina and James Valley colonies in Manitoba.

DEFINITION OF RURAL: The James Valley and Pembina colonies in southern Manitoba are engaged in diversified agricultural production. No details on the specific location were provided.

RESULTS RELATED TO RURAL AGING: The Hutterian Brethren promote home care by releasing family members from other daily responsibilities to care for elderly relatives. The communal ownership of property and the flexibility in the allocation of labour have negated the need for a nursing home. Of the three communities, only the Mennonites have introduced a nursing home.

CONCLUSIONS: The author argues that the internal structure of the community within which older adults are located accounts for the emergence of nursing homes and not the inexorable effects of industrialization. This comparative study suggests that the emergence of homes for the aged has at least two preconditions: no community economy or polity to provide a wider net for dependent elderly and an ideology that permits welfare or charity provisions.

MSHA-2 Research Group. (1999). *Follow-up to the Manitoba Study of Health and Aging (MSHA-2): Institutionalization in Later Life.* **Winnipeg, MB: Centre on Aging, University of Manitoba.**

OBJECTIVES: To determine the proportion of a sample of elders who moved to an institution between 1991/92 and 1996/97; to identify characteristics associated with a move to an institution; to provide a profile of the elders who were institutionalized and the types of moves they made; and to examine reasons for institutionalization from family caregivers' perspectives in the province of Manitoba.

METHODS: Data were from the Manitoba Study of Health and Aging (MSHA). The analyses were based on data collected from 1,745 individuals who were aged 65+ and living in the community in 1991/92, completed a 1991/92 in-person interview, and whose place of residence in 1996/97 was known. A person was considered as institutionalized if s/he resided in a personal care home (nursing home) or, at the time of follow-up, had a hospital stay of at least three months and was not expected to return to the community.

DEFINITION OF RURAL: Winnipeg/non-Winnipeg comparisons were made. Winnipeg is the major urban centre in the province; non-Winnipeg was defined as all areas outside of Winnipeg.

RESULTS RELATED TO RURAL AGING: Overall 12% of these older adults were institutionalized between 1991/92 and 1996/97. Place of residence did not emerge as significant; older adults in Winnipeg and those residing outside Winnipeg did not differ in the likelihood that they would be institutionalized by 1996/97. When the sample size was reduced in order to consider caregiver and older adult characteristics together, place of residence of the older adults was still not significant. No other Winnipeg/non-Winnipeg analyses were conducted.

CONCLUSIONS: This study highlights issues related to institutionalization in later life. No rural-specific implications are discussed.

Mustard, C., Finlayson, M., Derksen, S., & Berthelot, J.-M. (1999). What determines the need for nursing home admission in a universally insured population? *Journal of Health Services Research & Policy, 4*(4), 197-203.

OBJECTIVES: To examine the effects of income and education on the probability of nursing home entry in a universally insured elderly population in the province of Manitoba.

METHODS: Using a prospective observational study design, demographic characteristics, socioeconomic status, and health status were examined as predictors of nursing home admission from June 1986 to May 1989. The representative sample included 7,220 Manitoba residents aged 60+. Data from the 1986 Canada Census 2B questionnaire and from the Manitoba Health Services Insurance Plan's computerized administrative records of health care utilization were linked. Rural-urban residence was included as a control variable; 31% of the sample had a rural residence.

DEFINITION OF RURAL: No definition of rural was provided.

RESULTS RELATED TO RURAL AGING: Rural-urban place of residence emerged as a significant predictor of nursing home admission in the multivariate analyses. Urban residents were 1.6 times more likely to have been admitted than their rural counterparts. An increased risk of institutionalization also was associated with older age, male gender, unmarried status, lower household income, lower attained education, and having a disability.

CONCLUSIONS: The authors argued that their results emphasize the independent role of socioeconomic status in accentuating or accelerating the need for institutional care towards the end of life. No rural-urban specific conclusions were discussed.

See also DeCoster, C., Roos, N., & Shapiro, E. (1995); Frohlich, N., Markesteyn, T., Roos, N., Carriere, K. C., Black, C., DeCoster, C., Burchill, C. A., & MacWilliam, L. (1994); Roos, N. P., Shapiro, E., Bond, R., Black, C., Finlayson, G., Newburn-Cook, C., MacWilliam, L., Steinbach, C., Yogendran, M., & Walld, R. (2001); and Tomiak, M., Berthelot, J.-M., Guimond, E., & Mustard, C. A. (2000).

Roy, J. (1990). Les personnes âgées vivant à domicile et le désir d'hébergement en institution. (Elderly persons living at home and the desire of institutional placement). *Recherches Sociographiques, 31*(2), 227-239.

OBJECTIVES: To explore factors that influence older adults' decision to move to a care centre or a hospital extended care centre in the province of Quebec.

METHODS: Data were from a random sample of 290 adults aged 65+ living in their own homes in the district of Des Chenaux in the Trois-Rivieres region, based on the 1985 electoral provincial list. Respondents were interviewed at home in June 1988, using a questionnaire that covered primary environmental dimensions that affect the life of older adults, and factors related to health and services. Comparisons were made between respondents who were candidates for institutionalization and those who were not.

DEFINITION OF RURAL: Rural was defined as a population of < 5,000. A total of 10 rural municipalities were included; Sainte-Genevieve-de-Batiscan was the geographical centre.

RESULTS RELATED TO RURAL AGING: Only 10% of the respondents desired to move to an institution. In addition to age, factors related to the desire to be institutionalized were either of a social nature such as widowhood or an environmental nature such as poor quality of housing. Health (infirmities, medical advice, health deficiencies) had little influence on the desire to relocate from home to an institution.

CONCLUSIONS: This study places the social and environmental dimensions of older adults' lives at the centre of decision-making processes about staying in homes versus choosing to go to an institution.

Shapiro, E., & Tate, R. B. (1985). Predictors of long term care facility use among the elderly. *Canadian Journal on Aging, 4*(1), 11-19.

OBJECTIVES: To assess the impact of 28 sociodemographic and health status variables on nursing home admission in the province of Manitoba.

METHODS: Data were from the Manitoba Longitudinal Study on Aging (MLSA). Each of the 28 characteristics was compared for a group of 3,383 individuals aged 65+ and living in the community in 1971 who were followed-up in 1973 and 1977.

DEFINITION OF RURAL: Rural-urban comparisons were made but no definition of rural was provided.

RESULTS RELATED TO RURAL AGING: No rural-urban differences in the likelihood of being admitted to a nursing home emerged at 2 years or at 7 years.

CONCLUSIONS: The authors conclude that the elderly at risk of institutionalization can be identified relatively early since the short-term predictors continue to be associated with long term care facility use in the long run.

Thompson, L. (1997). Waiting time for nursing home admission in a voluntary single-entry system. *Canadian Journal on Aging, 16*(1), 17-29.

OBJECTIVES: To explore predictors of waiting time for nursing home admission in a typical, voluntary, single-entry system in the province of Saskatchewan.

METHODS: Data were from the database of the Saskatoon Coordinated Assessment Unit that assessed and prioritized applications for admission to nursing homes in the home care district of Saskatoon. Information was available on 777 clients who had been placed on the central waiting list for a first nursing home admission between September 1, 1991 and August 31, 1993. Thirty-two predictor variables for waiting time to nursing home admission were developed and time-to-event or survival analysis was used to analyze waiting times.

DEFINITION OF RURAL: Comparisons were made between Saskatoon and the surrounding rural districts.

RESULTS RELATED TO RURAL AGING: Overall median waiting time was 107 days. Residing in Saskatoon predicted faster admission compared with the surrounding district (95 vs. 224 days). In the multivariate analyses, rural-urban differences emerged only when the p-value was relaxed from $p \leq .001$ to $p \leq .05$.

CONCLUSIONS: The authors argue that their results suggest that publicly funded nursing homes in Canada select residents for admission based partly on administrative convenience and lighter care needs, rather than solely on independently assessed priority of need. No rural-specific implications are discussed.

Tomiak, M., Berthelot, J.-M., Guimond, E., & Mustard, C. A. (2000). Factors associated with nursing-home entry for elders in Manitoba, Canada. *Journal of Gerontology: Medical Sciences, 55A* **(5), M279-M287.**

OBJECTIVES: To assess the relative importance of predisposing, enabling, and need characteristics in predicting nursing home entry for older adults in the province of Manitoba.

METHODS: Data from the Manitoba Health Services Insurance Plan (MHSIP) records were linked with detailed demographic, socioeconomic, and activity limitation information obtained from the 1986 Census of Population and Statistics Canada's 1986 Health and Activity Limitation Survey. The MHSIP includes an overall registration file, physician services claims, hospital separations, nursing home entry and exit abstracts, and mortality events. The sample consisted of 5,153 adults aged 65+, 295 of whom entered nursing homes over the 5-year period from June 1986 to June 1991. Place of residence (rural vs. urban) was considered as an enabling characteristic. The dependent variable was the time between the start of the study and entry into a nursing home. Two regression models were fitted; the base-year model included predisposing, enabling, and need factors measured at baseline (June 1986) while the time-varying needs model relied on need variables updated on a yearly basis.

DEFINITION OF RURAL: Rural-urban comparisons were made but no definition of rural was provided.

RESULTS RELATED TO RURAL AGING: Living in an urban area increased the likelihood of nursing home admission for women only in the base-year model. A rural-urban difference was not significant in the time-varying needs model. Overall, age and need factors were the best predictors of nursing home entry.

CONCLUSIONS: The authors argue that gains in preventing or delaying nursing home entry can be achieved through intervention programs targeted at specific medical conditions such as Alzheimer's disease, musculoskeletal disorders, and stroke. They call for the collection of comprehensive, longitudinal data on an ongoing basis to better understand the impact of changes in predisposing, enabling, and need factors that occur after baseline.

See also DeCoster, C., Roos, N., & Shapiro, E. (1995); Frohlich, N., Markesteyn, T., Roos, N., Carriere, K. C., Black, C., DeCoster, C., Burchill, C. A., & MacWilliam, L. (1994); Mustard, C., Finlayson, M., Derksen, S., & Berthelot, J.-M. (1999); and Roos, N. P., Shapiro, E., Bond, R., Black, C., Finlayson, G., Newburn-Cook, C., MacWilliam, L., Steinbach, C., Yogendran, M., & Walld, R. (2001).

Nursing Homes: Structure/Services

Conn, D. K., Lee, V., Steingart, A., & Silberfeld, M. (1992). Psychiatric services: A survey of nursing homes and homes for the aged in Ontario. *Canadian Journal of Psychiatry, 37*(8), 525-530.

OBJECTIVES: To determine the perceived availability of, and need for, psychiatric services in nursing homes and homes for the aged across the province of Ontario.

METHODS: Mailed questionnaires were completed by medical directors (n = 269) and nursing directors (n = 320) of Ontario Ministry of Health nursing homes and Ontario Ministry of Community and Social Services homes for the aged. The overall response rate was 52%. Differences according to the region of the province and the population of the local town were examined.

DEFINITION OF RURAL: The southeast and southwest regions were described as "predominantly rural with a few large urban centres" (p. 526). The northern region was the most sparsely populated and considered as being under-serviced by physicians. Population sizes of the local towns were categorized as < 50,000, 50,000 to 200,000, and > 200,000.

RESULTS RELATED TO RURAL AGING: Perceived availability of psychiatrists was the greatest in larger urban areas and the least in rural areas. While 46% of the respondents indicated that a psychiatrist was available to their facility, differences emerged according to region and population of the local town. Only 34% of respondents in southwestern Ontario indicated that a visiting psychiatrist was available to their nursing home, compared to 48%, 56%, and 57% in the north, central, and southeast regions, respectively. Perceived availability was the greatest in the locations with a population > 200,000 (66%) and the least in locations with < 50,000 population (40%). A need for increased psychiatric services was identified by 74% of the respondents, with no significant differences according to region or population size. Breakdowns according to geographical location or community size were not presented for the number of hours of assessment and treatment from a psychiatrist per month, the presence of psychiatric or behavioural problems, or the need of psychotropic medication.

CONCLUSIONS: In the majority of long term care institutions, very few residents receive psychiatric care. The authors argue that planning is required to facilitate and encourage the development of efficient and effective psychiatric services for long term care facilities.

DeCoster, C., Roos, N., & Shapiro, E. (1995). A Population-based analysis of Manitoba's nursing home sector. *Canadian Journal on Aging, 14*(2), 319-334.

OBJECTIVES: To describe trends in nursing home and hospital use by the population aged 75+ across eight regions in the province of Manitoba.

METHODS: Data were from the Population Health Information System (PHIS) that used administrative data to develop measures of health and socioeconomic status. Drawing on data for the nursing home sector for 1989/90 and 1992/93, regional comparisons of nursing home bed ratios, admissions per 1,000 elderly, days of care per capita, mean expected length of stay for new admissions, median length of waiting time prior to admission, and selected hospital indicators for long-stay patients were examined.

DEFINITION OF RURAL: Winnipeg/non-Winnipeg and regional comparisons were made. Winnipeg is the major urban centre in the province; non-Winnipeg was defined as all areas outside of Winnipeg.

RESULTS RELATED TO RURAL AGING: From 1989/90 to 1992/93, the number of non-Winnipeg nursing home beds grew 5.4% compared to 2.6% in Winnipeg. The expected length of stay was similar across regions while the median length of stay in hospital for Winnipeg nursing home residents was longer than that of non-Winnipeg residents.

CONCLUSIONS: The authors argue that a population-based information system is a useful tool for managing the nursing home sector by highlighting the degree to which a province achieves distributional equity and equality of access to nursing home beds. The authors also conclude that Manitoba's single entry system using similar criteria contributes to equitable access to services.

See also Frohlich, N., Markesteyn, T., Roos, N., Carriere, K. C., Black, C., DeCoster, C., Burchill, C. A., & MacWilliam, L. (1994); Mustard, C., Finlayson, M., Derksen, S., & Berthelot, J.-M. (1999); Roos, N. P., Shapiro, E., Bond, R., Black, C., Finlayson, G., Newburn-Cook, C., MacWilliam, L., Steinbach, C., Yogendran, M., & Walld, R. (2001); and Tomiak, M., Berthelot, J.-M., Guimond, E., & Mustard, C. A. (2000).

Gladstone, J. W. (1992). Identifying the living arrangements of elderly married couples in long-term care institutions. *Canadian Journal on Aging, 11*(2), 184-196.

OBJECTIVES: To investigate the living arrangements of elderly married couples in homes for the aged (HFAs) and nursing homes (NHs) in the province of Ontario.

METHODS: Surveys mailed to HFAs and NHs were completed by 331 administrators in 1988 and 395 administrators in 1989; 272 of the administrators responded in both years. Information was gathered on the number of married couples living together, the number living apart but in the same institution, the reasons for living apart, and the number whose spouses live elsewhere.

DEFINITION OF RURAL: Population size was used to differentiate between communities that "were not defined in rural/urban terms because of the conceptual difficulties in making such distinctions" (p. 189).

RESULTS RELATED TO RURAL AGING: Population size had no effect on the number of married couples living together or apart in institutions, on the reasons for living separately, or on the number of married persons living in institutions whose spouses lived elsewhere.

CONCLUSIONS: The author suggests that the lack of difference according to community size may reflect different ways in which couples living in small and large communities draw upon social support. He calls for consideration of other community characteristics such as the cultural, ethnic, and racial composition.

Lahaie, U., & Theroux, J. (1992). Le Chez Nous accommodation with a difference for cognitively impaired persons in rural Manitoba. In G. M. Gutman (Ed.), *Shelter and care of persons with dementia* (pp. 73-97). Vancouver, BC: Simon Fraser University.

OBJECTIVES: To describe the development of a unit focusing on the needs of rural, mentally frail persons in the province of Manitoba.

METHODS: Le Chez Nous, the unit under study, was located in Foyer Notre-Dame, a 61-bed, long-term care facility. The unit was comprised of 12 beds for cognitively impaired individuals. This descriptive report covered geographic and demographic data, a historical overview, physical space, staffing, education, programming, the role of the family, and an evaluation of progress. The evaluation involved a family survey with 8 families, a staff survey, and an analysis of data on drug use, elopements, and acts of aggression.

DEFINITION OF RURAL: At the time of the study, Notre-Dame de Lourdes had a population of 708, with 24% aged 65+. It is located in the agricultural region of southwestern Manitoba.

RESULTS RELATED TO RURAL AGING: The mean age of Chez Nous residents was 85 and males outnumbered females 2:1. Family members noticed positive changes in the residents and attributed these changes to the environment, programming, and quality of staff. Three of six residents did not require antipsychotic medications after 16 months on the unit. There was a "dramatic decline" (p. 93) in elopements and a decrease in aggression accompanying segregation. Staff members also identified benefits for residents with the development of this new unit.

CONCLUSIONS: The authors argue that their model of care is adaptable to many existing long-term care environments, can be developed without government funding yet comply with standards, and can become a focus of community involvement. A small sample size limits the findings.

Note: This article also was published as a chapter in Novak, M. (Ed.). (1995). Aging and society: A Canadian reader. Toronto, ON: Nelson Canada.

Morgan, D. G., Semchuk, K. M., Stewart, N. J., & D'Arcy, C. (2003). The physical and social environments of small rural nursing homes: Assessing supportiveness for residents with dementia. *Canadian Journal on Aging, 22*(3), 283-296.

OBJECTIVES: To examine the physical and social environments as important therapeutic tools in the care of rural nursing home residents in the province of Saskatchewan.

METHODS: This study was conducted in seven small (15 to 35 beds), publicly funded nursing homes in one health authority. None of the facilities had separate dementia special care units (SCUs). The Physical Environmental Assessment Protocol (PEAP) was used to evaluate the facilities on nine key dimensions of dementia care environments. Two focus groups were held with registered nurses, nursing aides, and activity workers.

DEFINITION OF RURAL: Rural was defined as centres with populations of ≤ 15,000. The rural health authority had a population of 20,000, covered 16,000 square kilometres, and had a population density of 1.3 persons per square kilometre. The seven nursing homes were located in towns with populations ranging from 345 to 1,234.

RESULTS RELATED TO RURAL AGING: Facilities were most supportive in the provision of privacy and least supportive on maximizing awareness and orientation. In the focus groups, staff caregivers identified six special needs of residents with dementia that were difficult to meet in the nursing homes. Two needs were related to the physical environment (resident safety and a calm, quiet environment); four were related to the social environment (meaningful activity and one-to-one contact, opportunity to use remaining abilities, flexible policy, and knowledgeable caregivers who enjoy working with persons with dementia). Separate dementia SCUs were identified by a number of staff as one approach to managing dementia care but challenges in creating dementia units in small rural facilities also were identified.

CONCLUSIONS: The results provide support for conceptual models of dementia care settings that emphasize the interaction of organizational, social, and physical factors.

Morgan, D. G., Stewart, N. J., D'Arcy, K. C., & Werezak, L. J. (2004). Evaluating rural nursing home environments: Dementia special care units versus integrated facilities. *Aging & Mental Health, 8*(3), 256-265.

OBJECTIVES: To compare the physical and social environments of eight rural nursing homes with special care units (SCUs) for dementia with eight same-sized rural nursing homes that did not have SCUs in the province of Saskatchewan.

METHODS: The study was conducted in a sample of rural nursing homes with ≤ 100 beds. The eight facilities with SCUs were matched with non-SCU facilities on bed size and type of facility. A SCU is a specialized unit for individuals with behavioural disturbances associated with dementia. Two independent assessors evaluated the physical environment using nine dimensions of the Physical Environmental Assessment Protocol (PEAP) and the social environment using six subscales of the Nursing Unit Rating Scale (NURS).

DEFINITION OF RURAL: Rural was defined as centres with populations of ≤ 15,000. The populations of the communities where the facilities were located ranged from 924 to 14,980 for the SCUs, and from 488 to 14,051 for the non-SCUs.

RESULTS RELATED TO RURAL AGING: The SCUs were more supportive on six dimensions of the PEAP: maximizing awareness and orientation, maximizing safety and security, regulation of stimulation, quality of stimulation, opportunities for personal control, and continuity of the self. These units also were more supportive on the separation and stimulation subscales of the NURS, indicating the SCUs had greater separation of residents with dementia from other residents for activities of daily living and better control of non-meaningful stimulation.

CONCLUSIONS: The authors argue that the measurable environmental benefits are evident in rural facilities with SCUs designed to provide more therapeutic physical and social environments for residents with dementia. The findings suggest that it is feasible to create separate SCUs in small rural nursing homes, which in turn can lead to better care of rural residents with a dementia.

See also Morgan, D. G., Stewart, N. J., D'Arcy, C., Forbes, D., & Lawson, J. (2005); and Morgan, D. G., Stewart, N. J., D'Arcy, C., & Cammer, A. L. (2005).

Sarchuk, C. J., & Wiebe, P. (1992). Organization and coordination of services to individuals with dementia living in rural settings. In G. M. Gutman (Ed.), *Shelter and care of persons with dementia* **(pp. 183-192). Vancouver, BC: Simon Fraser University.**

OBJECTIVES: To describe the experience of providing services to individuals with dementia living in rural areas in the province of Manitoba, from the perspective of the Long Term Care Programs Division of the Manitoba Health Services Commission.

METHODS: This descriptive article begins with a discussion of the problems of providing dementia care in rural settings including the recruitment of home care staff, and then focuses on a Special Care Unit (SCU) in the Salem Home in Winkler. Opened in 1987, this SCU was to serve as a resource for the region and included an inpatient/resident unit, an outreach/consultation component, and an educational/research focus. The intent was not to have permanent admissions.

DEFINITION OF RURAL: Winkler is located in south central Manitoba. The Salem Home was a 125 bed personal care home (nursing home).

RESULTS RELATED TO RURAL AGING: Three initiatives to assist in caring for residents with dementia were highlighted: educational in-service programs for staff in long term care facilities, SCUs as a regional resource to personal care homes, and special care resource teams with psychogeriatric expertise (expansion to rural areas was dependent on funding). The 43 residents of the SCU in Salem Home ranged in age from 54 to 92. Being physically aggressive, disruptively noisy, and verbally abusive were the behavior problems most likely to be exhibited. Nurses' ratings of 22 clients who were followed up post-discharge suggested that 27% of the clients had substantial improvement, 9% had substantial to fair improvement, and 27% had died.

CONCLUSIONS: The authors argue that the concept of a SCU as a regional resource is promising and that the Salem Home SCU has been a valuable asset for referring facilities.

See also Thomson, K., Turner, L. C., & Wiebe, P. (1993-1994).

Shidler, S. (1998). A systemic perspective of life-prolonging treatment decision making. *Qualitative Health Research, 8*(2), 254-269.

OBJECTIVES: To describe the interactions and perceptions of individuals involved in life-prolonging treatment decisions in long-term care centres in a rural region in the province of Quebec.

METHODS: This ethnographic, ethnomethodological study was conducted in two public long-term care centres. Study participants included care centre residents (n = 35; 8 of whom faced a life-prolonging treatment decision during the study period); family members (n = 15; 10 in the decision-making events); and care centre personnel (n = 40 including 5 primary care physicians, 10 registered nurses, 8 licensed vocational nurses, 6 aides, 6 psycho-social workers, 4 housekeeping personnel, and 2 clinical administrators). Data collection involved taped, semi-structured interviews, participant observation, and document review.

DEFINITION OF RURAL: No definition of rural was provided. The two care centres had 75 and 50 beds, respectively.

RESULTS RELATED TO RURAL AGING: Eight life-prolonging decision-making events occurred during the study. Four themes were presented. These included: (1) wholeness: resident-system; (2) system and sub-systems: constellations; (3) punctuation: decision makers; and (4) equifinality: ongoing organization of communication. The participation of long-term care residents in their life-prolonging treatment decisions was not dependent simply on the communication between the physician and his/her patient. The decision makers, decision-making criteria, and patterns of communication evident in the eight cases did not necessarily conform to formal legal guidelines or to the established hierarchy of care/service organization. Rather, the results indicated that persons other than the three parties mentioned in legal guidelines (resident, physician, and proxy) may have information, and may facilitate the participation of the resident regarding his/her life-prolonging treatment wishes. In addition, it was found that the legal guidelines identifying the three key persons in the decision-making process (resident, physician, and proxy) do not adequately reflect the actors actually involved in these long-term care settings. Finally, the opportunity for the long-term care resident to participate in his/her life-prolonging treatment decision depends on the interaction between the members of the resident-system who have access to his/her treatment wishes.

CONCLUSIONS: The author argues that the opportunity of long-term care residents to participate in their life-prolonging treatment decisions can be facilitated by effective communication between members of a system of persons found in this setting. These results shift the focus of future inquiry, for both research and clinical practice, from the communication between physician and resident to the patterns of communication between all persons in the clinical setting who know the resident's treatment wishes.

Thomson, K., Turner, L. C., & Wiebe, P. (1993-1994). How SCUs help residents with mental health problems. *Journal of Long-Term Care Administration, 21*(4), 25-29.

OBJECTIVES: To explore the effectiveness of special care units (SCUs) for elderly residents with mental health problems in two personal care homes in the province of Manitoba.

METHODS: This article describes two 10-bed SCUs for elderly residents with behavior problems, the Salem Home SCU in rural Manitoba and the Bethania SCU in Winnipeg. Clients participated in a 6-month treatment program and then returned to their originating personal care home or residence. Detailed treatment plans were established and staff training was conducted to help staff prepare for the client's return. In addition, the SCU staff maintained an ongoing consultative role for a minimum of 6 months following readmission to the personal care home.

DEFINITION OF RURAL: The rural SCU was part of a 125-bed, personal care home (nursing home) located in Winkler, a community with a population of 6,000. The urban facility was located in Winnipeg (population 625,000).

RESULTS RELATED TO RURAL AGING: From 1988 to 1991, 48 clients were admitted to the rural SCU from personal care homes, hospitals, and a psychiatric hospital, and 38 were discharged. Median age was 80 years, with a range from 54 to 92. Among the rural admissions, 65% had dementia and 42% had calling out/verbal abuse as the primary behaviour problem. A case history of a client in the SCU provided specific information. Follow-up assessment of discharged clients, as rated by the referring personal care home staff, was positive; 59 percent of the rural clients were reported to have fair to substantial improvement in behavior.

CONCLUSIONS: The authors conclude that the SCUs provided effective treatment alternatives for individuals with mental health problems.

See also Sarchuk, C. J., & Wiebe, P. (1992).

Tourigny-Rivard, M.-F., & Drury, M. (1987). The effects of monthly psychiatric consultation in a nursing home. *The Gerontologist, 27*(3), 363-366.

OBJECTIVES: To assess the effectiveness of a monthly psychiatric teaching consultation in a 50-bed nursing home in a small, predominantly French-speaking farming community in the province of Ontario.

METHODS: A geriatric psychiatrist visited the nursing home once a month, discussed new referrals with the nursing staff, and offered a 1-hour in-service for the nurses. Over an 18-month period, 21 residents (8 males, 13 females) were seen in consultation. Nine staff members (6 nursing staff, 1 nursing home physician, and 2 administrators) provided written comments on any changes they observed since the consultations began. In addition, the consultant and one nurse reviewed each consultation case to study patterns and outcomes.

DEFINITION OF RURAL: The small farming community, approximately 40 miles from Ottawa, had a population of 1,700.

RESULTS RELATED TO RURAL AGING: Comments were largely positive, and focused more on the ways in which the consultation helped staff themselves to deal with residents rather than on how the consultation helped residents directly. Seven staff members indicated that the consultation helped to decrease the nurses' frustration level in dealing with behavioural problems and increased sensitivity to residents' needs. Administrators felt that depression was detected earlier, with opportunities for treatment offered as a result of the consultation. Overall, the perceptions were that the behavioural problems of 17 of the 21 residents (81%) were affected in at least one of the following three ways: improvement of the pathology or behavioural problem, improvement in the management, and increased tolerance towards the resident or the behaviour.

CONCLUSIONS: The authors conclude that regular psychiatric consultation in the nursing home can be very effective.

Tousignant, M., Hébert, R., Dubuc, N., Simoneau, F., & Dieleman, L. (2003).
Application of a case-mix classification based on the functional autonomy of the
residents for funding long-term care facilities. *Age and Ageing, 32,* **60-66.**

OBJECTIVES: To explore outcomes of a new model of long term care (LTC) funding in the Eastern Townships area in the province of Quebec.

METHODS: The study population included residents of all 11 LTC facilities (7 rural, 4 urban). Residents were assessed using the Functional Autonomy Measurement System (SMAF). This system allows for funding decisions to be based on the functional autonomy of the resident compared to the traditional method based predominantly on number of beds and hours of care. Using the new model referred to as ISO-SMAF, a facility's theoretical budget was calculated based on the adjusted cost per year associated with each ISO-SMAF profile derived from a previous economic study.

DEFINITION OF RURAL: The number of residents in the rural facilities ranged from 60 to 135; the range for the urban facilities was 48 to 386. Population size of the communities was not provided.

RESULTS RELATED TO RURAL AGING: With the exception of one facility, the percentage of residents assessed as having a high level of disability ranged from 65% to 80% in the rural facilities. The exception was a facility with only 23% assessed with high levels of disability. This facility specializes in mental health problems and 68% of its residents had profiles that reflected those problems. A comparison of the theoretical and available budget revealed shortfalls ranging from $41,488 to $3,181,988 in the rural facilities. The calculation of funding of both rural and urban facilities based on the severity of their residents' functional disabilities suggested an underfunding of facilities by the old methodology based on the number of beds and hours of care.

CONCLUSIONS: It is suggested that these results support the feasibility of applying the new funding approach. However, implementation of the ISO-SMAF classification must be supported by continued and computerized residents' medical files, which the authors argue allows for an accurate representation of the facility at any given point in time.

Wasko-Lacey, L., Mathews, M., & Bell, J. (2002). Quarterly medication reviews in long-term care. *Canadian Nurse, 98*(2), 27-31.

OBJECTIVES: To determine the extent to which quarterly medication reviews in long-term care (LTC) facilities are conducted and to assess the effects of these reviews in a rural health district in the province of Saskatchewan.

METHODS: Health records of 190 residents in 10 LTC facilities in the Midwest Health District were reviewed between February 6 and February 13, 2000. Residents had to be 65+ and to have continuously lived in the facilities for at least 4 months.

DEFINITION OF RURAL: The Midwest Health District in south-central Saskatchewan had a 2000 population of 17,701.

RESULTS RELATED TO RURAL AGING: Residents took an average of 63.1 doses of 8.02 different types of medications during a 1-week period. Adverse medication events were recorded for 16% of the residents while 32% had been physically restrained during the study period. Only 41% had a quarterly medication review, despite a Health District policy that each resident's medication regimen was to be reviewed at least every three months. Residents with a review had fewer doses per week, were less likely to have had an adverse event, and were less likely to have been physically restrained. However, quarterly reviews did not change the number of different medications prescribed.

CONCLUSIONS: The authors conclude that it is possible to reduce the use of medications in LTC facilities through the use of quarterly reviews.

Zieber, C. G., Hagen, B., Armstrong-Esther, C., & Aho, M. (2005). Pain and agitation in long-term care residents with dementia: Use of the Pittsburgh Agitation Scale. *International Journal of Palliative Nursing, 11*(2), 71-78.

OBJECTIVES: To explore the relationship between pain and agitation in long-term care (LTC) residents with dementia in rural western Canada.

METHODS: Using a descriptive correlational design, this exploratory study involved 58 residents with moderate to severe cognitive impairment in three LTC facilities. The facilities ranged in size from 41 to 70 beds (mean = 57). Six full-time registered nurses working in the facilities and three palliative care nurse consultants provided pain and agitation assessments. The Pittsburgh Agitation Scale (PAS) was used to assess agitation. Five proxy measures of pain were employed, including the Discomfort Scale for Dementia of the Alzheimer's Type (DS-DAT), number of pain diagnoses, use of analgesic medications, and pain ratings by both facility nurses and palliative care nurse consultants.

DEFINITION OF RURAL: The rural communities had populations of < 10,000.

RESULTS RELATED TO RURAL AGING: A moderately strong relationship existed between the total PAS agitation scores and the total DS-DAT pain scores. The PAS sub-score 'resisting care' was significantly correlated with the total DS-DAT scores and pain ratings by both facility nurses and palliative care nurse consultants.

CONCLUSIONS: While acknowledging the study limitations, the authors argue that their findings highlight the clinically important possibility that different types of agitation may be more associated with pain in residents with dementia than other types. The authors discuss the implications for nursing and call for more research.

Nursing Homes: Staffing Issues/Education

Morgan, D. G., Semchuk, K. M., Stewart, N. J., & D'Arcy, C. (2002). **Job strain among staff of rural nursing homes: A comparison of nurses, aides, and activity workers.** *Journal of Nursing Administration, 32*(3), 152-161.

OBJECTIVES: To examine differences in job strain among registered nurses, nursing aides, and activity workers in rural nursing homes in the province of Saskatchewan.

METHODS: The study was conducted in one rural health district in Saskatchewan. Data were from mailed survey questionnaires to all full-time, part-time, and casual registered nurses (n = 33), nursing aides (n = 65), and activity workers (n = 12). Two focus groups were held with direct care staff.

DEFINITION OF RURAL: The rural health district had a population of 20,000 and covered 16,000 square kilometres. The population density (1.3 persons per square kilometre) met the definition of a 'frontier' area (Wagenfeld, 2000). The seven nursing homes were located in towns with populations ranging from 345 to 1,234.

RESULTS RELATED TO RURAL AGING: Several differences in job content and strain were evident. Nursing aides reported significantly higher psychological demands and job strain than registered nurses, and lower decision authority than both registered nurses and activity workers. The activity workers scored higher on skill discretion and decision latitude than both the registered nurses and the nursing aides. Stress was a common theme in the focus groups; identified sources of stress included work load, insufficient skills, and issues related to the integration of residents with dementia with other residents.

CONCLUSIONS: This study provides insight into job strain in rural nursing homes and suggests possible intervention strategies to improve the work environment.

Morgan, D. G., Stewart, N. J., D'Arcy, C., & Cammer, A. L. (2005). Creating and sustaining dementia special care units in rural nursing homes: The critical role of nursing leadership. *Canadian Journal of Nursing Leadership,* 18(2), 74-99.

OBJECTIVES: To describe the development of special care units (SCUs) from the perspective of nursing Directors of Care (DOCs) in eight small rural nursing homes in the province of Saskatchewan.

METHODS: Data were from a larger study on rural SCUs. Eight facilities with ≤ 100 beds and with a SCU participated. A SCU is a specialized unit for individuals with behavioural disturbances associated with dementia. The DOC who was in charge at the time the SCU was planned and opened in each facility, as well as the current DOC if the person involved in setting up the unit was no longer in the position, was approached for an interview. Ten telephone interviews were conducted using a qualitative descriptive design. Verbatim transcripts were prepared and a thematic analysis was undertaken.

DEFINITION OF RURAL: Rural was defined as centres with populations of ≤ 15,000. The population of the communities ranged from 924 to 14,890.

RESULTS RELATED TO RURAL AGING: The role of nursing leadership in both creating and sustaining the unit over time emerged as critical. The fragile nature of these SCUs and the need for constant vigilance and effort to maintain an effective program also was evident. Four key leadership activities were identified: perpetual reinforcement and enforcement of SCU goals and ideals; support, guidance, and mentoring of staff; empowerment of staff; and liaison/public relations. Strategies for a successful SCU were identified. The positive and negative aspects of being in a rural setting were equally emphasized. These included perceptions about people being 'locked up', the distance for some residents from their home community, the demand to accept residents who did not fit the criteria but needed the security or enhanced staffing of the SCU, staffing, access to specialists, and demands on nursing directors.

CONCLUSIONS: Nursing leadership and supervision were essential for the creation and sustainability of the SCUs. Rurality posed challenges but also offered strengths to the process.

See also Morgan, D. G., Stewart, N. J., D'Arcy, C., Forbes, D., & Lawson, J. (2005); and Morgan, D. L., Stewart, N. J., D'Arcy, K. C., & Werezak, L. J. (2004).

Morgan, D. G., Stewart, N. J., D'Arcy, C., Forbes, D., & Lawson, J. (2005). Work stress and physical assault of nursing aides in rural nursing homes with and without dementia special care units. *Journal of Psychiatric and Mental Health Nursing,* ***12***, **347-358.**

OBJECTIVES: To compare nursing aides (NAs) employed in rural nursing homes with and without dementia special care units (SCUs) on exposure to and distress from disruptive behaviours exhibited by residents, job strain, and physical assault in the province of Saskatchewan.

METHODS: Data were drawn from a larger study in which all rural nursing homes of ≤100 beds that had an SCU (n = 8) were matched on size (± 5) and type (stand-alone, health centre, or hospital attached) to same-sized rural facilities with no SCU. A SCU is a specialized unit for individuals with behavioural disturbances associated with dementia. A mailed survey was completed by 355 NAs (186 in facilities with SCU, 169 in non-SCU facilities), with a focus on characteristics of the work environment, exposure to disruptive and aggressive behaviours, job strain, training, the impact of rural location on work, and demographic characteristics.

DEFINITION OF RURAL: Rural was defined as centres with populations of ≤ 15,000. The facilities were located in communities ranging in size from 488 to 14,051 (mean of 5,073).

RESULTS RELATED TO RURAL AGING: Compared to NAs in non-SCU facilities, NAs in nursing homes with a SCU reported significantly less exposure to disruptive behaviours (including aggressive and aversive behaviors). The groups did not differ on decision authority or skill discretion. A higher risk of being assaulted was significantly related to having a permanent position, increased job strain, and feeling inadequately prepared for dementia care. The NAs who worked more time on the SCU reported more assaults but less distress from disruptive behaviour, lower psychological job demands, lower job strain, and greater work autonomy.

CONCLUSIONS: A number of benefits for NAs working in rural nursing homes with SCUs were identified. The authors suggest that the provision of more dementia care training and the reduction of job demands and job strain may help to reduce work-related stress and physical assault of nursing aides employed in nursing homes.

See also Morgan, D. G., Stewart, N. J., D'Arcy, C., & Cammer, A. L. (2005); and Morgan, D. G., Stewart, N. J., D'Arcy, C., & Werezak, L. J. (2004).

Richardson, J., Moreland, J., & Fox, P. (2001). The state of evidence-based care in long-term care institutions: A provincial survey. *Canadian Journal on Aging,* *20*(3), 357-372.

OBJECTIVES: To determine the prevalence of awareness and use of practice guidelines in chronic care and long-term care (LTC) facilities, staff opinions about clinical conditions or problems important for developing clinical practice guidelines for care of geriatric LTC residents, and factors that promote change in clinical practice in the province of Ontario.

METHODS: Questionnaires were sent to the Directors of Nursing in all Ontario hospitals with 20+ chronic care beds, as well as nursing homes and homes for the aged with > 20 chronic and LTC beds. A total of 306 questionnaires were returned from two mailings, with a 71% response rate from hospital settings with chronic care beds and a 53% response rate from nursing home facilities. Questions focused on the type of facility and level of care offered, number of beds and nursing staff equivalents, the facility's funding mix, awareness/use of practice guidelines, types of problems/clinical conditions for which practice guidelines were needed, and the provision of 12 professional services. Practice guidelines were defined as "systematically developed statements to assist practitioners and patients with decisions about appropriate health care for a specific clinical circumstance..." (pp. 364-365).

DEFINITION OF RURAL: No definition of rural was provided; rural-urban comparisons were made.

RESULTS RELATED TO RURAL AGING: Forty percent of the facilities were aware of evidence-based guidelines, while only 22% used them. For rural facilities, these percentages were 18% for awareness and 7% for use, while the corresponding percentages for urban facilities were 25% and 16%, respectively. The guidelines being used involved skin and wound care, pain symptom management, continence, and stroke. The clinical problems that agencies identified as important for guideline development, irrespective of rural or urban location, were behavioral problems, continence, feeding problems, and problems with skin care.

CONCLUSIONS: Awareness and use of practice guidelines were quite low which may be due to the paucity of guidelines for geriatric practice and poor dissemination of those guidelines. Policy implications and directions for future research are discussed.

Skinkle, R. R., & Grant, P. R. (1988). An outcome evaluation of an in-service training program for nursing home aides. *Canadian Journal on Aging, 7*(1), 48-57.

OBJECTIVES: To evaluate an in-service training program for aides working in rural and urban nursing homes in the province of Saskatchewan.

METHODS: The in-service training program was designed to teach basic nursing skills, knowledge of basic nursing skills, the aging process, and the philosophy of long-term care. The program consisted of 90 modules which aides completed sequentially on their own time; completion time ranged from 6 to 18 months. The sample consisted of 86 nursing home aides from eight urban and eight rural Saskatchewan nursing homes. This included 41 graduates of the program (17 urban, 24 rural) and 45 aides who had not participated in the program (23 urban, 22 rural). Questionnaires were administered to groups of aides just prior to their shift.

DEFINITION OF RURAL: Rural nursing homes were located in small towns, villages, or rural municipalities; urban nursing homes were in cities.

RESULTS RELATED TO RURAL AGING: No significant rural-urban differences emerged. Graduates knew significantly more about basic nursing skills, the aging process, and the philosophy of long-term care than aides who had not participated in the program. They also were significantly more likely to say that their care team engaged in various aspects of good team functioning. Both groups tended to be positive in their general attitudes towards older adults. Characteristics such as other training or residents' needs were not taken into account. In addition, measures of quality of care provided were not obtained, making it difficult to ascertain if increases in knowledge translate into an improved quality of care.

CONCLUSIONS: The authors argue that this type of in-service training effectively communicates knowledge to nursing aides that, if applied, could increase the quality of care they provide to nursing home residents.

Physician Services

Curran, V., Hatcher, L., & Kirby, F. (2000). CME needs of rural physicians: How do we compare to our urban colleagues? *Canadian Journal of Rural Medicine, 5*(3), 131-138.

OBJECTIVES: To examine continuing medical education (CME) needs of physicians in the province of Newfoundland and Labrador.

METHODS: A needs assessment questionnaire was developed. Between March and June 1997, 867 questionnaires were distributed to all licensed and practicing physicians (specialists and family physicians). There were 339 questionnaires returned, for a response rate of 39%. Data were collected on demographics, learning patterns, level of participation in formal CME activities, learning needs, perceptions of the availability for CME programs, and learning program needs. Rural physicians accounted for 37% of the respondents.

DEFINITION OF RURAL: Rural was defined as communities with populations of < 10,000.

RESULTS RELATED TO RURAL AGING: Several rural-urban differences emerged. Rural physicians reported participating in a fewer number of formal CME programs, attending a smaller number of pharmaceutical company sponsored events, and spending more time in informal self-directed study than urban physicians. They also reported a greater need for advanced clinical skills and emergency medicine. Geriatrics was ranked third in the top 10 reported clinical skills CME needs by rural physicians while it was second for the urban physicians.

CONCLUSIONS: The authors argue that differences between the CME needs of urban and rural physicians continue to exist, with many of these differences related to the geographic isolation of rural physicians, and their distance from larger urban centres and from the only medical school in the province.

Fakhoury, W. K. H., & Roos, L. (1996). Access to and use of physician resources by the rural and urban populations in Manitoba. *Canadian Journal of Public Health, 87*(4), 248-252.

OBJECTIVES: To examine access to and use of physician resources for ambulatory care by residents of an urban area and rural areas in the province of Manitoba.

METHODS: Physician claims submitted to Manitoba Health in the fiscal years 1986/87 and 1991/92 were analyzed.

DEFINITION OF RURAL: All Manitoba Health regions were considered as rural regions, with the exception of Winnipeg which is the major urban centre in the province.

RESULTS RELATED TO RURAL AGING: In 1986/87, 56% of physicians practicing in Winnipeg were specialists compared to 16% in rural Manitoba. By 1991/92, these percentages had decreased to 54% and 14%, respectively. Overall, utilization rates for physician services increased over the study period, with the greatest increase in physician access for those aged 65 to 74. Among the 65 - 74 age group, most individuals in both urban and rural regions had at least one visit to a physician (1991/92: 90% urban males, 91% urban females, 87% rural males, 94% rural females). Similar percentages were evident for the 75+ group (1991: 95% urban males, 96% urban females, 91% rural males, 94% rural females). In the rural regions, the average number of visits per user in 1991 ranged from 7.42 for males aged 65 - 74 to 8.94 for females aged 75+. Patterns for change in services varied by age and sex.

CONCLUSIONS: In general, the 'utilization of physician resources rates' were relatively stable over time. The ratios for utilization, by age and sex, ranged from .88 (reflecting a decrease in utilization over time) to 1.12 (reflecting an increase in utilization over time). Most rates hovered between 1.01 to 1.03, reflecting little change over time. Statistical analyses were not conducted, however, making it difficult to determine which of the changes in access to physician services by age and sex were significant.

See also Finlayson, M., Lix, L., Finlayson, G. S., & Fong, T. (2005); Frohlich, N., Markesteyn, T., Roos, N., Carriere, K. C., Black, C., DeCoster, C., Burchill, C. A., & MacWilliam, L. (1994); Roos, N. P., Shapiro, E., Bond, R., Black, C., Finlayson, G., Newburn-Cook, C., MacWilliam, L., Steinbach, C., Yogendran, M., & Walld, R. (2001); and Tataryn, D. J., Roos, N. P., & Black, C. D. (1995).

Gorman, M., MacKnight, C., & Rockwood, K. (2004). Feasibility of telemedicine for specialized geriatric care of elderly people at a regional referral hospital. *Geriatrics Today, 7*(3), 93-97.

OBJECTIVES: To investigate whether telemedicine is a feasible adjunct to a specialized geriatric outreach program at a regional referral hospital and to examine patient attitudes toward teleconsultation in the province of Nova Scotia.

METHODS: Data were from 53 consecutive telemedicine consultations with 42 patients during a 2-year period by the Telemedicine in Geriatrics for Rural areas (TIGER) program in Antigonish and Halifax. The time period was November 30, 1999 to November 30, 2001. Patients were aged 17 to 88 (median age 74), 67% were women, and 90% had cognitive disorders. All patients received standard assessments, including a semi-structured Comprehensive Geriatric Assessment. Of the 42 patient/caregiver dyads surveyed, 33 (79%) returned a mailed, 26-item satisfaction questionnaire.

DEFINITION OF RURAL: Rural telemedicine links were located at Sydney, Neil's Harbour, Sherbrooke, Canso, and Glace Bay.

RESULTS RELATED TO RURAL AGING: Attitudes of both patients and caregivers indicated general satisfaction with the teleconference experience; all but one patient/caregiver dyad indicated they would use teleconsultation again. Patient/caregiver dyads reported cost and time savings by using teleconsultation. Compared with an in-person visit to Halifax, where the average direct cost was estimated at $390.16, patient/caregivers reported incurred direct costs of $27.55.

CONCLUSIONS: While recognizing that the study findings must be interpreted with caution due to the small sample size, teleconsultation appears to be feasible for older patients, their caregivers, and their physicians, and is a useful adjunct to the delivery of health care in rural areas of Canada. However, the authors argue that the two physicians must have a collaborative and respectful working relationship for teleconsultations to be successful. They call for rigorous testing of teleconsultation to determine its effectiveness as a routine adjunct to specialized geriatric care for rural older adults.

Houle, L. G., Salmoni, A. W., Pong, R. W., Laflamme, S., & Viverais-Dresler, G. A. (2001). **Predictors of family physician use among older residents of Ontario and an analysis of the Andersen-Newman Behavior Model.** *Canadian Journal on Aging, 20*(2), 233-249.

OBJECTIVES: To examine predictors of family physician use among older adults in the province of Ontario.

METHODS: Data were obtained from the 1990 Ontario Health Survey on a representative sample of 7,112 adults aged 65+ (mean age 72.69). Using the Andersen-Newman Behavior Model, variables of interest were the number of visits to a family physician in a 1-year period, predisposing characteristics (age, gender, education, living arrangement, physical activity, and health worries), enabling characteristics (family functioning, household income, medical coverage, ability to drive, and size of community), and need characteristics (self-rated health, general activity limitations, functional disability, number of health problems, sum of disability days, loneliness, and emotional state).

DEFINITION OF RURAL: Rural/non-rural comparisons were made; no definition of rural was provided.

RESULTS RELATED TO RURAL AGING: The number of health problems and self-rated health emerged as the most important predictors of family physician use. While a statistically significant rural/non-rural difference emerged, it contributed < 1 percent to the explained variance.

CONCLUSIONS: The authors conclude that the Andersen-Newman Behaviour Model may not be appropriate to study family physician use among older Canadians and suggest various alternative approaches.

Mathews, M., & Edwards, A. C. (2004). **Having a regular doctor: Rural, semi-urban and urban differences in Newfoundland.** *Canadian Journal of Rural Medicine, 9(3), 166-172.*

OBJECTIVES: To examine urban, semi-urban, and rural differences in the characteristics of adults aged 20+ who did and did not have a regular doctor in the province of Newfoundland.

METHODS: Data were from the 1995 Newfoundland Panel on Health and Medical Care study of 11,789 respondents from randomly selected households. There were 1,108 respondents aged 60 - 69 and 1,014 aged 70+.

DEFINITION OF RURAL: Rural communities had populations of < 10,000, semi-urban communities ranged in size from 10,000 to 99,999, and urban communities had populations of 100,000+.

RESULTS RELATED TO RURAL AGING: Fifteen percent of respondents of all ages did not have a regular doctor. Overall, rural residents were more likely not to have a regular doctor than residents of either urban or semi-urban communities. Among the rural respondents who did not have a physician, 7% were aged 60 - 69 and 4% were aged 70+. This compares to 10% and 4% for the semi-urban respondents and 8% and 1%, respectively, for the urban respondents in these age groups.

CONCLUSIONS: Place of residence was the strongest predictor of not having a regular doctor when all age groups were considered.

Pong, R. W., Salmoni, A., & Heard, S. (1999). Physician visits by older persons in Elliot Lake: Issues and challenges. In A. M. Mawhiney & J. Pitblado (Eds.), *Boom town blues: Elliot Lake, collapse and revival in a single-industry community* **(pp. 240-251). Toronto, ON: Dundurn Press.**

OBJECTIVES: To examine the frequency of visits to physicians for adults aged 50+, to estimate the total number of physician visits in a year, to determine the extent to which older residents had to seek medical care outside their community, and to identify problems experienced by those who had to leave the community for medical consultation in Elliot Lake in the province of Ontario.

METHODS: Data were from telephone and mail surveys completed for the Elliot Lake Seniors' Needs Assessment that began in 1994. Respondents were asked to indicate the number of times they had seen a family physician/general practitioner and/or a physician specialist in or outside Elliot Lake in the previous 12 months.

DEFINITION OF RURAL: Elliot Lake is a retirement community described as "a small city located in a region with chronic physician shortages" (p. 242).

RESULTS RELATED TO RURAL AGING: The mean numbers of visits to family physicians were 5.91 for the 65 - 69 age group, 7.36 for the 70 - 74 age group, and 5.66 for the 75+ age group. The corresponding mean numbers of visits to specialists were 1.22, 1.45, and 1.46 for each age group, respectively. Over half (54%) did not have to leave the community to see a physician although 66% of the specialist visits were outside Elliot Lake. Problems encountered by people who had to travel for medical appointments included a 'long wait for appointments' and 'poor weather'.

CONCLUSIONS: The authors discuss issues related to the availability of physicians and offer a number of strategies to deal with these issues.

Rockwood, K., Stadnyk, K., Carver, D., MacPherson, K. M., Beanlands, H. E., Powell, C., Stolee, P., Thomas, V. S., & Tonks, R. S. (2000). A clinimetric evaluation of specialized geriatric care for rural dwelling, frail older people. *Journal of the American Geriatrics Society, 48*(9), 1080-1085.

OBJECTIVES: To test a Comprehensive Geriatric Assessment (CGA) as an adjunct to usual care in three rural counties in the province of Nova Scotia.

METHODS: Data were from a randomized controlled trial with 3-, 6-, and 12-month follow-ups. A total of 182 frail older patients referred by family practitioners were assigned to the intervention (n = 95) or usual care (n = 87) groups. In addition to their usual care, the intervention group received 3-month implementation of CGA recommendations by a Mobile Geriatric Assessment Team (MGAT) with follow-up assessments at 3, 6, and 12 months. Geriatric nurse assessors, blinded to group assignment, performed each assessment. The CGA covered problems in 10 domains (mental status, emotional health, communication, mobility, balance, bowels, bladders, nutrition, daily activities, and social situation). Goal attainment scaling (GAS) recorded the degree of patient-related goal achievement between baseline and follow-up. Three types of goals were set, focusing on outcomes of care, process issues, and preventive practices. The ages of the control and intervention groups were 82.2 and 81.4 years, respectively; 58% of the control group and 57% of the intervention group were female.

DEFINITION OF RURAL: No definition of rural was provided.

RESULTS RELATED TO RURAL AGING: At 3 months, the intervention group was more likely to attain their goals compared with controls. Standard assessments of function (Barthel Index, Instrumental Activities of Daily Living), cognition (Mini-Mental State Examination), and quality of life (modified Spitzer Quality-of-Life index) showed no difference over 12 months. There also were no differences in survival as measured by the number of days (intervention: 320, control: 294) or the time to institutionalization (intervention: 340, control: 342 days).

CONCLUSIONS: The authors argue that although the intervention did not prolong life or delay institutionalization, clinically important benefits were observed. They conclude that an interdisciplinary MGAT can target rural-dwelling frail older persons, perform in-home CGAs, and develop an intervention strategy. Future research is needed in other locations to determine if the model can be successfully replicated and whether the benefits are cost-effective.

Tataryn, D. J., Roos, N. P., & Black, C. D. (1995). Utilization of physician resources for ambulatory care. *Medical Care, 33*(Suppl. 12), DS84-DS99.

OBJECTIVES: To describe ambulatory physician service use by residents in 1991/92 in the province of Manitoba.

METHODS: Physician claims submitted to Manitoba Health in the fiscal year 1991/92 were analyzed. An ambulatory physician visit was defined as any contact with a physician that occurred while the patient was not a hospital in-patient and included office, outpatient, emergency, and nursing home visits.

DEFINITION OF RURAL: 'Largely rural' non-Winnipeg health regions were compared to the Winnipeg health region. Winnipeg is the major urban centre in the province; non-Winnipeg was defined as all areas outside of Winnipeg.

RESULTS RELATED TO RURAL AGING: Individuals aged 65+ had higher rates of contact with physicians than their younger counterparts but accounted for only about 20% of the physician contacts. Winnipeg residents were much more likely than rural residents to have a consult and to visit medical specialists (i.e., general internists, those with a subspecialty such as geriatrics, etc.). Among the 65 - 74 age group, physician contact rates (visits per 100 residents) were 21.4 for rural males and 27.9 for rural females compared to 24.2 for urban males and 33.0 for urban females. For the 70+ age group, the rates were 18.1 for rural males, 30.0 for rural females, 20.5 for urban males, and 33.0 for urban females. Average physician expenditures were lower for older rural residents than for older urban residents. In the rural regions, the average cost ranged from $3.95/resident for males aged 75+ to $6.43/resident for females aged 75+.

CONCLUSIONS: Although residents aged 75+ (6% of the population) made twice as many visits per capita compared to younger adults, their actual demand on the system was small and accounted for just less than 10% of expenditures on physician services. In a discussion at the end of the article (pp. D596 – D599), the Editors comment that, because the elderly represent such a small group, even with the doubling of the senior population in Manitoba over the next several years, the impact on the need for physician services will be modest.

See also Fakhoury, W. K. H., & Roos, L. (1996); Finlayson, M., Lix, L., Finlayson, G. S., & Fong, T. (2005); Frohlich, N., Markesteyn, T., Roos, N., Carriere, K. C., Black, C., DeCoster, C., Burchill, C. A., & MacWilliam, L. (1994); and Roos, N. P., Shapiro, E., Bond, R., Black, C., Finlayson, G., Newburn-Cook, C., MacWilliam, L., Steinbach, C., Yogendran, M., & Walld, R. (2001).

Service Planning/Delivery Models

Brymer, C., Cormack, C., & Spezowka, K.-A. (1998). Improving the care of the elderly in a rural county through education. *Gerontology & Geriatrics Education, 19*(1), 55-64.

OBJECTIVES: To examine a geriatric educational intervention for non-physician health care professionals in a rural county in the province of Ontario.

METHODS: Four geriatric educational seminars were offered, focusing on medication use, physical assessment, mental status assessment, and elder abuse. A total of 28 one-hour presentations were given at three different times during the day and at all three hospitals in the county. At the beginning of each session, participants answered questions related to topic-specific current practice; these 4-5 questions were developed specifically for this study (included in the article). At the end of the session, a 6-item questionnaire on satisfaction with the presentation and content was completed. Three months following the sessions, questionnaires focusing on current practice were mailed to the participants' homes. Total score indexes were calculated for each topic. There were 164 participants (67 registered nurses, 26 registered practical nurses, 21 social workers/occupational therapists/physiotherapists, 20 community case managers, and 30 from other health-care related areas). Sample sizes for a comparison of pre- and post-tests varied by topic area (medication use, n = 67; physical assessment, n = 90; mental status assessment, n = 94; and elder abuse, n = 82).

DEFINITION OF RURAL: No definition of rural was provided. The county was described as a "large rural county in Southwestern Ontario" (p. 56).

RESULTS RELATED TO RURAL AGING: A total of 164 participants attended at least one seminar; 66 individuals participated in all four seminars. Statistically significant improvements were evident in each area, with the greatest improvements in medication use and physical assessment. Satisfaction with the presenters, content, pace, and format was rated as good-to-excellent by participants. No differences according to discipline were evident in the scores or the improvement in scores.

CONCLUSIONS: The authors conclude that a needs-based educational intervention can improve practice with regards to assessment of the elderly and is feasible even in small communities.

Cloutier Fisher, D. (2000). *Long-term care restructuring in rural Ontario: Retrieving community narratives through a case study approach.* **Doctoral dissertation, University of Guelph, Guelph, ON. Retrieved from:**

OBJECTIVES: To examine how restructuring processes have affected the ability of elderly and disabled persons, reliant upon public sector services, to remain in their communities in the province of Ontario.

METHODS: This doctoral dissertation research involved a case study of small communities in Wellington County, Ontario. Semi-structured interviews were conducted with 24 long-term care service users and their caregivers (14 elderly clients, 4 disabled clients, and 6 caregivers), 17 service providers, and 8 community representatives, between June 1997 and February 1998.

DEFINITION OF RURAL: Wellington County has two 'anchoring' small town communities, Harriston and Palmerston. The 1996 populations were 2,008 and 2,468, respectively. In 1996, the percentages of persons aged 65+ were 22% for Harriston and 18% for Palmerston.

RESULTS RELATED TO RURAL AGING: The results emphasized the particular vulnerabilities of service users who were disabled, who had both physical and mental health needs, and who had low incomes. One of the most disruptive outcomes of restructuring for service users was the replacement of a known service provider with someone from another agency because of the available service dollars in the latter. The majority of individuals seemed ill-equipped to cope themselves or to engage private care on their own behalf, even when warned to expect cuts. Individuals, family members, and formal care providers were forced to enlist the support of a diverse range of formal and informal supportive services in order to maintain independence.

CONCLUSIONS: The author identifies many unanswered questions regarding restructuring of long-term care and, more generally, the role of government in contemporary society.

See also Cloutier Fisher, D., & Joseph, A. E. (2000).

Cloutier-Fisher, D., & Joseph, A. E. (2000). Long-term care restructuring in rural Ontario: Retrieving community service user and provider narratives. *Social Science & Medicine, 50*(7-8), 1037-1045.

OBJECTIVES: To examine the community-based long-term care (LTC) restructuring that was initiated in 1996 in the province of Ontario.

METHODS: A case study of two small rural towns (Harriston and Palmerston) in Wellington County, Ontario was undertaken to develop a 'situated understanding' of service-user and service-provider perspectives on service coordination issues and on service cuts, particularly as they affected the ability of elderly people reliant on publicly-funded community services to stay in their homes and to continue to 'age in place'. Interviews were conducted from 1997 to 1998 with 13 female and 1 male community-service users aged 71 to 98 and 17 providers (12 front-line workers, planners, and administrators employed by agencies providing community services, the local District Health Council, and the local Community Care Access Centre; and 5 staff at the Palmerston and District General Hospital).

DEFINITION OF RURAL: Harriston had a 1996 population of 2,008, with 22% aged 65+. Palmerston had 2,468 residents, with 18% aged 65+.

RESULTS RELATED TO RURAL AGING: Prior to presenting the case study, the antecedents and key features of LTC restructuring were examined. Several themes emerged from the case study. These related to service co-ordination, negative reactions to service cuts, and concerns regarding the limits of community care as a means of supporting older adults' desire to age in place. This desire to age in place and stay at home lead some older adults to create their own solutions to maintain independence.

CONCLUSIONS: The authors argue that a managed competition system introduced as the centrepiece of LTC reform has resulted in increasing diversity and uncertainty for both users and providers. Despite continued attempts to 'cut and paste' support packages, the restructuring of publicly-funded community services, combined with a substantial re-investment in LTC facilities, appears to make some elderly people more vulnerable to institutionalization.

See also Cloutier Fisher, D. S. (2000).

Crilly, R. G., Harris, D., Stolee, P., & Ellett, F. K. (1999). A framework for development of geriatric services in rural areas. *Gerontology & Geriatrics Education, 20*(1), 59-72.

OBJECTIVES: To describe the development and conceptual framework for a community initiative to improve care for older adults in the southwestern region of the province of Ontario.

METHODS: A process of exploration and interaction with local communities led to the development of the 'Models Project' in which the Southwestern Ontario Regional Geriatric Program (RGP) worked with two largely rural communities to develop local expertise in geriatric assessment and improve care of older adults. Organizational development principles were used to guide the project.

DEFINITION OF RURAL: No definition of rural was provided. The two communities were described as "largely rural" (p. 60).

RESULTS RELATED TO RURAL AGING: The three phases of the initiative were described. Phase 1 was the exploratory stage that identified significant gaps in knowledge about older adults and specific health problems; the difficulty of applying the concept of a comprehensive geriatric assessment in a local agency/institution where there was a lack of sufficient critical mass of clients, and a lack of many of the usual members of the team; and the lack of availability of specialized geriatric services outside the major urban centre in the region. An expanded view of comprehensive geriatric assessment provided a vision for community development of services for the elderly. Phase 2 was an interaction phase, lasting about 2 years. The RGP provided comprehensive geriatric assessments, consultation, and education throughout the region. This phase highlighted the concentrated effort required to convert new knowledge into a change in practice, the unrealistic expectations that all workers would view the problems of geriatric patients as their primary focus, and the question of whether the existing system would enable change in practice to occur. Phase 3 involved the implementation of the 'Models Project' that saw the RGP work with two rural communities to develop local geriatric resources to meet each community's needs. The conceptual framework that guided the 'Models Project' was outlined.

CONCLUSIONS: The authors argue that the 'Models Project' serves to illustrate principles and processes that may be of value for other communities with scarce specialized geriatric resources and that it can be used to improve care of older patients.

See also Harris, D., Crilly, R. G., Stolee, P., & Ellett, F. K. (1999).

Fraser, B. S. (1989). *Service planning for the elderly in rural communities: Learning from the One-Stop Access initiative.* **Master's thesis, University of Guelph, Guelph, ON.**

OBJECTIVES: To present a framework for identifying rural service planning problems, drawing on a case study of One-Stop Access in the province of Ontario.

METHODS: The case study was conducted in Huron County. One-Stop Access was developed for the Ontario government in 1987 as "a way of providing a single point of access or entry to the range of community-based services available to assist the elderly" (p. 47). A community consultation was undertaken from October to December 1987. A public meeting of individuals representing various agencies was followed by face-to-face interviews. Information was collected on the current health and social services available in the county, types of interagency relationships that exist, perceived gaps in services, and the response in general to the One-Stop Access concept.

DEFINITION OF RURAL: Huron County is a predominantly rural area of southwestern Ontario. Its 1986 population was 56,000; 69% resided in communities of < 2,500 or in open countryside. In 1986, 16% of the population was aged 65+.

RESULTS RELATED TO RURAL AGING: The interrelationship between generic and rural service planning issues in community-based health and social services for the elderly was examined. Ecological dimensions (small dispersed populations, low absolute numbers of inhabitants, and relative isolation/distance from urban places) were viewed as geographical constraints that affected community services. These effects included problems with efficient and effective service delivery, increased travel time and cost, issues of decreased communication and limited information sharing, and local rivalries. Sociocultural characteristics (small locally responsive agencies, sense of autonomy/self-reliance, distrust of government and change, and independence) were seen as organizational constraints. Their effects on community services included responsive small local agencies, limited interagency collaboration, territoriality and lack of co-ordination, communication problems, threats to autonomy, animosity toward top-down initiatives, and anti-government sentiments.

CONCLUSIONS: The author argues that careful identification of rural populations and skillful integration of solutions to the problems within new models of delivery have the potential to address long standing issues in rural service provision.

See also Fraser, B., & Fuller, A. M. (1989); and Wolfe, J., Fraser, B., & Fuller, A. M. (1991).

Fraser, B., & Fuller, A. M. (1989). One-Stop Access for senior citizens: A model of integrated service delivery for rural areas. In S. J. Lewis (Ed.), *Aging and health: Linking research and public policy* (pp. 101-109). Chelsea, MI: Lewis Publishers.

OBJECTIVES: To discuss issues faced in the development of a model of One-Stop Access in a predominantly rural area in the province of Ontario.

METHODS: This initiative involved collaboration between the Board of Health, and the Gerontology Research Centre and the School of Rural Planning and Development at the University of Guelph. The One-Stop Access concept was introduced by the Ontario government in 1987 and proposed a "system which would provide a single point of entry for community services, comprehensive functional assessments, and referral to appropriate services via a case management system" (p. 102). A community consultation process was undertaken, with further information sharing and feedback obtained at two public meetings (no details provided).

DEFINITION OF RURAL: No definition of rural was provided.

RESULTS RELATED TO RURAL AGING: The issues of rurality, the role of the local authority, the case management system, and the extent of decentralization were discussed. The primary components in the One-Stop Access Model were identified and included the local authority, the management unit, a citizen's advisory council, and the service providers.

CONCLUSIONS: The authors argue that in this type of model, commitment from individuals at all levels is critical. Training and upgrading also are necessary support features for the system as a whole, along with the need for balance between the provision of integrated services at the community level and the cost of such provision. Efforts to coordinate, evaluate, and streamline programs are discussed as ongoing challenges.

See also Fraser, B. S. (1989); and Wolfe, J., Fraser, B., & Fuller, A. M. (1991).

Gunderson, W., Marshall, K., Stewart, N., & Morgan, D. (1995). *Needs assessment for dementia care: Midwest Health District.* **Saskatoon, SK: Midwest Health Distrcit and College of Nursing, University of Saskatchewan.**

OBJECTIVES: To conduct a needs assessment for dementia care in the Midwest Health District in the province of Saskatchewan in order to estimate the number of persons with special needs related to Alzheimer's disease and related disorders, to describe problem behaviours and their impact on safety, and to examine issues related to environments for care and available resources.

METHODS: Key informant interviews (n = 100) were completed in nine communities from December 1994 to January 1995. Respondents were selected by the Local Co-ordinating Committees at the community level to represent acute care and/or long-term care facilities (n = 40; Director of Care, Direct Care Staff, Activity Worker, and Resident Council), Home Care (n = 19; Nursing Co-ordinator, Direct Care Staff, and Assessor), and community other than Home Care (n = 41; Physician, Pastoral Care, Housing Manager, and Alzheimer Support Group). Identical questions were used with each respondent group. Content analysis of interviews was done to identify themes. Information on the number of dementia cases was provided by the key informants and then verified with the Local Co-ordinating Committee.

DEFINITION OF RURAL: The nine communities were Dinsmore, Milden, Beechy, Elrose, Kyle, Lucky Lake, Outlook, Rosetown, and Davidson.

RESULTS RELATED TO RURAL AGING: A total of 256 cases of dementia were identified (165 in facilities, 78 in Home Care, and 19 in the community but not receiving Home Care service). Among facility residents with dementia, 47% were in Stages 5 or 6 of the Global Deterioration Scale (GDS). The estimated prevalence of problem behaviours in long-term care was 34%. In Home Care, 63% of clients with dementia were in GDS Stages 5 or 6. The corresponding percentage for the community group not receiving Home Care was 37%. The prevalence of dementia was estimated at 295 to 306 cases, based on age-standardized rates. Five needs were identified: these related to a safe environment, programs for persons with dementia and their caregivers, improved methods of assessment of persons with dementia, education, and quality of life for persons with dementia and their caregivers.

CONCLUSIONS: The authors suggest that the number of dementia cases is an underestimate and identify the Midwest Health District as a unique case for needs-based funding. A number of recommendations related to dementia care are provided.

Hanlon, N., & Halseth, G. (2005). The greying of resource communities in northern British Columbia: Implications for health care delivery in already-underserviced communities. *The Canadian Geographer, 49*(1), 1-24.

OBJECTIVES: To examine the context of aging in rural and remote locations of northern British Columbia, with the purpose of highlighting impending challenges for health care service provision.

METHODS: Existing data on the demographics related to population change from 1991 to 2001 in northern British Columbia and on the availability of services to support seniors who age in place were reviewed. Three case studies were presented.

DEFINITION OF RURAL: 'Northern British Columbia' was defined as the territory under the jurisdiction of the Northern Health Region. The case studies were conducted in Kitimat (2001 pop. 10,771), Mackenzie (2001 pop. 5,489), and Fort Nelson (2001 pop. 4,438).

RESULTS RELATED TO RURAL AGING: Most northern local health areas (LHAs) experienced faster growth in the 65 - 79 age group than the rest of the province. This reflects the faster out-migration of non-seniors. The growth of the 80+ group was lower than provincial rates, with the smaller and more remote LHAs recording overall negative growth rates. The authors discuss the challenges in providing services in rural and remote communities that enable seniors to remain in their own homes and communities as long as possible (e.g., assisted housing, home care). They also discuss the impact that restructuring of the acute care sector has had on the continuum of care and provision of support to seniors. In terms of continuing care, the northern region had, in 1998/99, 917 long-term care and extended care beds. By 2002/03, this had increased to 986 beds. However, that increase was more than offset by the increase in the ratio of the oldest-old. In addition, these beds were concentrated in the 16 largest centres, with 23% of the overall extended care capacity entirely co-located in acute care hospitals. The result was that smaller communities often lacked local continuing care beds. The three case studies highlighted the connection between industrial and public welfare services restructuring.

CONCLUSIONS: The authors argue that needs are unmet in smaller communities in northern B.C., with delivery mechanisms off-loading tremendous costs, such as transportation, onto clients. They also argue that population aging in areas that have never dealt with this issue before has served to highlight important questions about how to provide for needs of seniors that the policy and community context are not presently equipped to meet.

Harris, D., Crilly, R. G., Stolee, P., & Ellett, F. K. (1999). Improving a system of care for elderly persons in rural areas. *The Gerontologist, 39*(3), 362-367.

OBJECTIVES: To describe a community initiative to improve the care of elders in largely rural areas in the province of Ontario.

METHODS: An organization development framework guided pilot projects in two communities, with support from the Southwestern Regional Geriatric Program (RGP).

DEFINITION OF RURAL: Site 1 included 3 small towns and the surrounding areas; 21% of its population was aged 65+. Site 2 was a small city with a population of 32,000 and its surrounding area; 14% of the population was aged 65+. This site was already intensely serviced by the RGP.

RESULTS RELATED TO RURAL AGING: Four overlapping stages in the development of this initiative were described: (1) assess the potential for action; (2) get the whole system in the room (e.g., getting all the stakeholders together to promote community wide discussion); (3) focus on the future; and (4) structure tasks that people can do for themselves. Two interdisciplinary teams representing primary service agencies in the communities were trained to serve as local resources in geriatric assessment and intervention. Assessments were conducted to identify where skills and knowledge could be enhanced, and to identify system problems that the steering committees needed to address through means other than training. Through the resource teams, the communities developed a more integrated and coordinated approach to care for the elderly population.

CONCLUSIONS: The authors conclude that a training program is only a partial solution to improving care for elderly individuals. Barriers that hinder the transfer of skills and knowledge to worksites also need to be removed. The process provided insights into the implementation of system change.

See also Crilly, R. G., Harris, D., Stolee, P., & Ellett, F. K. (1999).

Hemingway, D., & MacLeod, T. (2004). Living north of 65 years: A community-based process to hear the voices of northern seniors. *Rural Social Work, 9*, 137-146.

OBJECTIVES: To identify the health needs of older adults in the northern area of the province of British Columbia through a community-based, capacity-building process.

METHODS: The project began in Fall 2000 and concluded in Spring 2002. It involved older adults from eight communities. Regionally-based Community Advisory Committees (CACs) and a Task Force on Seniors' Health (each composed of seniors and trusted allies) were established. The CACs approved each aspect of the work which included hosting a local community forum; drafting, revising, piloting, and distributing a survey instrument (entitled "Living North of Sixty-Five Years"); organizing a regional seniors' consultative forum; analyzing survey and forum data; identifying the key findings; and ultimately, presenting recommendations to the Health Board.

DEFINITION OF RURAL: The eight communities were Robson Valley, Prince George, Vanderhoof, Mackenzie, Fraser Lake, Fort St. James, Burns Lake, and Granisle.

RESULTS RELATED TO RURAL AGING: This article described the community-participation process. Recommendations to the Northern Interior Regional Health Board were outlined. These ranged from establishing a regional seniors' telephone information line to ensuring a range of housing options are available to allow individuals to age in place. Successes, limitations, and potential implications for policy development, service delivery, and social work practice with older adults in smaller northern and rural communities were discussed.

CONCLUSIONS: The authors argue that the participatory approach can guide social work practitioners and researchers who work with older adults during a time of cutbacks and policy changes within the health care system.

See also Prince George Task Force on Seniors' Health and Community Action Committees (2002).

Joseph, A. E., & Cloutier, D. S. (1990). A framework for modeling the consumption of health services by the rural elderly. *Social Science & Medicine, 30*(1), 45-52.

OBJECTIVES: To describe a framework for conceptualizing the process of older adults' service utilization at both the aggregate (user and non-user characteristics) and individual (decision-making) levels, and to test the framework in the province of Ontario.

METHODS: Data were from a survey conducted in Summer 1987 in Grey County, Ontario. A stratified random sample of 202 residents aged 65+ from Meaford (n = 126) and Markdale (n = 76) was drawn from school support lists. In-person interviews focused on the use of health and social services in the past 2 years, demographic characteristics, and residential histories. Services studied here included: VON nursing, VON footcare, public health nursing, physiotherapy, homemaking, and meals-on-wheels. Sixty percent of the respondents were aged 65 – 74; 65% were females. The authors state that "No formal statistical evaluation is attempted" (p. 49) as their sample may not be considered as representative, and because of issues of sample size and low use rates.

DEFINITION OF RURAL: Grey County is situated beyond the commuting zones of Toronto, Kitchener-Waterloo, and London in southwestern Ontario. Meaford had a 1986 population of 4,380 (21.7% aged 65+) and Markdale's 1986 population was 1,226 (28.6% aged 65+).

RESULTS RELATED TO RURAL AGING: The framework identified 2 models to explain the route to service use in situations where needs potentially can be satisfied by one or more community support services. Model 1 represented the conventional, aggregate approach to the description of usage patterns, and sought to characterize differences and similarities in use among groups defined on the basis of variables such as age and marital status. Model 2 was specific to the individual (or household), and divided the decision on use/non-use of an available service into 3 elements: perceived degree of service importance, perceived quality of local service, and perceived accessibility. A negative decision may occur at any one of these three steps. The testing of the models was difficult, given the low rate of use. Less than 10% used any one service over the past 2 years (VON nursing [8%], VON footcare [4%], public health nursing [3%], physiotherapy [2%], homemaking [8%], and meals-on-wheels [3%]).

CONCLUSIONS: The findings underscore the complex and dynamic nature of service provision and utilization issues in rural communities. The authors call for research that examines the relationships between housing form/choice and service use.

See also Joseph, A. E., & Cloutier, D. S. (1990); Joseph, A. E., & Cloutier, D. S. (1991); and Joseph, A. E. (1992).

Joseph, A. E., & Hollett, R. G. (1993). On the use of socio-demographic indicators in local health planning: A Canadian non-metropolitan perspective. *Social Science & Medicine, 37*(6), 813-822.

OBJECTIVES: To examine the use of sociodemographic indicators in mental health services planning, taking into account local settlement conditions and trends as well as general knowledge of the spatial etiology of mental illness, and using a county in the province of Ontario as an example.

METHODS: Data from 22 municipalities in the County of Wellington in southern Ontario were extracted from the Hospital Medical Records Institute (HMRI) and the 1986 Census of Canada. Hospital separations for each municipality from 1981/82 to 1985/86 were obtained from HMRI; breakdowns by age and sex were not available. Eight mental disorders listed under the Ontario Broad Code were examined: alcohol psychosis, schizophrenia, affective psychosis, other forms of psychosis, neuroses, alcoholism, drug dependence, and personality disorders and other non-psychotic disorders. Utilization rates per 1,000 population were calculated for all diagnoses; for schizophrenia, affective psychosis, and other forms of psychosis as a group; and for the other 5 disorders as a group. Twenty indicators were selected from the 1986 Census as descriptors of the municipalities; 18 represented sociodemographic variables, and 2 characterized the geographic structure of the county (townships vs. villages/towns vs. city; distance from Guelph).

DEFINITION OF RURAL: The County of Wellington had a 1986 population of 139,435. It includes the City of Guelph, 9 towns/villages, and 12 townships. The City of Guelph had a 1986 population of 78,225; the 21 remaining municipalities ranged in size from 653 to 6,168 in 1986.

RESULTS RELATED TO RURAL AGING: The 5-year hospital utilization rates for all mental disorders varied by municipality from 1.14 to 13.58 per 1,000 population. The average rate for the 9 towns and villages was 9.52 compared to 8.19 for the City of Guelph and 3.02 for the 12 townships. Multivariate analysis revealed strong relationships between rates of hospitalizations for mental illness and the demographic maturity and gender composition of municipal populations. Rates tended to be highest in communities with substantial relative concentrations of older persons, particularly elderly women.

CONCLUSIONS: The authors discuss the importance of service and amenity-led migration in the accumulation of older people in nucleated rural communities and suggest that it is this order accumulation that underlies the differences between townships, towns/villages, and the City of Guelph rather than the nature of the community per se. While recognizing data limitations, including the lack of information about outpatient services, they conclude that local settlement patterns and trends are important for the application and interpretation of sociodemographic indicators of health services planning.

Kelley, M. L., & MacLean, M. J. (1997). Interdisciplinary continuing education in a rural and remote area: The approach of the Northern Educational Centre for Aging and Health. *Educational Gerontology, 23*(7), 631-649.

OBJECTIVES: To describe an interdisciplinary continuing education approach for health care practitioners in a rural remote environment in the province of Ontario.

METHODS: Existing literature on rural health care practice and interdisciplinary education and teamwork was briefly reviewed. The experience of the Northern Educational Centre for Aging and Health (NECAH) in planning and delivering a 5-day interdisciplinary educational program in palliative care offered in 1994 was used to illustrate issues of rural health care practice and implications for practitioners' educational needs. Eighty-seven delegates representing regional agencies and several health care disciplines, and 40 hospice volunteers attended the educational sessions. Over one-half (54%) of the participants were practicing in 13 different rural and remote communities with populations of ≤ 10,000.

DEFINITION OF RURAL: The NECAH is located at Lakehead University in Thunder Bay. Thunder Bay (population 120,000) serves as the major economic and service centre for northwestern Ontario. The area has a population density of < 1 person per square mile.

RESULTS RELATED TO RURAL AGING: The planners deliberately employed a broad definition of palliative care in order to appropriately address the region's health care realities, where palliative care was performed as part of a generalist practice. Practitioners throughout the region were consulted by the program planners to identify educational needs and preferred approaches to program delivery. Networking among delegates was emphasized. Communication across disciplinary boundaries was promoted through the educational methods used during the initiative.

CONCLUSIONS: The authors argue that the NECAH approach serves as an educational model specific to health care practitioners working in rural and remote environments.

McGee, P., Tuokko, H., MacCourt, P., & Donnelly, M. (2004). Factors affecting the mental health of older adults in rural and urban communities: An exploration. *Canadian Journal of Community Mental Health, 23*(2), 117-126.

OBJECTIVES: To describe factors affecting the mental health of older adults in rural and mid-sized communities in the province of British Columbia, from the perspectives of community stakeholders.

METHODS: Eight focus groups were held with participants identified by key individuals in the mental health area as those with knowledge or experience to provide information about factors affecting the mental health of older persons. Participants (n = 63) were from two mid-size urban and four rural communities. The questions focused on factors that affect the mental health of older adults, how their communities were addressing these factors, innovative strategies, gaps in services, and the challenges encountered. Sessions were audio-taped and then transcribed verbatim.

DEFINITION OF RURAL: No definition of rural was provided.

RESULTS RELATED TO RURAL AGING: Six categories of factors affecting the mental health of older adults were identified, including clinical, physical, organizational, educational, psychosocial, and spiritual factors. Participants in both rural and urban communities described variability in the availability and accessibility of personnel, services, and programs. For rural residents, interdisciplinary mental health teams, day services, and transportation services often were unavailable or severely limited.

CONCLUSIONS: The authors call for innovative strategies to meet the needs of seniors, particularly those living in rural areas.

Mitten, C., Donaldson, C., & Mandeville, P. (2003). Priority setting in a Canadian long-term care setting: A case study using program budgeting and marginal analysis. *Canadian Journal on Aging, 22*(3), 311-321.

OBJECTIVES: To examine the use of program budgeting and marginal analysis (PBMA), an economic framework used widely by health authorities in a number of different countries, within the context of the long-term care (LTC) services offered in Claresholm in the province of Alberta.

METHODS: A case study of Claresholm was undertaken in 2000. Prior to the study, older adults in this community had 2 options: live in their own homes and rely on informal caregivers or enter a 100-bed LTC facility. A program budget for LTC in Claresholm was derived. A 10-member expert panel met 4 times in late 2000. Following a presentation of the existing mode of service delivery and supporting evidence from the literature, including various service-delivery options, the panel devised an expansion wish list and sought to identify areas for resource release to fund the potential expansions. A follow-up survey also was conducted with the expert panel members.

DEFINITION OF RURAL: Claresholm is located 120 kilometres south of Calgary. In 2001, 24% of its population was aged 65+ compared to 10% for Alberta. Its overall population was expanding at a lower rate than the provincial average (6% vs. 10% from 1996 to 2001).

RESULTS RELATED TO RURAL AGING: Recommendations included implementing adult day and adult night support programs, and converting long-term beds to convalescent beds. Funding for these changes was identified through allocating provincial 'Broda' funding and altering nursing assistant and physiotherapy activity. In the follow-up survey, there was unanimous agreement that PBMA added value to the priority setting process.

CONCLUSIONS: The authors conclude that PBMA was an effective, resource-neutral framework in aiding decision makers with redesigning LTC services in Claresholm. They argue that PBMA has the potential to be of value in the priority-setting process in health care systems.

Prince George Task Force on Seniors' Health and Community Action Committees. (2001). *North of 65 years: Report of the research into health services for seniors in the Northern Interior Health Region of British Columbia.* **Prince George, BC: Northern Interior Regional Health Board.**

OBJECTIVES: To provide the Northern Interior Regional Health Board (NIRHB) evidence-based information to help plan effective services for seniors in the province of British Columbia.

METHODS: This descriptive report outlined a participatory project undertaken in Fall 2000 with eight Community Advisory Committees to the NIRHB and the results of a survey entitled 'Living North of Sixty Five'. The survey was developed with input from seniors, and then distributed by volunteers from the Regional Community Advisory Committees. A total of 670 surveys were returned, representing almost 12% of the regional senior population. Two Community Advisory Committees, representing Valemount and McBride, were formed after the survey process began and elected to comment on senior health services in their communities separately.

DEFINITION OF RURAL: Surveys were returned from residents of Burns Lake, Dunster, Fort Fraser, Fort St. James, Fraser Lake, Francois Lake, Granisle, Hixon, Mackenzie, McBride, McLeod Lake, Oosta Lake, Prince George, Robson Valley, Tachet Reserve, Topley Landing, Valemount, Vandenhoof, and Wisteria.

RESULTS RELATED TO RURAL AGING: The report examined housing and living situations, future plans, help and services, health care needs, access to health services, nutrition, dental, lifestyle, and overall concerns. The respondents' opinions covered a wide range of individual perspectives, including an independent stance and the rejection of all kinds of help. There appeared to be a contradictory willingness to identify serious and urgent health care needs and to deny the need for assistance.

CONCLUSIONS: The authors argue that services need to be in place before a crisis presents itself. Services that enhance and support a senior's sense of dignity and independence need not be perceived as weakness or the first step on a slippery slope into dependency.

See also Hemingway, D., & MacLeod, T. (2004).

Regional Steering Committee for Geriatric Services in the North Peace River Region. (1986). *A new beginning: A review of the needs of seniors in the Peace River Health Unit. Volume 1: Executive summary;* **and** *A new beginning: A review of the needs of seniors in the North Peace Region. Volume 2: Technical report & Volume 3: Directory of agencies.* **Peace River, AB: The Regional Interdisciplinary Steering Committee for Geriatric Services in the North Peace River Region.**

OBJECTIVES: To assess the needs of older adults in the Peace River area in the province of Alberta.

METHODS: The project began in September 1985. Phase 1 involved the compilation of a registry of 3,000 people aged 65+. A listing of area agencies with services and programs for seniors was developed and 20 key agencies were interviewed about program delivery problems, future programming needs, and information needs. A survey of more than 400 seniors was completed by volunteer interviewers

DEFINITION OF RURAL: At the time of the study, the Peace River Health Unit District served about 40,000 people. The area covered 44,256 square kilometres and was largely rural and small town although there were six larger towns.

RESULTS RELATED TO RURAL AGING: The local agencies' lack of autonomy was identified as an issue; they often had to originate new programs as directed from head offices elsewhere. Areas for new programs ranged from physiotherapy departments in hospitals to expanded recreational programming to religious support groups. Needs were identified in terms of quality of life, medical, accommodation, transportation, financial, outreach programming, general programming, and information needs.

CONCLUSIONS: The report provides several recommendations to better meet the needs of older adults.

Salmoni, A. W., Sahai, V., Heard, S., Pong, R., & Lewko, J. (1996). Predicting future long-term-care needs in a community. *Canadian Journal of Public Health, 87*(6), 418-421.

OBJECTIVES: To estimate the number of severely disabled older adults expected in the next 5 to 10 years in a small northern community in the province of Ontario.

METHODS: Data were from a seniors' needs assessment conducted in Elliot Lake, Ontario in 1995. Telephone interviews were conducted with 3,448 residents of Elliot Lake aged 50+ (90% of total). Severely disabled was defined as having 2+ activities of daily living (ADL) disabilities (eating, dressing, grooming, walking, getting in/out of bed, and bathing/showering). Three prediction models were examined.

DEFINITION OF RURAL: No definition of rural was provided and the population size of Elliott Lake was not given.

RESULTS RELATED TO RURAL AGING: The three prediction methods provided a range of estimates of long-term care needs. Assuming that residents remain in the community, projections varied from 58 to 181 residents who will be aged 65+ in 5 years and will be severely disabled. The 10-year projections ranged from 80 to 205.

CONCLUSIONS: At a minimum, the projections identified the need for 35 - 58 long-term care beds in 5 years and 48 - 80 beds in 10 years to meet the demands of the severely disabled older population.

Shapiro, E., Tate, R. B., Wright, B., & Plohman, J. (2000). Changes in the perception of health care policy and delivery among Manitoba elders during the downsizing of the hospital sector. *Canadian Journal on Aging, 19*(1), 18-34.

OBJECTIVES: To examine changes in older adults' opinions about health care during the downsizing of the Winnipeg hospital sector in the province of Manitoba.

METHODS: A province-wide representative sample of individuals aged 65+ was interviewed in 1993 (n = 1,116) and re-interviewed in 1994 (n = 1,005). Questions focused on their perceptions of access to and quality of health care. Individuals who had been hospitalized during the six months prior to either interview were asked about the care and attention they received. Comparisons were made according to place of residence and admission/no admission to hospital during the time period.

DEFINITION OF RURAL: Winnipeg/non-Winnipeg comparisons were made. Winnipeg is the major urban centre in the province; non-Winnipeg was defined as all areas outside of Winnipeg.

RESULTS RELATED TO RURAL AGING: Both non-Winnipeg and Winnipeg residents had less favorable opinions about the overall quality of care after the Winnipeg hospital downsizing. Logistic regressions confirmed that place of residence (Winnipeg/non-Winnipeg) was not a factor in changing perceptions of the overall quality of care. The opinions about quality and access among those who had been hospitalized when most of the beds were being closed were significantly more favorable than among those hospitalized before the bed closures or not hospitalized at all; no Winnipeg/non-Winnipeg comparisons were presented.

CONCLUSIONS: The authors argue that, in similar circumstances, government needs to inform the public about the need for change and publicize their commitment to protecting access and standards of care.

Skinner, M. W. (2005). *Voluntarism and long-term care in the countryside: Exploring the implications of health care restructuring for voluntary sector providers in rural Ontario (1995-2003).* **Doctoral dissertation, Queen's University, Kingston, ON. Retrieved from:**
http://proquest.umi.com/pqdweb?index=0&did=954011521&SrchMode=1&sid =7&Fmt=13&VInst=PROD&VType=PQD&RQT=309&VName=PQD&TS=1172605 716&clientId=12301

OBJECTIVES: To examine the relationship between public service restructuring and voluntarism as it relates to the delivery of health care services in rural and small town settings in the province of Ontario.

METHODS: This dissertation involves a qualitative case study of three communities. In-depth interviews were conducted with 72 key informants between July and December 2003, and a review of existing literature and government legislation, policies, and documents was completed.

DEFINITION OF RURAL: The communities included the town of Blind River (population 3,969), the town of St. Marys (population 6,293), and the township of North Grenville (population 13,581) to represent remote hinterland, rural hinterland, and urban countryside settings, respectively.

RESULTS RELATED TO RURAL AGING: A comprehensive explanation of how voluntary sector providers were struggling to reconcile the long-standing issues of service provision in rural areas with the downloading of responsibilities for direct service provision associated with public service restructuring was presented. Rural providers operated within a context defined by relatively smaller and dispersed populations, shortage of qualified health professionals, limited pools of volunteers, and lack of privacy. The rural and small town settings lacked the economies of scale to sustain the range of long-term care services required in the community. At the same time, the volunteer sector providers had an ability to develop mutually beneficial partnerships and networks with local institutions and government.

CONCLUSIONS: This research contributes to the limited empirical base on long-term care issues in rural areas. Implications for future research are discussed.

Stolee, P., Kessler, L., & Le Clair, J. K. (1996). A community development and outreach program in geriatric mental health: Four years' experience. *Journal of the American Geriatrics Society, 44*(3), 314-320.

OBJECTIVES: To describe a geriatric mental health outreach program based on a community development model and to review 4 years of experience with this program in Brant County in the province of Ontario.

METHODS: The geriatric mental health outreach program of a regional psychiatric hospital served a primarily non-urban area, with offices in the community rather than in the hospital. It targeted community-dwelling or institutionalized older persons with late-onset mental health problems and/or behavioral disturbances, persons with long-standing psychiatric disorders with age-related changes, and their caregivers. Program components included an interprofessional Home Visit Team (HVT), a Specialized Information and Resource Service (SIRS), educational service initiatives, and an ongoing active role in planning and coordination in the local health care system.

DEFINITION OF RURAL: No definition of rural was provided. The area served was described as a non-urban area.

RESULTS RELATED TO RURAL AGING: Between January 1991 and December 1994, 637 individuals were referred to the HVT program. The average age was 78.1 years and 65% were female. Cognitive impairment, behavioral disturbances, physical/medical problems, and depression were the most common reasons for referral to the outreach program. SIRS received approximately 5 information inquiries per month in addition to the general inquiries about the outreach program. Information most frequently requested related to community services, behaviour issues, and medications. Information packages and educational tools were developed to be used in a 'train the trainer' model. Pilot educational service initiatives were undertaken in long-term care facilities, community agencies, temporary full-time developmental rotations, and an education/development group for family practitioners. Members of the outreach team worked with a number of community groups and agencies in the planning, developing, and coordinating of the health and social services system.

CONCLUSIONS: The program is a multifaceted effort to make efficient use of scarce, specialized resources in a manner that is sensitive and responsive to local circumstances and needs. The authors argue that their experience to date has shown evidence of the feasibility and potential benefits of a comprehensive approach to community development and outreach in geriatric mental health.

Whitfield, K. (2005). *Health service planning with individuals with dementia: Towards a model for inclusion.* **Doctoral dissertation, University of Waterloo, Waterloo, ON. Retrieved from:**
http://proquest.umi.com/pqdweb?index=0&did=1216757511&SrchMode=1&si
d=8&Fmt=13&VInst=PROD&VType=PQD&RQT=309&VName=PQD&TS=117260
5792&clientId=12301

OBJECTIVES: To identify characteristics required by rural Alzheimer Society chapters to successfully facilitate the inclusion of persons with dementia and living in the community, in decision-making about health services and supports in the province of Ontario.

METHODS: This doctoral dissertation relies on a case study approach with the Alzheimer Society of Grey-Bruce and the Alzheimer Society of Haldimand and Norfolk. A total of 59 key informants were interviewed, including 24 representatives from the Alzheimer Society organizations, 16 experts in dementia care, 11 people with dementia, and 8 mental health and disability sector experts. Key documents also were reviewed.

DEFINITION OF RURAL: The office of the Alzheimer Society of Grey-Bruce is situated in Owen Sound and has a service area covering all Grey County and Bruce County. These counties are largely rural (2002 population of the area was 152,965). The office of the Alzheimer Society of Haldimand and Norfolk is located in Simcoe, and has a service area covering Haldimand County and Norfolk County. These counties are largely rural, with a 2002 population of 104,670.

RESULTS RELATED TO RURAL AGING: The rural nature of the communities served by these two organizations was perceived to have an impact on planning and evaluation, and on health services. The challenges of being an organization that serves a mainly rural community included: getting board representation, fundraising that was described as very competitive, the distance to a major learning and/or research centre, and isolation of individuals from their neighbours and the lack of public transportation. Fewer specialized services, access to services, and few experts who want to work in the area were identified as having a negative impact in terms of health services. Positive impacts were a high level of neighbourly help, the greater cooperation among service providers, and that most service providers lived in the community where they worked, making it easier for clients to get help. There also were perceived implications of rurality on the involvement of people with dementia in planning and decision-making about health services. Attending meetings was identified as the most difficult. Persons with dementia experienced some negativity and resistance when initiating a relationship with the Alzheimer organization in their community while some also had positive experiences. Commonalities between the dementia care, mental health, and disability sectors relevant to the inclusion of consumers in service related decisions were identified. These included a key message of human rights and self-determination, a history of oppression and advocacy, a need to develop service organizations where the consumer plays a more central decision making role, and the promotion of a planning philosophy that is person focused. A model of inclusion was presented.

CONCLUSIONS: The author concludes that persons with dementia who serve as members of governing boards will most likely contribute to organizational level inclusion, and calls for research to explore potential outcomes.

Wolfe, J., Fraser, B., & Fuller, A. M. (1991). Issues and perspectives on services planning for the rural elderly: The One-Stop Access model, Huron County, Ontario. In K. M. Cossey (Ed.), *Rural environments and the elderly: Impact, contributions and needs fulfillment* (pp. 16-43). Sackville, NB: Rural and Small Town Research and Studies Programme, Department of Geography, Mount Allison University.

OBJECTIVES: To examine elements of public policy with respect to rural social service provision from the perspectives of central agencies, municipal leaders, service providers, and older adults, drawing on an example of the One-Stop Access Model in Huron County in the province of Ontario.

METHODS: A community consultation process was undertaken in Huron County. Interviews and meetings were held with a variety of agencies, organizations, and individuals. The One-Stop Access Model targeted planning and coordination of services for older adults.

DEFINITION OF RURAL: Huron County is a predominantly agricultural area in southwestern Ontario. Its 1986 population was 56,000.

RESULTS RELATED TO RURAL AGING: The consultative process revealed that quality services were being provided in the county, these services were unevenly distributed across the county, information about services was not readily accessible, local access was important to consumers, and communication was a critical factor to the program success. Issues such as the role of the local authority and case management were discussed. Four key factors related to decentralization (community visibility and communication; ease of contact between case managers, client, and service providers; peer interaction among case managers; and cost) were examined from the perspectives of clients/consumers, case managers, service providers, and the system.

CONCLUSIONS: The authors argue that this experiment in service planning provides insight into issues and perspectives that can improve planning processes in rural communities.

See also Fraser, B. S. (1989); and Fraser, B., & Fuller, A. M. (1989).

Service Use/Non-use

Cloutier, D. S. (1988). *Theoretical and empirical perspectives on the use of health and social services by the rural elderly.* **Master's thesis, University of Guelph, Guelph, ON.**

OBJECTIVES: To investigate the use of health and social support services by independent, community-dwelling older adults in two communities in Grey County in the province of Ontario.

METHODS: A survey of 202 elderly persons from the Town of Meaford (n = 126) and the Village of Markdale (n = 76) was conducted in July and August 1987. Random samples were drawn from the 1984 school support lists, with the final selection stratified by age. Interviews focused on residential history, personal and transportation mobility, social support and information networks, health and social service awareness and use, and personal information. Two service packages were considered: services that come to the individuals in their homes (e.g., VON nursing and footcare, public health nursing, physiotherapy, homemaking, meals-on-wheels) and services that the individual must leave the home to obtain (e.g., those from family doctors, hospitals, optometrists, dentists, chiropractors, foot clinics, or geriatric clinics).

DEFINITION OF RURAL: In 1986, Meaford's total population was 4,380; 21.7% were aged 65+. The population of Markdale was 1,226, with 28.6% aged 65+.

RESULTS RELATED TO RURAL AGING: Age, gender, marital status, rating one's health as poor, and having favourable impressions of services were significantly related to the use of services, as were local supply conditions, type of housing, and residential history (mover vs. non-mover). A predisposition towards the use of inside-home services was observed for elderly persons who had a small action space (low personal and transportation mobility), who relied upon formal support information sources, and who had limited informal support networks available during periods of illness.

CONCLUSIONS: The author concludes that outside-home services are important to the majority of elderly individuals whereas the use of inside-home services is influenced by circumstances and characteristics of individuals and of the service environment. Future research directions include an examination of the relationship between informal social support network and service use, the role of perceptions of service use, and the importance of perceptions of isolation with respect to service availability.

See also Joseph, A. E., & Cloutier, D. (1990).

Finlayson, M., Lix, L., Finlayson, G. S., & Fong, T. (2005). Trends in the utilization of specific health care services among older Manitobans: 1985 to 2000. *Canadian Journal on Aging, 24*(Suppl. 1), 15-27.

OBJECTIVES: To examine 16-year trends in the utilization of hospital and physician services by older adults aged 75+ in the province of Manitoba.

METHODS: Data were from the Manitoba Population Health Research Data Repository of all patient contacts with hospitals, physicians, and nursing homes. Trends from 1985/86 to 2000/01 were examined for hospital services (separations, short-stay days, long-stay days, cataract surgeries, and hip/knee replacements) and physician care (overall visit rate and proportion having 7+ visits).

DEFINITION OF RURAL: Winnipeg/non-Winnipeg comparisons were made. Winnipeg is the major urban centre in the province. The non-Winnipeg Regional Health Authorities (RHA) were further classified as northern (Nor-Man, Burntwood, Churchill RHAs), central (Central, Interlake, Marquette, North Eastman, Parkland RHAs), and southern (Brandon, South Eastman, South Westman RHAs).

RESULTS RELATED TO RURAL AGING: Changes in the use of health care services among the 75+ age groups were evident, with the extent of change varying with the service under consideration, age, and location of residence. The rate of hospital separations and the rate of short-stay hospital days were higher for the non-Winnipeg population than the Winnipeg population. The Winnipeg region had substantially higher rates for cataract procedures than the non-Winnipeg regions; there was no difference for hip and knee replacement. A great proportion of the Winnipeg population made intensive use of physicians each year (defined as 7+ visits) compared to the non-Winnipeg population. Regional variations also were evident for some types of services. For example, for cataract surgery, the Winnipeg versus non-Winnipeg gap was reduced by 12% whereas the gap expanded for hip and knee replacement surgery.

CONCLUSIONS: The authors conclude that examining utilization data at the provincial level masks important differences in the direction or the extent of change over time that emerges when regional or age group comparisons are made. They call for increased sensitivity to regional differences in population distribution, use patterns, and local health care priorities when planning health services.

See also De Coster, C., Bruce, S., & Kozyrskyj, A. (2005); Fakhoury, W. K. H., & Roos, L. (1996); Frohlich, N., Markesteyn, T., Roos, N., Carriere, K. C., Black, C., DeCoster, C., Burchill, C. A., & MacWilliam, L. (1994); Kozyrskyj, A. L., Black, C., Chateau, D., & Steinbach, C. (2005); Roos, N. P., Shapiro, E., Bond, R., Black, C., Finlayson, G., Newburn-Cook, C., MacWilliam, L., Steinbach, C., Yogendran, M., & Walld, R. (2001); and Tataryn, D. J., Roos, N. P., & Black, C. D. (1995).

Frohlich, N., Markesteyn, T., Roos, N., Carriere, K. C., Black, C., DeCoster, C., Burchill, C. A., & MacWilliam, L. (1994). *A report on the health status, socio-economic risk and health care use of the Manitoba population 1992-93 and overview of the 1990-91 to 1992-93 findings*. Winnipeg, MB: Manitoba Centre for Health Policy and Evaluation, University of Manitoba. Retrieved from: http://www.umanitoba.ca/centres/mchp/reports/pdfs/1994/Populis.pdf

OBJECTIVES: To examine use of health care services from 1990/91 to 1992/93 in the province of Manitoba.

METHODS: Data were from the Manitoba Population Health Information System (PHIS). The PHIS is population-based and designed to track the health status and health care resource use of Manitoba residents.

DEFINITION OF RURAL: Winnipeg/non-Winnipeg comparisons were made. Winnipeg is the major urban centre in the province; non-Winnipeg was defined as those health regions outside of Winnipeg. Information also was provided on specific health regions.

RESULTS RELATED TO RURAL AGING: In 1992/93, there was relatively little variation in nursing home utilization across the province. Excluding the Norman and Thompson regions, where the small elderly population makes rates unstable, the number of nursing home residents per 1,000 population aged 75+ ranged from 124 in Parklands to 140 in Westman. In 1992/93, the percentage of individuals having at least one contact with physicians was virtually identical for Winnipeg and non-Winnipeg males and females aged 65 - 74 and 75+.

CONCLUSIONS: The authors call for closer examination of the determinants of health and programs designed to generate good health across the entire population.

See also DeCoster, C., Roos, N., & Shapiro, E. (1995); Fakhoury, W. K. H., & Roos, L. (1996); Finlayson, M., Lix, L., Finlayson, G. S., & Fong, T. (2005); Mustard, C., Finlayson, M., Derksen, S., & Berthelot, J.-M. (1999); Roos, N. P., Shapiro, E., Bond, R., Black, C., Finlayson, G., Newburn-Cook, C., MacWilliam, L., Steinbach, C., Yogendran, M., & Walld, R. (2001); Tataryn, D. J., Roos, N. P., & Black, C. D. (1995); and Tomiak, M., Berthelot, J.-M., Guimond, E., & Mustard, C. A. (2000).

Hanlon, N. T. (1994). *Geographical perspectives on the links between social support networks and health care utilization among the elderly population of Ontario.* **Master's thesis, University of Guelph, Guelph, ON.**

OBJECTIVES: To examine the relationship of informal support networks to residential location, living arrangements, and the use of selected health care services among individuals aged 55+ in the province of Ontario.

METHODS: Data were from 12,938 individuals aged 55+ who participated in the 1990 Ontario Health Survey (OHS). The OHS sample was designed to target a population of 1,000 in each of the province's 43 Public Health Units (PHUs). Factors studied included the number of family and peer support contacts, residential location, living arrangements, age, gender, level of education, and activity limitations. Health care services were measured by visits to general physicians, consultations with specialist physicians, and hospitalizations over a 12-month period.

DEFINITION OF RURAL: Within each PHU, urban was defined as residence in the urban core and urban fringe areas of Census Metropolitan Areas or Census Agglomerations. Households in the rest of the PHU were classified as rural.

RESULTS RELATED TO RURAL AGING: Significant associations emerged between residential location and both family and peer informal support network size. Older adults in rural households had higher levels of family and peer contacts living outside their homes than their urban counterparts. Urban residence had a significant negative relationship with the frequent use of general practitioners and hospitalizations, and a significant positive relationship with specialist visits. Compared to urban residents, rural older individuals with a disability were more likely to be hospitalized but those who lived alone were less likely to consult a specialist.

CONCLUSIONS: The author calls for recognition of the effects of geography on social interaction, informal care, and formal care. The limitations of a definition of rural as "simply anything that is not urban" (p. 98) are discussed. Implication for policy and suggestions for future study are presented.

James, A. M. (1994). *Aging in urban and rural areas: Where are the differences? A study of health care utilization by the elderly population of eastern Ontario.* **Doctoral dissertation, Queen's University, Kingston, ON.**

OBJECTIVES: To examine rural-urban differences in the supply of services for seniors and the use of services by this age group, to reinterpret aging and service use as a gendered process, and to understand the potential role that long-term care reform will have on future service delivery in the province of Ontario.

METHODS: Data were collected in 1991 and 1992 on the supply of health and social services and consumption of services by the elderly population in the Census Divisions of Frontenac, Lennox, and Addington. Separate questionnaire surveys were administered to suppliers of health and social services (n = 80), and to a sample of urban and rural individuals aged 65+ living independently in the study area (n = 220; 81 – rural, 139 - urban). Questionnaires were distributed by four seniors' organizations and to 250 randomly selected seniors listed in the *Might's Kingston and District City Directory*.

DEFINITION OF RURAL: The urban core consisted of the City of Kingston, Kingston Township, and Pittsburg Township. The fringe included the Townships of Portland, Storringto, Loughborough, the Village of Bath, Wolfe Island, Amherst Island, Ernestown, and Howe Island. The remaining municipalities were designated as rural. In these analyses, the fringe and the rural areas were combined.

RESULTS RELATED TO RURAL AGING: While a wide range of services existed in rural areas, the rural agencies often had limited staff, constrained availability, and different eligibility criteria than the urban agencies. In terms of service use, there appeared to be rural-urban differences for some services (e.g., VON footcare – 20% rural, 10% urban; senior day centre – 8% rural, 23% urban; friendly visitors – 16% rural, 5% urban) and no differences for other services (e.g., public health unit nurse – 3% rural, 4% urban). Overall, a higher percentage of rural older adults reported service use than was evident for their urban counterparts. Rural widowed women represented the largest percentage of users. The potentially biased nature of the sample due to the over-representation of elderly women in the rural sample was noted.

CONCLUSIONS: The author argues that, while service availability is part of the explanation for service use, a more complex set of processes intertwined with age, gender, residential history, and mobility needs to be taken into account.

Joseph, A. E., & Cloutier, D. S. (1990). *The utilization of health and social services by the rural elderly: An approach and case study* **(Occasional papers in Geography, No. 15). Guelph, ON: Department of Geography, University of Guelph.**

OBJECTIVES: To present a framework for modeling the use of health and social services by rural older adults, to apply the framework in Grey County in the province of Ontario, and to assess the potential use of the framework for future research.

METHODS: The case study was carried out in six communities (Townships of Artemesia, St. Vincent, and Euphrasia; the Village of Markdale; the Town of Meaford; and the City of Owen Sound). Random samples of community-dwelling residents stratified by age group (65 - 74 and 75+) were drawn from school support lists. In-person interviews were conducted with 202 respondents in Summer 1987 and 186 respondents in Fall 1988. Services included VON nursing, VON footcare, public health nursing, physiotherapy, homemaking, meals-on-wheels, doctors, hospitals, optometrists, and dentists. The questionnaire was included in an Appendix.

DEFINITION OF RURAL: Grey County had 16% of its 1986 population aged 65+. Total population sizes varied (Township of Artemesia – 2,040; Township of St. Vincent – 1,955; Township of Euphrasia – 1,350; Town of Markdale – 1,226; Village of Meaford – 4,380; City of Owen Sound – 19,805).

RESULTS RELATED TO RURAL AGING: Use of VON nursing and use of homemaking services were highest in Owen Sound, followed by the Townships, and then Meaford/Markdale. Respondents in Owen Sound were more reliant on formal sources of information (doctor/hospital, VON/public health nurse, and phone book/brochures) compared to respondents in the other settings, suggestive of a relationship between service use and awareness of formal services. Transportation mobility status did not differ overall or by age group across the three locations (townships vs. town/village vs. city). There was virtually no difference in doctor visits across the three locations. However, the percentage of Owen Sound and township respondents reporting hospitalizations was similar and higher than those for Meaford/Markdale respondents. Differences in service-seeking behaviour existed between home and apartment dwellers. Finally, residential mobility/migration was important to consider with regard to service use.

CONCLUSIONS: The authors argue for policy decisions to be based on more than a single indicator. They call for an investigation of the range of options and outcomes of expansion of in-home support services in rural areas.

See also Cloutier Fisher, D. (2000); Cloutier Fisher, D., & Joseph, A. E. (2000); Joseph, A. E., & Cloutier, D. S. (1990); Joseph, A. E., & Cloutier, D. S. (1991); and Joseph, A. E. (1992).

Morgan, D. G., Semchuk, K. M., Stewart, N. J., & D'Arcy, C. (2002). **Rural families caring for a relative with dementia: Barriers to use of formal services.** *Social Science & Medicine, 55,* 1129-1142.

OBJECTIVES: To describe the study development process and to report selected findings regarding the use of formal supportive services such as home care and support groups by family caregivers in the province of Saskatchewan.

METHODS: The project used a multi-stage, community-based approach to facilitate the planning of a study of rural dementia care. Both an exploratory, qualitative design and a descriptive design were employed. Focus groups were held with formal and informal caregivers in the facilities and the community, with random selection used when possible. Six focus groups involved formal care providers, including Directors of Care in nursing homes, hospitals, and home care, the district's Director of Health Care Services, nursing home personnel, home care personnel, health district board members, and physicians. Two focus groups were held with family caregivers of individuals with dementia living at home or in a facility.

DEFINITION OF RURAL: The rural health district had a population of 20,000 and covered 16,000 square kilometres. The population density (1.3 persons per square kilometre), met the definition of a 'frontier' area (Wagenfeld, 2000). The seven nursing homes were located in towns with populations ranging from 345 to 1,234.

RESULTS RELATED TO RURAL AGING: Participants identified several barriers to the use of formal services. These barriers were: the stigma of dementia, lack of privacy, beliefs and attitudes, lack of awareness, financial barriers, acceptability and accessibility of services, and challenges in service delivery. Home care staff described the consequences of not using support services for caregivers. Often help was not sought until a crisis and the caregiver's health was a concern. Strategies for increasing the use of community-based services were suggested, including the need for public education about available services.

CONCLUSIONS: While caregivers experience stress in caring for a relative with dementia, home care staff perceive that caregivers are reluctant to use services that might help them. The authors call for longitudinal studies to examine the decision-making process that rural family caregivers use in determining if and when formal community-based services will be used, and to explore differences in the perspectives of family and formal caregivers.

MSHA-2 Research Group. (1999). *Follow-up to the Manitoba Study of Health and Aging (MSHA-2): Community-based Service Use in Manitoba by Older Adults and their Caregivers.* **Winnipeg, MB: Centre on Aging, University of Manitoba.**

OBJECTIVES: To examine the likelihood of community-based service use, to explore family caregivers' views about the reliability of services and their satisfaction with services, to identify older adults' and family caregivers' characteristics, and to determine reasons for not using services in the province of Manitoba.

METHODS: Data were from the 1996/97 Manitoba Study of Health and Aging (MSHA). In 1991/92, a random sample of 1,763 individuals aged 65+ was interviewed in-person and those who screened as having possible cognitive impairment were invited to a clinical assessment. Caregivers were selected based on the older persons' physical and cognitive functioning; 388 in-person interviews were completed. In 1996/97, 211 older adult-caregiver dyads completed interviews. In addition, 108 caregivers who had not been interviewed in 1991/92 and who were caring for an older adult who was cognitively intact in 1991/92 but cognitively impaired in 1996/97 were interviewed. The sample for this report (n = 293) consisted of 130 dyads involving older adults with cognitive impairment and 163 dyads where the older adult was cognitively intact. Services included homemaker/cleaning services, personal care services, in-home nursing services, home-delivered meals, day centres, day hospitals, respite services in hospitals, respite services in nursing homes, and in-home respite services.

DEFINITION OF RURAL: Winnipeg/non-Winnipeg comparisons were made. Winnipeg is the major urban centre in the province; non-Winnipeg was defined as all areas outside of Winnipeg.

RESULTS RELATED TO RURAL AGING: Older adults living in Winnipeg were no more likely to use at least one service, homemaking/cleaning services, personal care services, or in-home services than those who lived elsewhere in the province. Less than 10% of the sample had made use of the other services. Therefore, no Winnipeg/non-Winnipeg comparisons were made. Living in Winnipeg was associated with not using home-delivered meals because family/friends were providing assistance. Caregivers of older adults who resided outside Winnipeg were more likely to be unaware of day centres, day hospitals, and nursing home respite than their urban counterparts.

CONCLUSIONS: The study highlights issues related to both the use and non-use of community services in Manitoba. The authors call for more in-depth analyses on this topic.

See also Strain, L. A., & Blandford, A. A. (2002).

Racher, F. E. (2003). *Accessing Health Services: The Experience of Elderly Rural Couples*. Doctoral dissertation, University of Calgary, Calgary, AB. Retrieved from:
http://proquest.umi.com/pqdweb?index=0&did=765336951&SrchMode=1&sid
=9&Fmt=13&VInst=PROD&VType=PQD&RQT=309&VName=PQD&TS=1172605
917&clientId=12301

OBJECTIVES: To understand the experiences of elderly rural couples as they accessed health services in the southwestern region of the province of Manitoba.

METHODS: This dissertation focused on six elderly couples residing in their own homes in rural communities. The couples participated in conjoint conversational interviews to describe in detail and give meaning to their personal experiences in accessing health services. A series of interviews were conducted from April to November 2002.

DEFINITION OF RURAL: Two communities had populations of < 1,000 people and very limited health services. The other two communities had populations between 1,500 and 3,000, and hospital and physician services were available on a 24-hour basis. All were located in southwestern Manitoba.

RESULTS RELATED TO RURAL AGING: The findings were discussed in terms of the characteristics of the elderly rural couples, their experiences in accessing and using health professionals and health services, issues and concerns identified by the couples, and decision-making processes and problem solving strategies used by the couples. A descriptive theoretical couple-environment reciprocity framework for adaptation to change was developed.

CONCLUSIONS: The author argues that refocusing from individual spousal caregivers or care receivers to the couple as a unit has implications for creative and more appropriate program planning and policy development.

See also Racher, F. (1996) and Racher, F. E. (2002). Further information regarding the methodology is available in Racher, F. E., Kaufert, J. M., & Havens, B. (2000). Conjoint research interviews with frail, elderly couples: Methodological implications. Journal of Family Nursing, 6(4), 367-379.

Strain, L. A., & Blandford, A. A. (2002). Community-based services for the taking but few takers: Reasons for non-use. *Journal of Applied Gerontology, 21*(2), 220-235.

OBJECTIVES: To examine reasons for not using community-based services and the characteristics associated with these reasons among older person-caregiver dyads in the province of Manitoba.

METHODS: Data were from the Manitoba Study of Health and Aging (MSHA). In 1991/92, a random sample of 1,763 individuals aged 65+ was interviewed in person and those who screened as having possible cognitive impairment were invited to a clinical assessment. Caregivers were selected based on the older persons' physical and cognitive functioning; 388 in-person interviews were completed. In 1996/97, 211 older adult-caregiver dyads completed interviews. In addition, 108 caregivers who had not been interviewed in 1991/92 and who were caring for an older adult who was cognitively intact in 1991/92 but cognitively impaired in 1996/97 were interviewed. The sample size for these analyses was 293. Services included homemaker/cleaning services, personal care services, in-home nursing services, home-delivered meals, day centres, day hospitals, respite services in hospitals, respite services in nursing homes, and in-home respite services. Characteristics of both older adults and caregivers were examined.

DEFINITION OF RURAL: No definition of rural was provided. Comparisons were made between the major urban centre (Winnipeg) and a combined category of small cities, towns, villages, and farms.

RESULTS RELATED TO RURAL AGING: Service non-use was relatively high and varied according to the service. With the exception of hospital respite, the most frequent reason for non-use was that the older persons' health did not necessitate use. Place of residence emerged as significant for home-delivered meals, day centres, day hospitals, and nursing home respite, when controlling for other characteristics. Living in a major urban centre was associated with not using home-delivered meals because family/friends were providing assistance. Caregivers of older adults who resided outside the major urban centre were more likely to be unaware of day centres than their urban counterparts. They also were more likely to be unaware of day hospitals and nursing home respite.

CONCLUSIONS: Non-use of community-based services was prevalent among this sample of older person-caregiver dyads. Place of residence was a significant characteristic in terms of awareness of day centres, day hospitals, and nursing home respite. As day hospitals and nursing home respite were not available province-wide, these findings were not surprising. Day centres were more readily available but a different program name may have been used. The authors call for more in-depth examination of service non-use.

See also MSHA-2 Research Group (1999).

HEALTH PROMOTION/SCREENING

Health Promotion

Graham, E. L. D. (2005). Rural-urban differences in self-care behaviours of older Canadians: The effects of access to primary care. Master's thesis, Simon Fraser University, Vancouver, BC. Retrieved from: http://proquest.umi.com/pqdweb?index=1&sid=1&srchmode=1&vinst=PROD& fmt=13&startpage=1&clientid=12301&vname=PQD&did=1196390821&scaling =FULL&ts=1172597598&vtype=PQD&rqt=309&TS=1172597602&clientId=1230 1

OBJECTIVES: To explore the effects of access to primary care on the self-care of older Canadians, across five residential categories.

METHODS: This thesis research draws on a sample of 24,281 respondents aged 65+ from the master files of Statistics Canada's 2001 Canadian Community Health Survey. Variables examined included self-care behaviours (daily fruit and vegetable consumption, frequency of engagement in physical activity, daily participation in physical activity, smoking status, and weekly alcohol consumption), residential status, age, sex, marital status, education, household income, race/colour, self-perceived health status, health utility index score, number of chronic coniditons, having/not having a regular doctor, consulting any health professional, and self-perceived unmet health care needs. Logistic regression models including residential status as an independent variable were developed for each of the 5 self-care behaviours.

DEFINITION OF RURAL: Based on the 1996 census definition, rural areas were defined as "sparsely populated lands lying outside urban areas" and urban areas had "minimum population concentrations of 1,000 and a population density of at least 400 per square kilometer" (Statistics Canada, 1996, pp. 58 & 61). Rural was further classified as 'rural fringe' and 'rural area outside a CMA', while urban areas were categorized as 'urban core', 'urban fringe' and 'urban area outside CMA'.

Rural-urban residence was measured on a 5-category continuum, based on 1996 Census data and Statistics Canada definitions. These categories were urban core (large area around a census metropolitan area [CMA] or census agglomeration [CA] with a population of >10,000); urban fringe (area with population 1,000 to 9,999 in the CMA/CA boundary but not adjacent to the urban core); urban outside of a CMA/CA (not within boundaries of CMA/CA but has a population 1,000 to 9,999); rural fringe (within a CMA/CA that is not classified as urban core or urban fringe and has a population < 1,000); and rural outside a CMA/CA (all remaining areas).

RESULTS RELATED TO RURAL AGING: Self-care behaviour did not vary substantively across residential status. Several predictors of self-care emerged although none of the independent variables fully explained the association between access to primary care and self-care.

CONCLUSIONS: Since previous research employs dichotomous rural/urban comparisons, the author argues that the examination of a 5-category residential status measure is an important and unique contribution to the literature. Directions for future research are discussed.

Penning, M. J., Blandford, A. A., & Chappell, N. L. (1993). *Outcome evaluation of the "Discover Choices" community program.* **Winnipeg, MB: Centre on Aging, University of Manitoba.**

OBJECTIVES: To evaluate Discover Choices, a community-based health promotion program implemented by Health and Welfare Canada's Prairie Region office in 1988 in the provinces of Manitoba and Saskatchewan. The overall goal of the program was to encourage older adults to make informed choices about their health.

METHODS: Data for this outcome evaluation were collected prior to implementation of the program, approximately six months after initial implementation, and approximately one year later. Personal interviews were conducted with the target group who were aged 55 to 74, not working full-time, had ≤ 12 years of education, and had an annual income of ≤ $10,000 per individual or ≤ $18,000 per household (initial sample size of 720). Data for the secondary target group (aged 75+; those aged 55 to 74 with higher education, income, etc; family and friends of the primary target group; general public) were collected via mailed questionnaires at two points in time.

DEFINITION OF RURAL: Non-urban was defined as outside of Winnipeg, Saskatoon, or Regina (major centres in the two provinces).

RESULTS RELATED TO RURAL AGING: The report provided detailed findings from the outcome evaluation. Of relevance here are findings regarding urban/non-urban differences. Overall, individuals living in non-urban areas were more likely than their urban counterparts to demonstrate a change (e.g., increased knowledge of health issues and coping abilities) that was consistent with the goals and objectives of the Discover Choices program.

CONCLUSIONS: The results suggest that Discover Choices was more effective in non-urban areas than in urban areas. Further research over a longer time period is required.

See also Penning, M. J., & Chappell, N. L. (1993).

Penning, M. J., & Chappell, N. L. (1993). Health promotion and disadvantaged elderly: Rural-urban differences. In C. N. Bull (Ed.), *Aging in rural America* (1st Ed.) (pp. 117-133). Thousand Oaks, CA: Sage Publications.

OBJECTIVES: To examine whether rural-urban differences existed in the effectiveness of Discover Choices, a health promotion program launched in September 1988 by the Health Promotion Directorate of Health and Welfare Canada, in the provinces of Manitoba and Saskatchewan. The program's goal was to encourage economically disadvantaged older adults to make informed choices about their health, by increasing their knowledge of factors affecting health as well as through social support, community development, and self-development.

METHODS: Personal interviews were conducted with a random sample of 532 individuals aged 55 to 74 in Manitoba and Saskatchewan during Summer 1988, prior to program implementation. Participants were re-interviewed approximately 18 months later, following completion of all aspects of the program. Over one-half (54%) of the sample was aged 65 to 74. Forty percent lived in or near small towns or villages.

DEFINITION OF RURAL: The 5 categories of residence based on population size were < 500; 500 – 4,999; 5,000 – 99,999; 100,000 – 499,999; and 500,000+.

RESULTS RELATED TO RURAL AGING: Rural-urban differences in health knowledge were not evident at baseline or follow-up although such knowledge increased from baseline to program completion, particularly among respondents in more rural areas. Individuals in smaller rural areas attributed significantly greater importance to preventive health behaviours at both baseline and follow-up than those living in more urban areas. In terms of health locus of control, no rural-urban differences were evident in a belief in chance outcomes or a belief in the efficacy of self-care. Differences emerged for medical skepticism, with those living in smaller rural or larger urban being more skeptical than those in communities of moderate size. Greater involvement in leisure activities and greater access to informal networks also were more evident among rural than urban residents. Urban elders were advantaged in terms of their knowledge about seniors' organizations.

CONCLUSIONS: The findings offer only limited support to the view that rural older adults are comparatively disadvantaged. While rural residents were more economically disadvantaged, similar differences in health-related indicators were not evident. The authors conclude that older adults living in more rural, smaller urban areas benefited more from the Discover Choices program than those living in the larger urban areas.

See also Penning, M. J., & Chappell, N. L. (1993).

Thurston, W. E., & Blundell-Gosselin, H. J. (2005). The farm as a setting for health promotion: Results of a needs assessment in south central Alberta. *Health & Place, 11*(1), 31-43.

OBJECTIVES: To explore the farm as a setting where health promotion and prevention programs can be implemented in order to reduce injuries and health problems in the province of Alberta.

METHODS: Data were from a cross-sectional, occupational health and safety needs assessment of 347 farms in south central Alberta. Mailed questionnaires were sent out between January and March 1994 to self-identified farmers on the Farm Business Communications List Service Group, a business that compiled names of people from magazine subscription lists for marketing purposes. Both male and female farmers were included. Information was collected on the farmers' familiarity with farm living; thoughts on farm safety; people managing and working on the farm; type of commodity, economics, and equipment; off-farm work; income; and the availability of resources. Sample size was 563 for analyses relying on individual responses and 347 for farm responses. There were 94 farmers aged 60 - 69 and 36 aged 70+.

DEFINITION OF RURAL: The farms were located in four municipalities and three counties surrounding Calgary, a major urban centre in the province. The types of farming were primarily beef and grain production.

RESULTS RELATED TO RURAL AGING: Age emerged as significantly related to family income. People with a family income of less than $25,000 were more likely to be in the 60 - 69 age group while the highest income group was the 40 - 49 age group. No other age-specific differences were reported.

CONCLUSIONS: The authors emphasize the heterogeneity among these farms. They argue that this suggests few health issues for which the farm is the most appropriate setting for an intervention. They encourage an ecological approach that takes into account both the composition and context of rural settings, and one that is coordinated across the multiple settings in which rural people live and work.

Screening

Ahmad, F., Stewart, D. E., Cameron, J. I., & Hyman, I. (2001). Rural physicians' perspectives on cervical and breast cancer screening: A gender-based analysis. *Journal of Women's Health & Gender-Based Medicine, 10*(2), 201-208.

OBJECTIVES: To determine if there were significant gender differences in practices and perceptions of barriers to breast and cervical cancer screening among rural family physicians in the province of Ontario.

METHODS: This cross-sectional study involved 191 family physicians who practiced in 5 rural Public Health Units (PHU) in Ontario (response rate 53%). A mailed survey was used to collect information on sociodemographic characteristics, knowledge of screening guidelines, likelihood or intention to screen, the rate or percentage of performed screenings, and perceived barriers to screening. The physicians' mean age was 44.4 years, 68% were males, and the mean number of years in practice was 16.6 years. Practice locations within the rural PHUs were characterized as rural (29%), towns (61%), and small cities (10%).

DEFINITION OF RURAL: Rural areas had populations of < 500, towns had 500 – 10,000 population, and small cities had 10,001 – 100,000 population.

RESULTS RELATED TO RURAL AGING: Over 90% of the physicians reported that they were very likely to conduct a Pap test and clinical breast examination (CBE) during a periodic health examination, and they had high levels of confidence and comfort in performing these procedures. Female (28%) and male (23%) physicians were equally likely to conduct pap tests for patients aged 70+ while female physicians (74%) were more likely than male physicians (60%) to do so for the 50 - 69 age group. A similar pattern emerged for clinical breast examinations (patients aged 70+: 63% of female physicians, 56% of male physicians; patients aged 50 - 69: 81% of female physicians, 69% of male physicians). No gender differences were evident for mammography screening, irrespective of the patient's age. No distinctions according to the age of the patient were provided with regards to the likelihood of conducting screening, levels of confidence and comfort, and knowledge of breast and cervical cancer screening guidelines. In addition, differences according to the practice locale (rural, town, small city) were not provided although all were in rural PHUs.

CONCLUSIONS: These findings suggest that physicians' gender plays a role in sex-sensitive examinations, such as Pap tests and clinical breast examinations. The authors identify a need to facilitate physician-patient interactions for sex-sensitive cancer screening examinations by health education initiatives targeting male physicians and women themselves. The feasibility of sex-sensitive cancer screening examinations provided by a same-sex health provider also should be explored.

Calam, B., Bass, M., & Deagle, G. (1992). Pap smear screening rates: Coverage on the southern Queen Charlotte Islands. *Canadian Family Physician, 38*, 1103-1109.

OBJECTIVES: To determine the percentage of eligible females in a rural family practice population who have had adequate cervical screening, in the Queen Charlotte Islands in the province of British Columbia.

METHODS: This cross-sectional study involved chart reviews for a random sample of 196 females aged 18+ who had a chart in the local clinic's system, and who had made at least 2 visits to the clinic in the previous 5 years. Variables included age at December 31, 1990; racial origin (Haida vs. non-native); and location (central [residing in Skidegate or Queen Charlotte City] vs. outlying [requiring a ferry or more than 30 km road trip to reach the central clinic]). Women were classified as overdue for a Pap smear, never screened, or adequately screened, based on the clinic's recall protocol and the recommended screening intervals.

DEFINITION OF RURAL: Queen Charlotte City is on the Queen Charlotte Islands, 150 kilometres off the northwest coast of British Columbia. A 3-physician group practice offers both outpatient and hospital care and serves a population of approximately 300, including Haida Indians.

RESULTS RELATED TO RURAL AGING: Significantly fewer Haida women than non-native women had adequate cervical screening. Among the 60+ age group, 82% of the non-natives and 50% of the natives were categorized as adequately screened.

CONCLUSIONS: The authors speculate that screening efforts, and particularly recall letters, may work best for non-native women. They call for qualitative research to elucidate cultural factors that could aid in planning screening programs that would be accepted by all women at risk in the community.

Calam, B., Norgrove, L., Brown, D., & Wilson, M. A. (1999). Pap screening clinics with native women in Skidegate, Haida Gwaii: Need for innovation. *Canadian Family Physician, 45*, 355-360.

OBJECTIVES: To design, implement, and evaluate a pilot program, in consultation with community representatives, in order to address the Pap screening needs of First Nations women 40 years and older on a rural reserve in the province of British Columbia.

METHODS: A Pap screening outreach program was developed that marked a departure from the usual screening approach in the community. The main components of program were: identification of key links to the population, consultation with the community to design an outreach process, identification of underscreened women, implementation of community Pap screening clinics conducted by 2 female physicians at the Skidegate Health Centre, and evaluation of the pilot program. Two half-day Pap clinics were held in March 1992 with invitations sent to women aged 40+ who were identified as 'overdue' for Pap smears through chart reviews.

DEFINITION OF RURAL: The communities of Haidi Gwaii, Queen Charlotte Islands, are rural settlements located off the northwest coast of British Columbia. Three salaried family physicians provide outpatient medical care out of a clinic based in Queen Charlotte city. Physicians also visit a community health centre seven kilometres away on the Haida reserve of Skidegate. The health centre is staffed by two community health representatives, nurses, and other support personnel.

RESULTS RELATED TO RURAL AGING: There were 74 native females aged 40+ residing in Skidegate at the time of the pilot program; 30 were aged 60+. Twenty-eight met the inclusion criteria, including 17 aged 60+ (61%). Of those aged 60+, only 43% were adequately screened. Of the 28 meeting the inclusion critieria, 27 were identified as overdue for Pap screening (one woman whose screening status was unknown could not be contacted). Four additional women could not be contacted, leaving a 'viable' sample of 23. Twelve of those women agreed to participate and 11 kept appointments. The 11 females were screened at the Pap clinic, for a participation rate of 48%. This resulted in an increase of 15% over the previously recorded screening rate for this population. Age-related information for the 11 participating females was not provided. All participants indicated that the outreach clinic was a better venue than individual appointments at the main clinic.

CONCLUSIONS: Community consultations led to the development of a small-scale outreach program for a population at risk for cervical cancer. The First Nations community health representatives were key links for the process that involved family physicians and office staff at a local clinic on a rural reserve. More screening clinics of this type and evaluation for sustainability are proposed.

Leslie, W. D., MacWilliam, L., Lix, L., Caetano, P., & Finlayson, G. S. (2005). A population-based study of osteoporosis testing and treatment following introduction of a new bone densitometry service. *Osteoporosis International, 16*(7), 773-782.

OBJECTIVES: To evaluate the change in physician osteoporosis testing and prescribing, following introduction of a dual-energy x-ray absorptiometry (DXA) testing service in a geographic region that had previously had very limited access in the province of Manitoba.

METHODS: Data were from the Manitoba Health administrative database. Age-adjusted annual bone testing rates in women aged 50+ from 1995 to 2002 were calculated as were rates for dispensing of new osteoporosis prescriptions from 1996 to 2002. The rates were stratified by geographical location (urban and rural health regions serviced by the new program in 1999 [new] and the remaining urban and rural health regions which had relatively unchanged DXA access [control]). Regression models of DXA testing rates and osteoporosis prescription rates were created for all older women in these regions. Selected analyses focused solely on the 65+ age group.

DEFINITION OF RURAL: The urban regions consisted of the Winnipeg and Brandon health regions. The remaining health regions serviced by the programs were considered as rural.

RESULTS RELATED TO RURAL AGING: There was a statistically significant increase in bone density testing and BMD-guided osteoporosis treatment in the urban (new) and rural (new) regions following introduction of the DXA testing service, relative to the control regions.

CONCLUSIONS: These results suggest that the local availability of the bone density testing service led to an increase in objective test-guided therapy with some reduction in the use of empiric and preventive strategies. There was a neutral effect on overall use of these agents.

Tatla, R. K., Paszat, L. F., Bondy, S. J., Chen, Z., Chiarelli, A. M., & Mai, V. (2003). Socioeconomic status and returning for a second screen in the Ontario breast screening program. *The Breast, 12*(4), 237-246.

OBJECTIVES: To examine the relationship between geographically derived socioeconomic status (SES) and returning for a second breast screen among women recommended for biennial mammography by the Ontario Breast Cancer Screening Program (OBSP) in the province of Ontario. The OBSP is an organized screening program with 90 sites; the target population is women aged 50+ who have no acute breast symptoms, and no history of breast cancer or breast augmentation.

METHODS: This retrospective cohort study involved 57,902 women aged 50 to 69 who were initially screened between January 1, 1995 and December 31, 1997 by the OBSP. The sample included 10,873 women aged 60 - 64 and 9,394 aged 65 - 69. Women were considered to have returned for a second screen if they returned within 3 years of their initial screen. Descriptive/clinical information was collected by the OBSP at the time of booking an appointment and at the initial screen. Explanatory factors in this analysis included age, rurality, preferred language, initial mammography results, previous mammography history, and referral by a health professional.

DEFINITION OF RURAL: Consistent with the 1996 Census definition, urban areas were defined as having a minimum population of 1,000 and a population density of 400 per square kilometre. Rural areas were the territories outside urban areas.

RESULTS RELATED TO RURAL AGING: Twenty-three percent of the sample resided in rural regions. Among the group aged 60 - 64 at the time of the initial screen, 75% of the urban and 79% of the rural women had returned for a second screen within 3 years. The corresponding figures for the group aged 65 - 69 at the time of the initial screen were 74% urban and 79% rural. Socioeconomic status (SES) was related to returning for a second screen. However, rurality modified that relationship, a finding not previously reported. Compared to women in the highest ('richest') quintile, urban women in the first and second quintile were less likely to return; this relationship was not found in rural women. Younger women (50 - 64) were more likely to return for the second screening than those aged 65+. Overall, women residing in rural areas were more likely to return for a second screening compared to their urban counterparts.

CONCLUSIONS: The authors note that rurality has not been previously identified as a modifier of the relationship between SES and returning for a second screen. They argue that low SES women aged 50 - 69, particularly in urban areas, need to be specifically targeted to increase their likelihood of re-attendance for breast cancer screening within an organized program.

Worrall, G. (1991). Screening healthy people for diabetes: Is it worthwhile? *The Journal of Family Practice, 33*(2), 155-160.

OBJECTIVES: To estimate the prevalence of previously unknown diabetes mellitus in a rural, apparently healthy population aged 40+ in the province of Newfoundland.

METHODS: The study was conducted between July 1, 1989 and January 1, 1990 in the Gander and District Hospital Board area. A 1 in 5 random sample of healthy patients aged 40+ attending six rural family physician offices was selected from the active patients' files. These individuals were invited to have their fasting plasma glucose (FPG) level tested with a reflectance glucometre. If the FPG was $\geq$ 7.8 mmol/L (140.5 mg/dL), a second FPG test was done on a later day. The sample of 1,264 patients contained 139 known patients with diabetes. Of the remaining 1,125 patients, 936 (83%) were tested.

DEFINITION OF RURAL: Gander is a town located in the northeastern part of the island of Newfoundland. Its 2001 population was 9,651, with a population density of 92.6 persons per square mile.

RESULTS RELATED TO RURAL AGING: On the first test, 23 patients had an elevated FPG level but only 9 did so on the second test. One new patient with diabetes was found for each 15 patients already diagnosed; the prevalence of unknown diabetes in the study population was 0.7%. The author reports that, as a result of this survey, the estimated prevalence of diabetes in the population aged 40+ rose marginally from 11.0% to 11.7%, and the estimated prevalence for the entire population rose from 4.4% to 4.6%. The prevalence of diabetes increased with age, for both males and females, with a marked increase after the age of 55.

CONCLUSIONS: The authors conclude that routine screening for diabetes mellitus in otherwise healthy patients aged 40+ is not worthwhile and argue that such screening should be restricted to high-risk groups. These results from one rural area of Newfoundland must be interpreted with care and cannot be considered as generalizable.

COMMENTS: **Martínez Acevedo, M., de la Fuente, L., Ferreras, M.R., & Turbián, J.L. (1992). Screening for diabetes.** *Journal of Family Practice, 34*(42), 397. In their letter to the Editor, these authors presented data from an epidemiological study of diabetes mellitus in a neighbourhood of Toledo, Spain. In their study, 3% of people examined were diabetic; 67% were unaware of their diabetes. They argued that the conditions under which basic medical care is carried out can be important in determining the usefulness of a screening test and urged caution in generalizing from Worrall's results.

INFORMAL CARE/SUPPORT

Caregiving

Bédard, M., Koivuranta, A., & Stuckey, A. (2004). **Health impact on caregivers of providing informal care to a cognitively impaired older adult: Rural versus urban settings.** *Canadian Journal of Rural Medicine, 9*(1), 15-23.

OBJECTIVES: To investigate potential rural-urban differences in the health impact on caregivers of cognitively impaired individuals in the northern area of the province of Ontario.

METHODS: This descriptive study involved convenience samples of caregivers of older adults with possible or probable Alzheimer's disease or other forms of dementia from rural (n = 20) and urban (n = 17) northern Ontario. Caregivers were identified through local agencies, advertising, and networks. Data obtained from the caregivers included: demographic information; activities of daily living and frequency of behaviour problems (Dysfunctional Behaviour Rating Instrument [DBRI]) of care recipients; the type and quantity of supports available and used by caregivers; global health indices; caregiver burden (Zarit); and healthy behaviours (Health-Promoting Lifestyle Profile). The caregivers were predominantly female (rural - 75%, urban - 82%). Only 25% of the rural caregivers were spouses; the corresponding figure for the urban group was 41%. Being employed full-time was reported for 7 rural and 1 urban caregivers.

DEFINITION OF RURAL: The rural community was a town with < 15,000 residents and located approximately a 1.5–hour drive from the urban centre. It had a 57-bed hospital with emergency coverage; specialists' services were provided by out-of-town physicians. The urban community had a population of approximately 125,000. Services included an acute hospital, rehabilitation/chronic care hospital, a psychiatric hospital, and several services for older adults and their caregivers.

RESULTS RELATED TO RURAL AGING: Most caregivers reported good health. Personal burden tended to be higher than role burden. The health behaviours engaged in most frequently by rural caregivers were participating in leisure/physical activities, reporting physical signs/symptoms, being aware of what is most important in life, and eating breakfast. For the urban caregivers, the top four behaviours were eating breakfast, looking forward to the future, being aware of what is most important in life, and accepting things one cannot change. Rural caregivers had access to fewer formal supports but did not report greater burden, poorer health status, or fewer healthy behaviours than urban caregivers. Small sample sizes limit the findings.

CONCLUSIONS: The authors argue that rural caregivers may have special needs regarding the management of behaviour problems exhibited by care recipients and in the promotion of healthy behaviours for themselves. They call for future research using better sampling techniques to identify the needs of rural caregivers.

Hallman, B. C. (1997). *The Spatiality of Eldercare: Towards a Gendered Geography of the Aging Family.* Doctoral dissertation, University of Guelph, Guelph, ON. Retrieved from: http://proquest.umi.com/pqdweb?index=0&did=736877301&SrchMode=1&sid =10&Fmt=13&VInst=PROD&VType=PQD&RQT=309&VName=PQD&TS=117260 6003&clientId=12301

OBJECTIVES: To examine gendered spatial behaviour and place context in relation to family caregiving to elderly relatives (eldercare) in Canada.

METHODS: This dissertation research draws on data from the 1991 Work & Family survey and the 1995 Work & Eldercare survey conducted by the Work and Eldercare Research Group of the Canadian Aging Research Network (CARNET). The Work & Family sample consisted of 1,149 employed men and women who reported that, at least once in the prior 6 months, they provided assistance to one elderly relative living independently in the community (n = 836) or to two elderly relatives living at the same location (n = 313). The Work & Eldercare sample consisted of 163 employed caregivers who did not co-reside with the elderly relatives and who indicated in the 1991 survey that they were willing to participate in further projects; 85% were aged 36 to 55. The effects of caregiver gender, time-distance, and elder's place of residence on eldercare were examined. An analysis of aggregate patterns and relationships was undertaken as well as a qualitative analysis of individual caregiver comments and selected caregiver profiles emphasizing the experience of caregiving. Time-distance was a measure of the geographical separation between the caregiver and the elderly relative (1 - 30 minutes, 31 - 120 minutes, > 120 minutes). Information was obtained on the size of the community in which the elderly relative lived; 22% resided in rural communities/small towns.

DEFINITION OF RURAL: Population size was used to differentiate between communities: rural communities/small towns with populations of < 10,000, urban places of 10,000 to 99,999, and larger urban centres with populations of 100,000+.

RESULTS RELATED TO RURAL AGING: Several research questions were addressed. Of relevance here are the findings regarding community type. Most of the caregivers were providing care to a female relative (88% rural, 92% small urban, and 88% large urban). There was virtually no difference in the caregivers' gender across the three community types. No significant place effects were evident for the provision of any of four eldercare tasks groups, with the exception of male caregivers providing help with household chores and maintenance for elderly relatives living in large urban centres. There was a trend for female caregivers with rural elderly relatives to have the highest rates of task performance. The average frequency of assistance with personal care decreased with increasing community size but no statistically significant differences were evident for transportation/shopping, household chores and maintenance, or emotional support. Feelings of obligation to care did not vary significantly by place nor did the availability of other family members to care for the elderly relatives. Comments by respondents who identified place or community effects on caregiving behaviour noted service limitations in their elderly relatives' communities but also the supportive nature of some communities and neighbourhoods.

CONCLUSIONS: Place context did not appear to have any major effect on eldercare provisions as studied here. The dissertation concludes with a discussion of the social policy implications of the research, theoretical constructs from structuration theory and social feminism, and suggestions for further research.

Hawranik, P. (1985). Caring for aging parents: Divided allegiances. *Journal of Gerontological Nursing, 11*(10), 19-22.

OBJECTIVES: To assess the relationship between the coping strategies of family caregivers and the support systems of the caregiver and parent, the health status of the elderly parent, and the social adjustment of the elderly parent in a rural sample in the province of Manitoba.

METHODS: This exploratory study involved families in one rural region of Manitoba. Both the elderly parent and the primary child caregiver were interviewed. The Ways of Coping Checklist was completed by the primary caregiver. A second questionnaire was completed by the elderly parent and included the Index of Incapacity and the Social Adjustment Scale. Of the families studied, 19 were receiving formal services and 23 were receiving informal services or no services at all. The 18 families with an elderly parent with organic brain disease were excluded from the analyses presented here as the parent was unable to participate. The majority of both children and parents were female (no percentages provided). The ages of the caregivers ranged from 30 to 74 years; parents ranged in age from 70 to 99 years.

DEFINITION OF RURAL: No definition of rural was provided.

RESULTS RELATED TO RURAL AGING: No relationships were found between the caregivers' coping strategies and support systems, parent's health status, or parent's social adjustment (data not shown). There were few differences in the coping strategies employed by the different groups. Most of the caregivers were resigned to the stressful situation they encountered in caring for their parents.

CONCLUSIONS: The implications for health professionals are discussed. The author calls for further research on coping strategies of caregivers.

Hildebrand, E. A. (1986). *Adult children as caregivers to elderly parents: A Mennonite exploration.* **Master's thesis, University of Manitoba, Winnipeg, MB.**

OBJECTIVES: To examine the parental support system of a rural Mennonite population in terms of the type of support provided to the parent by an adult child, the quantity of services that are provided, the quality of the intergenerational relationship, and the strain associated with the caregiver role in a small southern town in the province of Manitoba.

METHODS: This thesis research involved separate interviews with a purposive sample of 37 respondents (15 adult children aged 40+, 15 parents aged 68+, and 7 children-in-law aged 42+) to determine the different perceptions of the caregiving situation. These individuals were from a relatively liberal and socially integrated church conference. A separate group of 14 members from a more conservative church (8 adult children and 6 parents) were interviewed as an adult children panel and a parent panel. Type of support included emotional support and companionship, transportation, household repairs, financial assistance, help with housekeeping, shopping, yard work, decision-making, business and financial matters, and care during times of illness. The Zarit Burden Interview was used to measure caregiver burden.

DEFINITION OF RURAL: Steinbach is located 38 miles southeast of Winnipeg and had a population of approximately 7,000 at the time of the study. Almost 80% of the population was Mennonite.

RESULTS RELATED TO RURAL AGING: The majority of adult children provided both affective and instrumental support to their parents. Emotional support was viewed by both parents and adult children as valued and vital. The low level of caregiving strain reported by adult children was partially attributed to strong affective ties which were both in evidence and expressed by both generations. One of the faith principles of the more conservative group was a strong belief in self-denial; this adult children group reported virtually no feelings of burden in the areas of a lack of personal time or interference with social life although slight feelings of burden were evident in terms of trying to provide both parent and family, a lack of sharing of caregiving responsibilities by other family members, and feeling that the parent was somewhat dependent.

CONCLUSIONS: The relative homogeneity of the findings was attributed to both cultural and religious factors associated with the Mennonite belief system such as the norms of filial responsibility, strong family ties, and mutual aid and service for others. Methodological considerations including the small sample size and sample bias are discussed. The author identified areas for future research.

Hubley, A. M., Hemingway, D., & Michalos, A. C. (2003). A comparison of older informal caregivers and non-caregivers living in non-metropolitan areas. *Social Indicators Research, 61,* **241-258.**

OBJECTIVES: To examine differences in the quality of life, health, and social support between older married caregivers and non-caregivers and to examine differences in age identity in the northern region of British Columbia.

METHODS: Data were from a quality of life survey of 875 individuals aged 55+ living in northern British Columbia's non-metropolitan communities. Questionnaires were provided to a number of agencies/organizations such as seniors' organizations, recreation centres, and native health centres, and were included in a freely distributed seniors' newspaper. The analyses focused on quality of life, health (SF-36), social support, and age identity. The sample was limited to married individuals aged 65+, due to an interest in older adults and to the results of preliminary analyses that indicated that marital status was a potentially confounding variable in the caregiver/non-caregiver comparisons. The sample consisted of 239 married, community-dwelling respondents ranging in age from 65 to 86 years, with an average age of 71.8 years. There were 63 caregivers and 176 non-caregivers; 49% were female. Care receivers were primarily spouses (85%).

DEFINITION OF RURAL: No definition of rural was provided. Reference was made to the non-metropolitan communities where the study was undertaken.

RESULTS RELATED TO RURAL AGING: Older married caregivers and non-caregivers were not significantly different in terms of quality of life, self-reported health, and most aspects of social support and age identity. Caregivers were less satisfied than non-caregivers with their romantic relationships although there was no difference in satisfaction with their living partners. Caregivers felt older mentally than non-caregivers but there were no differences in social or physical age.

CONCLUSIONS: Caregiver status alone does not appear to be related to lower quality of life, poorer mental and physical health, lower levels of social support, or older age identities. The authors speculate that their caregiving group may not have high levels of demands as caregivers were not experiencing caregiver stress, thereby explaining the lack of differences between the caregivers and non-caregivers.

Keating, N., Fast, J., Frederick, J., Cranswick, K., & Perrier, C. (1999). *Eldercare in Canada: Context, content and consequences* (Catalogue No. 89-570-XPE). **Ottawa, ON: Statistics Canada.**

OBJECTIVES: To describe the nature, extent, and consequences of informal eldercare for seniors with high care needs in Canada.

METHODS: Data were from Statistics Canada's 1996 General Social Survey (GSS) for the community-dwelling seniors and from the 1994/95 National Population Health Survey (NPHS) for seniors living in institutional settings. The GSS analyses involved all respondents aged 65+ irrespective of whether they received assistance (n = 5,952) and all respondents who provided care to a person aged 65+ (n = 1,366). Assistance was defined as help with tasks because of a long-term health problem, because of a temporarily difficult time, or because of the way things were done in the senior's household. Eldercare was defined as assistance provided to someone aged 65+ because of the individual's long-term health or physical limitation. Tasks included meal preparation and clean up, house cleaning, laundry and sewing, household maintenance and outside work, shopping for groceries or other necessities, transportation, banking or bill paying, personal care, emotional care, and/or checking up to make sure the older adult is okay.

DEFINITION OF RURAL: Rural residence was defined as living in rural fringe areas and rural areas outside of a census metropolitan area (CMA). Urban residence included living in urban core, urban fringe, and urban areas outside CMAs.

RESULTS RELATED TO RURAL AGING: Of relevance here are the findings related to urban/rural residence. There were no differences in the proportions of rural and urban residents with regards to four groups of assistance (assistance with at least one task as a result of a long-term health problem, assistance with at least one task as a result of a temporarily difficult time, assistance with at least one task as a result of 'the way they do things', and no assistance). Approximately 20% of seniors in each group lived in rural areas. When examining the group who received assistance for a long-term health problem, compared to other groups and controlling for other factors, rural dwellers were more likely than urban residents to receive assistance for long-term health problems. About 25% of caregivers lived in rural areas. There were no rural-urban differences in the proportion of male caregivers and the number of hours of care males provided. Rural female caregivers were somewhat more predominant and provided slightly more hours of care than their urban counterparts. In addition, rural women gave slightly more hours of care. However, in the regression analyses, there were no rural-urban differences for meal preparation, housekeeping, home maintenance and repair, shopping for groceries, transportation, or personal care. Among female caregivers, there were significant rural-urban differences in the time spent on bill paying (rural women spent more time) but this was not evident for males. In terms of consequences, rural female caregivers had higher levels of guilt and had fewer potential economic opportunities than the urban counterparts but there were no rural-urban differences for male caregivers. No rural-urban differences were evident for either males or females with regard to socioeconomic consequences, burden, or job adjustments.

CONCLUSIONS: The findings indicate that older adults receive both assistance and care from members of their informal networks. The authors argue that Canadians are actively involved in caring for seniors in need, and for many, the cost of caring is high.

Keefe, J. M. (1996). *The impact of community context on the relationship between employment and caregiving among Canadian women.* **Doctoral dissertation, University of Guelph, Guelph, ON. Retrieved from:**
http://proquest.umi.com/pqdweb?index=0&did=736559671&SrchMode=1&sid=11&Fmt=13&VInst=PROD&VType=PQD&RQT=309&VName=PQD&TS=1172606103&clientId=12301

OBJECTIVES: To examine the importance of community context in understanding the relationship between employment and caring for elderly relatives for women aged 30 to 64 in Canada.

METHODS: This dissertation was divided into three chapters, each with its own research questions, methods, and findings. Chapter 1 focused on the likelihood of women being employed and helping elderly kin within different community contexts, drawing on data from Statistics Canada's 1990 General Social Survey (GSS). In Chapter 2, the likelihood of combining employment and helping elderly kin in rural areas in three Canadian regions was examined using data from the GSS and the 1991 Census of Canada. In Chapter 3, the balancing of caring for elderly kin and paid work among Canadian women was examined, drawing on the 1991/92 Canadian Work and Family Survey.

DEFINITION OF RURAL: In Chapter 1, rural areas/small towns included nucleated communities of < 10,000 as well as the dispersed population in the countryside while urban areas represented an amalgamation of census agglomerations (CAs – population 10,000 to 99,999) with census metropolitan areas (CMAs – population 100,000+). In Chapter 2, the census categories of urban (1,000+) and rural (< 1,000) were used. In Chapter 3, rural areas/villages with < 2,500 population or dispersed populations in rural townships or municipalities were combined with towns having a population of 2,500 - 9,999 and compared to urban centres with populations of 10,000+.

RESULTS RELATED TO RURAL AGING: Analysis of the GSS data revealed rural-urban differences in providing help to elderly parents only among non-employed women. The complexity of this relationship was demonstrated when regional variations were considered. The rural-urban differences in the likelihood that employed women provided help to elderly parents in the Atlantic region were opposite to those in British Columbia. Reporting only national data had the effect of averaging these relationships. The analysis of employment patterns within more specific categorizations of rural using the 1991 Canadian Census revealed that employment opportunities decreased as the size of the community decreased. Using data from the Canadian Work and Family Survey, predictors of work and family outcomes and stress were found to be different in rural compared to urban contexts. Factors associated with caregiving to older adults tended to be the most significant predictors of work and family outcomes in rural areas, while childcare responsibilities tended to be the most significant predictor in urban areas.

CONCLUSIONS: The author argues that future research in the area of work and eldercare needs to consider the distinctive characteristics of rural social and economic structures, especially as manifested among different regions of the country. Policy implications and strategies for assisting employed caregivers are discussed.

See also Keefe, J. (1999).

Keefe, J. (1999). The likelihood of combining employment and helping elderly kin in rural and urban areas among Canadian regions. *Canadian Journal of Regional Science, 20*(3), 367-387.

OBJECTIVES: To understand the likelihood of women combining employment with helping elderly parents in rural versus urban contexts in Canada.

METHODS: Data were from Statistics Canada's 1990 General Social Survey (GSS), a household survey of non-institutionalized individuals aged 15+ living in the 10 Canadian provinces. These analyses focused on the sub-sample of women aged 30 to 64 (n = 3,643), weighted to be representative of female Canadians in that age group. Only three regions, Atlantic Canada (Newfoundland, Nova Scotia, New Brunswick, and Prince Edward Island), British Columbia, and Ontario were compared. Employment status (employed vs. not employed) and the nature of employment were examined. Proximity to elderly parents and the provision of help to elderly parents were included in the analysis.

DEFINITION OF RURAL: Rural areas and small towns were defined as nucleated communities of < 10,000 persons as well as dispersed populations in the countryside. The latter category was constructed using Statistics Canada's postal code conversion file. Urban areas represented an amalgamation of census agglomerations (CAs – population 10,000 to 99,999) and census metropolitan areas (CMAs – population 100,000+).

RESULTS RELATED TO RURAL AGING: In all three regions, rural women were less likely to be employed than their urban counterparts. Employed rural women in the Atlantic region were far less likely to be employed full-year and more likely to be employed in jobs that do not allow them sufficient weeks to qualify for unemployment insurance than those in urban regions. Similar trends were evident for British Columbia and Ontario but the measure of association was not as strong. At a national level, women in rural areas were slightly more likely than urban women to have proximate elderly kin although the relationship was weak. Regional variations existed, with rural women in the Atlantic region being more likely than the urban women to have kin nearby. In British Columbia, the opposite was true, while in Ontario the association was too weak to warrant importance. Significant relationships between providing assistance to elderly parents and community context, while controlling for employment status within the three regions, were evident. Regional variations once again emerged.

CONCLUSIONS: National generalizations about the likelihood of women being employed and willing to provide help to elderly parents within rural versus urban areas overlook the effects of region. There were variations across the country. Implications for policy are presented.

See also Keefe, J. M. (1996).

Keefe, J. (1999). *The nature of caregiving by community context: A profile of informal caregiving in Canada's rural and urban areas.* **Halifax, NS: Department of Gerontology, Mount Saint Vincent University.**

OBJECTIVES: To obtain a profile of the nature of family caregiving in rural and urban areas in order to determine differences in the type of services performed by family caregivers, in the amount of care provided, and in their experience of burden, as well as a profile of the nature of caregiving received by elderly persons in rural versus urban areas including the type and amount of care received from family caregivers in Canada.

METHODS: This report begins with a review of the literature, followed by analysis of data from Statistics Canada's 1996 General Social Survey (GSS). Two subsamples were selected for the analyses: respondents aged 65+ (n = 5,952) including 672 older individuals who received assistance from informal support only because of their long-term health problem or disability; and informal caregivers who provide assistance to individuals aged 65+ because of a long-term health problem or disability (n = 1,038). The amount of informal support and the source of assistance (informal, formal, a mix of informal and formal) with seven types of tasks were examined (meal preparation, housecleaning, house maintenance, grocery shopping, transportation, banking/bill paying, and personal care).

DEFINITION OF RURAL: Rural areas/small towns included the nucleated communities of < 10,000 and the dispersed population in the countryside. Urban areas represented an amalgamation of census agglomerations (CAs – population 10,000 to 99,999) with census metropolitan areas (CMAs – population 100,000+). Rural-urban differences in the province of Prince Edward Island (PEI) were not accessible due to confidentiality issues; as over half of the population was rural, PEI respondents were considered as rural residents.

RESULTS RELATED TO RURAL AGING: Few rural-urban differences were evident in the amount or source of assistance received by these older adults. Rural-urban residence did not emerge as a significant factor in a regression analysis that examined the number of tasks with which elderly persons received help from informal supports. Significant regional differences emerged. From the perspective of the caregiver, caregivers in rural areas were slightly more likely to be providing assistance to elderly persons. Discrepancies in rural-urban differences in the amount of care provided were found, depending on the measure employed.

CONCLUSIONS: The author concludes that there were very few concrete findings to support the creation of a distinctive policy for elderly persons or their caregivers in rural areas. Areas for potential policy implications and for future research are discussed, as are the limitations due to the dichotomization of rural and urban.

See also Keefe, J., & Side, K. (2003).

Keefe, J., & Side, K. (2003). *Net loss population settlement patterns and maintenance of rural health status: A case study in Atlantic Canada.* **Halifax, NS: Mount Saint Vincent University. Retrieved from:**
<u>http://www.msvu.ca/mdcaging/PDFs/ruralhealth.pdf</u>

OBJECTIVES: To analyze patterns of social support among rural Canadians and to inform policy directions toward sustainable and healthy rural communities within an Atlantic Canada context.

METHODS: This report draws on various Statistics Canada data sources, including Statistic Canada's 1996 General Social Survey (GSS). Data from a case study of Parrsboro, Nova Scotia also were discussed.

DEFINITION OF RURAL: In the GSS analyses, the Census definition was used, where rural included all individuals living in the rural fringes of census metropolitan areas (CMAs) and census agglomerations (CAs) as well as individuals living in rural areas outside CMAs or CAs (i.e., population living outside urban places (places with population ≥ 1,000) or outside places with population densities of ≥ 400 people per square kilometre. In the GSS, respondents from Prince Edward Island were considered as rural residents.

RESULTS RELATED TO RURAL AGING: Of relevance here are the findings on the provision and receipt of unpaid care or assistance to older adults. In the 2001 Census, one-fifth of rural Atlantic Canadians reported that they provided such care, an increase of 1% from 1996. Women were more likely to be providing this care than men. Older rural Canadians were significantly more likely to give and to receive assistance with both household and non-household activities of daily living and with emotional support. Assistance due to a long-term health problem or physical limitations was provided for an average of 2.9 tasks by the 50 - 64 age group compared to an average of 1.3 among the 80+ age group. In terms of receiving of assistance, the 80+ aged group received assistance on the highest number of tasks.

CONCLUSIONS: The authors outline policy considerations, and urge analysts and decision makers to consider inter- and intra-regional variations as well as rural and regional lenses when developing social and economic policy.

See also Keefe, J. (1999).

MacRae, H. M. (1995). Women and caring: Constructing self through others. *Journal of Women & Aging, 7*(1/2), 145-167.

OBJECTIVES: To explore the meaning of caring and the construction of a meaningful component of self-identity, from the perspective of rural elderly women in the province of Nova Scotia.

METHODS: Data were from a study designed to examine self-identity in later life and the ways it was maintained. In-depth, semi-structured interviews were conducted with 142 women aged 65 to 98 living in a small town in Nova Scotia. Respondents lived in three different settings: 101 women in their own homes or private apartments in the community, 31 women residing in two local apartment complexes, and 10 women living in the 'well elderly' wing of the local nursing home. Individuals in their own homes were selected by knocking on every fifth house on every street in the town while a random sample was taken of the apartment dwellers. Virtually all nursing home residents on the wing were included. Many of the women (64%) were widowed and few had worked outside the home at full-time jobs. A modified version of Kuhn's TST (20-statement-test) or the *Who am I?* test was completed by 100 of the women; additional data were obtained from more explicit questions and direct probes during the interview.

DEFINITION OF RURAL: The town had a population of approximately 6,500 residents at the time of the study.

RESULTS RELATED TO RURAL AGING: Although the vast majority of the respondents scored high on self-esteem and presented an overall positive sense of self (data not shown), answering the question *Who am I?* was often difficult as these women were not accustomed to thinking about themselves. Their self-identity was built around relationships and experience rather than statuses and formal roles. The women described themselves in terms of 'doing for others', personal attributes such as 'helpful', 'good-hearted', 'generous', and 'kind', and familial roles as wife, mother, homemaker, and grandmother. Caring for others was a route to self-meaning. The importance of the historical, social, and cultural context was discussed. The community in which these women resided was viewed as a positive resource for both identity construction and its maintenance.

CONCLUSIONS: The focus on interpersonal relationships with others appears to be a wise identity investment for later life. The author argues that women learn to care through a socialization process and not, as the psychological view holds, because caring is a naturally feminine activity. Future research is needed to explore the nature and basis of identity throughout the life course and the importance people attach to their social statuses and roles, relationships, and other life experiences.

See also MacRae, H. (1996).

Smale, B., & Dupuis, S. L. (2004). *In their own voices: A profile of dementia caregivers in Ontario.* **Waterloo, ON: Murray Alzheimer Research and Education Program, University of Waterloo. Retrieved from:** http://www.marep.uwaterloo.ca/PDF/InTheirOwnVoices1-SurveyResults.pdf

OBJECTIVES: To provide a comprehensive profile of caregivers of persons with Alzheimer's disease, including their involvement in providing assistance in activities of daily living, their perceptions and use of formal community support services and informal social resources, perceived barriers to their use, and the various impacts felt and coping resources drawn on as part of their caregiving, in the province of Ontario.

METHODS: This study was comprised of three stages. Stage 1 involved questionnaires completed by a sample of informal community-based caregivers of persons with Alzheimer's disease or a related dementia still living in the community or recently moved to a long-term care facility (within 6 months of the questionnaire). Questionnaires were distributed to members and service users by about 100 selected agencies and over 60 long-term care facilities. The study was promoted through Ontario's Community Care Access Centres and the local media. Approximately 11,000 questionnaires were distributed; 2,244 were returned and completed in a useable form, yielding a response rate of approximately 20%. Stage 2 consisted of 14 focus groups with caregivers and care providers. Stage 3 also relied on focus group participants.

DEFINITION OF RURAL: Communities were divided into rural (population < 10,000), mid-sized (population 10,000 to 99,999), and urban communities (population 100,000+).

RESULTS RELATED TO RURAL AGING: This report from Stage 1 included a comparison of the caregivers' use and perceptions of support services based on the size of the community in which the care receiver lived (rural 24%, mid-sized 37%, urban 40%). Overall, community size appeared to have little impact. No significant differences according to community size were found for the likelihood of providing assistance with basic or instrumental activities of daily living (with the exception of yard work), the provision of emotional support, arrangement of recreational activities, making social visits/providing companionship, or doing telephone check-ups. There also were no differences in the use of community support services, with the exception of adult day programs and transportation services that were used less often by those whose care receivers resided in mid-sized rather than rural or urban communities. Receiving help with caregiving tasks from friends/neighbours was slightly less likely in mid-sized communities while direct support from religious groups was slightly lower in the urban communities. Some differences according to community size were evident with regard to the perceived need of support services. In-home respite services and support groups other than Alzheimer's disease support groups were more likely to be identified by caregivers of individuals in rural communities while the reverse was true for homemaker services. A significantly higher percentage of caregivers of urban care receivers reported several barriers to accessing community support services compared to their counterparts caring for individuals in rural or mid-sized communities.

CONCLUSIONS: Caregivers caring for individuals in rural communities used community support services as much as those caring for residents of larger communities. They also generally did not perceive the barriers to their access to be as constraining as those in larger communities. The authors speculate that community size may not effectively capture the situation of those caregivers in more remote areas who may have greater difficulty accessing services.

Note: Two reports provide details on the focus groups conducted with rural and urban caregivers: Smale, B., & Dupuis, S. L. (2004). Stage 2: The Focus Groups; Smale, B., & Dupuis, S. L. (2004). Stage 3 : Working Focus Groups. Retrieved from:
http://www.marep.uwaterloo.ca/research/

Perceptions/Beliefs about Caregiving

Bond, J. B., Jr., Harvey, C. D. H., & Hildebrand, E. A. (1987). Familial support of the elderly in a rural Mennonite community. *Canadian Journal on Aging, 6*(1), 7-17.

OBJECTIVES: To investigate perceptions of caregiving burden on middle-aged offspring living with elderly parents in a rural Mennonite community in the province of Manitoba.

METHODS: Pastors from three congregations (General Conference Mennonite [GC], Evangelical Mennonite Conference [EMC], and Lutheran) with a common ethnic heritage and social milieu were interviewed and asked to identify two-generation families who were members of their congregation and living within 50 kilometres of town. Middle-aged offspring were telephoned to determine their willingness to participate. In-person interviews were conducted with 38 individuals (24 biological children and 14 children-in-law). Members' religiosity was assessed using items which measured participation in congregational activities, talking and reading about religion, prayer, and financial contributions to the church. Burden was measured using 11 items from the Zarit Burden Interview. The sample ranged in age from 31 to 63; 20 were female. There were 16 from the Lutheran congregation, 13 from the EMC, and 9 from the GC.

DEFINITION OF RURAL: The rural Manitoba town had a 1981 population of 6,676. The surrounding area is agricultural, with feed grains, wheat, and fodder being produced. A language other than English or French was the mother tongue of 3,415 residents, reflecting the migration of German-speaking Mennonites to this community.

RESULTS RELATED TO RURAL AGING: No marked differences were found between the congregation leaders' perceptions of doctrine that dictates care for older family members. Lutheran respondents reported a lower level of religiosity than either Mennonite group but there were no differences in perceived caregiving burden. Regardless of religious denomination, persons reporting a greater degree of religiosity also reported a lesser degree of burden.

CONCLUSIONS: The authors acknowledge the small and non-random nature of their sample, and suggest more extensive investigation of religious variables and familial care for older parents.

Skoe, E. E., Matthews, M., Pratt, M. W., & Curror, S. E. (1996). The ethic of care: Stability over time, gender differences, and correlates in mid- to late adulthood. *Psychology and Aging, 11*(2), 280-292.

OBJECTIVES: To assess care reasoning levels following Gilligan's care ethic (1982) and its correlates in two studies, one conducted in a rural county in eastern Canada and one in a metropolitan area in eastern Canada.

METHODS: The first study involved 30 female and 30 male community-dwelling volunteers aged 60 to 80 in a rural county. The mean ages were 68.6 for females and 71.7 for males. All participants were parents; 83% of the women and 100% of the males had been employed outside the home. The Ethic of Care Interview (ECI) measure that consists of four dilemmas was administered in a structured interview. In addition to a real-life conflict generated by the participants, the three standardized interpersonal dilemmas involved conflicts surrounding unplanned pregnancy, marital fidelity, and care for a parent. Five ethics of care levels were scored: survival (caring for self), the transition from survival to responsibility, the conventions of goodness (caring for others), the transition from a conventional to a reflective care perspective, and the ethics of care (caring for both self and others). Study 2 involved a sample from a moderately-sized metropolitan area and thus is not discussed below.

DEFINITION OF RURAL: No definition of rural was provided.

RESULTS RELATED TO RURAL AGING: These rural women scored significantly higher on the ECI than did rural men. More women than men generated interpersonal real-life dilemmas and more men than women generated impersonal ones. Respondents scoring higher in care also felt more positively about their physical health and experience of aging.

CONCLUSIONS: Unlike previous research on late adolescents and young adults, gender differences were found in this study. The authors speculate that this may be due to sample and location differences such as single students versus married people, small towns versus large cities, or cohort differences. They argue that the results support the construct validity of the ECI and point to its potential role in adults' personal adaptation.

Storm, C., Storm, T., & Strike-Schurman, J. (1985). Obligations for care: Beliefs in a small Canadian town. *Canadian Journal on Aging, 4*(2), 75-85.

OBJECTIVES: To explore women's perceptions of obligations to assist a frail old person with physical care, financial aid, and psychological support in a small town in Atlantic Canada.

METHODS: The study involved 20 women from each of 4 age groups (18 - 25, 30 - 45, 50 - 65, and 65 - 85). The young adults (aged 18 - 25) were selected from undergraduate students, individuals aged 30 - 45 and 50 - 65 were sampled from a list of volunteers identified by church and social groups, and the 65 - 85 year olds were selected from private apartment complexes where tenants were largely older adults. In-person interviews were conducted in which respondents were asked to imagine a hypothetical old person whose circumstances and resources were described, and then to respond to a series of questions about care needs. They completed a questionnaire and provided information about demographic characteristics and previous experiences with older adults. The three younger groups also completed a questionnaire concerning the degree of obligation of various individuals, government, and the church to help frail older persons with physical, financial, and psychological needs.

DEFINITION OF RURAL: No definition of rural was provided. The study took place in a "small town" (p. 75).

RESULTS RELATED TO RURAL AGING: Children were considered the principal source of assistance, regardless of type of need, by all age groups. This obligation decreased significantly with increasing geographical distance. There was a perceived greater obligation to assist when the child's financial resources were greater. The government was perceived as having a substantial obligation, equal to or greater than that of any more personal source of assistance source except for children in favorable circumstances. Siblings, friends, and the church were perceived to be common sources of assistance, particularly psychological assistance. When gender was mentioned, women were assumed to be the natural caretakers.

CONCLUSIONS: The expectation that children would be the primary source of assistance was confirmed although this obligation was affected by financial circumstances and geographical proximity. The limits to generalizability due to the sample being restricted to women living in a small town are acknowledged.

Social Support/Isolation

Béland, F., & Groupe de Recherche Interdisciplinaire en Santé. (1987). Multigenerational households in a contemporary perspective. *International Journal of Aging and Human Development, 25*(2), 147-166.

OBJECTIVES: To examine factors associated with the frequency of multigenerational households of older adults in the province of Quebec.

METHODS: Data on individuals aged 65+ living in private homes (not institutional settings) were from the 1981 Census of Canada. Two types of multigenerational households were examined: households headed by the elderly as evidenced by the contribution of the older to the younger generation, and households headed by the younger generation where the contribution was from the younger to the older generation. The population of the geographical area, sex, age, home ownership, and living arrangements were examined. Population size was divided into 0 – 4,999 (28%), 5,000 – 29,999 (7%), 30,000 - 99,999 (7%), and 100,000+ inhabitants (58%). Females accounted for 57% of the sample; 40% were aged 65 - 69; and 54% resided in a home owned by the head of the household.

DEFINITION OF RURAL: Rural included regions with < 1,000 inhabitants or with < 400 inhabitants per square kilometre (Statistics Canada, 1981) and small towns with < 5,000 residents.

RESULTS RELATED TO RURAL AGING: The most frequently reported living arrangements were living with a spouse only (39%) or living alone (23%). Multigenerational households accounted for 39% of the respondents' living arrangements, including living in someone's home (17%), being the head of the multigenerational household (16%), or being the spouse of the head of such a household (6%). Living arrangements did not vary with rural or urban location. Elderly women residing in rural areas, small towns, or mid-sized cities were less likely to reside in another person's home than those in large metropolitan areas although this effect was small compared to those of age and gender.

CONCLUSIONS: The authors conclude that the effects of rural and small town locations on multigenerational households were minimal. They suggest that rural residents may have adopted an urban lifestyle and that the pattern of inheritance of the farm by younger generations may have an urban counterpart. Future research needs to consider a combination of occupation and geographical location as well as ethnic differences.

Bond, J. B., Jr., & Harvey, C. D. H. (1991). Ethnicity and intergenerational perceptions of family solidarity. *International Journal of Aging and Human Development, 33*(1), 33-44.

OBJECTIVES: To explore intergenerational interactions between Mennonite and non-Mennonite rural older parents and their middle-aged children in the province of Manitoba.

METHODS: Data were from 138 matched pairs of older parents and their middle-aged children. The middle-aged sample was selected from rural Manitobans between the ages of 35 and 65, and living in separate households in 10 contiguous census sub-divisions. The sub-divisions were targeted so that approximately one-half of the respondents would be Mennonite. Each middle-aged respondent was asked to select a parent to participate; a random sample of parents was then selected. Mailed questionnaires and/or a telephone survey were conducted with the middle-aged sample; the parents were interviewed in-person. Five dimensions of family solidarity were measured.

DEFINITION OF RURAL: Reference was made to rural Manitoba but no specific definition was provided.

RESULTS RELATED TO RURAL AGING: Middle-aged offspring typically reported less family solidarity than did parents. The exception was functional solidarity where the middle-aged children reported stronger solidarity than did their parents. The children indicated they provided more care than the parents said they received. More intergenerational differences were evident for the Mennonites than the non-Mennonites.

CONCLUSIONS: The authors suggest that generational differences in perception exist in rural settings as they do in urban locations. They call for further research with larger sample sizes and various ethnic groups.

Cape, E. (1987). Aging women in rural settings. In V. W. Marshall (Ed.), *Aging in Canada: Social perspectives* **(2nd ed.) (pp. 84-99). Markham, ON: Fitzhenry & Whiteside.**

OBJECTIVES: To explore diversity in the informal support services available to elderly females in country settings in the province of Ontario.

METHODS: A purposive sample was selected on the basis of county (Haliburton and Northumberland), type of location (open country or small settlement), age, and predominant background (rural 'natives' and urban 'transplants'). Interviews were conducted by elderly rural women living in the area and completed with 168 women (42% aged 60 - 69, 37% aged 70 - 79, 21% aged 80+).

DEFINITION OF RURAL: Two rural regions were studied: Haliburton County and Northumberland County. Both counties are beyond commuting distance from a metropolitan centre. In Haliburton, aging 'summer people' had become year-round residents and cottage areas were turning into stable communities of winterized homes; the towns were somewhat larger and more urban in their character. Northumberland County is almost entirely open country and agricultural, with mixed farming and large dairy herds; the villages are traditional farm settlements.

RESULTS RELATED TO RURAL AGING: Only 6 women lived with their children and over 85% indicated that this was not a preferred option. Children and paid employees were the most likely sources of assistance. Planned social events primarily involved children and their families while neighbours provided more casual contact. Transportation was identified as a problem in maintaining personal friendships by 22% of the respondents. The 80+ age group was 4 times more likely to report this problem. Mental health needs were largely ignored by the women, even though 27% reported experiencing periods of serious depression in the previous year.

CONCLUSIONS: The informal support network appeared to be working well for these older women although a substantial proportion of help came from paid employees. The author calls for longitudinal research to determine whether new country dwellers develop sufficient rural roots to sustain them in a non-metropolitan environment.

Corin, E. (1987). The relationship between formal and informal social support networks in rural and urban contexts. In V. W. Marshall (Ed.), *Aging in Canada: Social perspectives* (2nd ed.) (pp. 367-398). Markham, ON: Fitzhenry & Whiteside.

OBJECTIVES: To explore personal and sociocultural factors related to social support among older adults in the province of Quebec.

METHODS: Interviews were conducted with a sample of 239 individuals aged 65+, stratified according to age, sex, and environment (rural, urban middle class [Ste-Foy] and urban deprived area [Inner City]). Three different maps of social networks were drawn: the Wider Network (WN) that included all people identified in response to questions about categories of social relations, the Current Network (CN) that was comprised of all people seen at least once a month, and the Behavioural Network (BN) which was comprised of all persons in touch with the respondent during the past week. Relationships were grouped as children, siblings and kin, and friends and neighbours.

DEFINITION OF RURAL: No definition of rural was provided.

RESULTS RELATED TO RURAL AGING: The social networks of rural residents were generally more similar to those of the urban middle class respondents than those of the urban deprived area. However, rural older adults were more likely to rely almost exclusively on their nuclear family, often on their spouse, for emotional and instrumental support.

CONCLUSIONS: The authors conclude that characteristics of communities are related to the functioning of the social support systems. They argue that planning needs for one rural setting are not necessarily transferable to another one.

Havens, B., Hall, M., Sylvestre, G., & Jivan, T. (2004). Social isolation and loneliness: Differences between older rural and urban Manitobans. *Canadian Journal on Aging, 23*(2), 129-140.

OBJECTIVES: To identify factors associated with social isolation and loneliness for very old rural and urban adults in the province of Manitoba.

METHODS: Data were from the 1996 Aging in Manitoba (AIM) Study which involved follow-up interviews of 1,868 survivors who had participated in earlier waves of the study. Respondents were aged 72 to 104, with 34% of the rural sub-sample and 32% of the urban sub-sample aged 85+. Information was collected through in-person interviews. Social isolation was measured by a life space index. The loneliness measure was a combination of scores on a loneliness scale and two single-item questions from the Netherlands NESTOR studies in aging. Factors examined included age, gender, marital status, perceived adequacy of current income, perceived adequacy of future income, living alone, recent moves, proximity to relatives, perception of seniors' activeness in the community, perception of community's respect, life satisfaction, self-rated health, the number of chronic illnesses, mental status, assistance with basic and instrumental activities of daily living (ADLs and IADLS), the number of days in hospital, the number of physician visits, and home care. Separate multiple regression models were constructed for rural (n = 1,032) and urban (n = 836) sub-samples.

DEFINITION OF RURAL: No definition of rural was provided.

RESULTS RELATED TO RURAL AGING: There were no rural-urban differences in the likelihood of social isolation or loneliness. Factors related to isolation for the rural sub-sample were living alone, living far from relatives, low life satisfaction, declining cognition, and needing help with 3+ ADLs. For the urban sub-sample, being aged 85+, living alone, and needing help with 3+ IADLs were significant. Factors associated with loneliness for the rural sub-sample were perceived inadequacy of future income, living alone, feeling seniors were not respected, low life satisfaction, and having 4+ chronic illnesses. Being widowed and having 4+ chronic illnesses were the only factors that emerged as relevant for the urban sub-sample.

CONCLUSIONS: The authors conclude that while social isolation and loneliness may be related concepts, their associated factors may be quite different. They argue that both social isolation and loneliness are significant issues for older persons, regardless of geographical location.

Mackenzie, P. (2004). Social work practice with rural elderly. In M. J. Holosko & M. D. Feit (Eds.), *Social work practice with the elderly* (3rd ed.) (pp. 275-301). Toronto, ON: Canadian Scholars' Press.

OBJECTIVES: To discuss social work practice with rural older adults, drawing on results of a study in the province of Saskatchewan.

METHODS: This book chapter highlighted selected findings from an in-depth qualitative study conducted with elderly women in rural Saskatchewan. No details about the methodology were provided.

DEFINITION OF RURAL: No definition of rural was provided. A discussion of the concept of rural is presented.

RESULTS RELATED TO RURAL AGING: Almost all respondents were able to describe their involvement with a varied, responsive, and resourceful social network. All had at least one member living in close proximity. Most had several other kin members close by, and reported feeling well-supported and involved in a large and caring family. There was a preference to obtain help from the informal network and to "pick and choose" formal services (p. 286). Some were exercising their right to live with a certain amount of risk. Overall, the women felt very safe in their communities. The sense of personal safety emerged as a major theme in the study. The roles for rural gerontological social work are discussed, including animating, coordinating and supporting social networks; working with families; revisiting community social work and developing/coordinating community programs; research on rural aging; and, family counseling and grief work.

CONCLUSIONS: The author provides eight specific recommendations for action. She argues that the voices of the women in her study challenge policymakers to explore innovative patterns of community life.

MacRae, H. (1996). Strong and enduring ties: Older women and their friends. *Canadian Journal on Aging, 15*(3), 374-392.

OBJECTIVES: To examine friendship in later life among women aged 65+ living in a small town in the province of Nova Scotia.

METHODS: In-depth, semi-structured interviews were completed with 142 women aged 65 to 98 (mean age 76.9) residing in three different settings. Women living in their own homes or private apartments (n = 101) were recruited by knocking on the door of every fifth house on the street through the entire town. Women living in apartment dwelling (n = 31) were drawn at random from two local seniors' apartment complexes while those living in nursing homes (n = 10) also were randomly selected from a wing for the 'more well elderly'. Respondents were asked questions concerning their friends in general and about their 'close friends'. Both quantitative (e.g., number and length of friendships and amount of contact) and qualitative data were gathered.

DEFINITION OF RURAL: The community had a population of 6,500.

RESULTS RELATED TO RURAL AGING: These older women were actively involved with friends. Most identified at least one close or intimate friend although 4 out of 10 nursing home residents indicated that they had no close friends. Many respondents established new friendships as well as maintaining older ones. The women had no difficulty defining what friendship meant to them. The criteria included being a confidant, trust, being loyal and being there through good and bad times, and sharing. The women differentiated between friends and close friends, old friends, and those acquired more recently. Friendships were viewed as important for identity maintenance, particularly when they provided an opportunity for involvement in a more or less equal or reciprocal relationship.

CONCLUSIONS: The results highlight the involvement of older women in relationships with friends. Directions for future research include the subjective meaning of friends and the types of friends, the nature and function of all friendship ties in friendship networks, the influence of the scarcity of kin or the need for assistance on the acquisition of new friends, the influence of social class, and longitudinal research that examines changes in friendships over time.

See also MacRae, H. M. (1995).

Martin-Matthews, A. (1988). Social supports of the rural widowed elderly. *The Journal of Rural Health, 4*(3), 57-70.

OBJECTIVES: To provide a brief demographic profile of rural aging in Canada and an overview of Canadian research findings on the rural aged in general, and to examine issues facing older, rural widowed individuals in the province of Ontario.

METHODS: Data were from a study of 152 widowed residents of two urban and two rural communities in southern Ontario. Most (84%) were female; the average age was 73 years (range 60 - 90). The length of widowhood ranged from < 1 year to 54 years (mean = 10.6 years). Three categories of social support were explored: perceived support (appraisal, belonging, tangible, esteem); patterns of support (number of supporters, face-to-face contact, telephone contact); and preferred sources of support (with 12 typical life situations such as feeling dizzy at home, changing a light bulb, and a companion for holidays).

DEFINITION OF RURAL: The rural communities were a rural town with a population of 3,600 and a rural village with 1,120 residents.

RESULTS RELATED TO RURAL AGING: More similarities than differences in the social support patterns of this sample of rural and urban widowed elders were evident. Both groups indicated high levels of perceived social support overall. In terms of the pattern of support, rural respondents reported higher levels of face-to-face contact with siblings and higher levels of telephone contact with children than their urban counterparts. For preferred sources of support, rural widowed elderly participants were more likely to ask for help from a friend or neighbour for transportation compared to their urban counterparts, and were less likely to go for a walk alone. Rural participants also had lower socioeconomic status and had been widowed for a shorter period of time which may account for the rural-urban difference in support. Despite these findings, 56% perceived that living in a rural area was an advantage in widowhood, 33% favored the urban setting, 5% felt there was no difference, and 5% were unable to answer.

CONCLUSIONS: Overall, there were few rural-urban differences in the social support of these elderly women.

McCay, B. J. (1987). Old people and social relations in a Newfoundland "outport". In H. Strange & M. Teitelbaum (Eds.), *Aging and cultural diversity: New directions and annotated bibliography* **(1st ed.) (pp. 61-87). South Hadley, MA: Bergin and Garvey.**

OBJECTIVES: To describe the situation of older adults in an outport fishing community on Fogo Island in the province of Newfoundland

METHODS: This anthropological study was based on field work conducted from 1972 to 1974. Thus, the ethnographic present of this analysis was the early 1970s.

DEFINITION OF RURAL: Grey Rock (a pseudonym) had a 1971 population of 406 individuals, with 12.8% aged 65+. Men outnumbered women, a skewedness that continues into old age. The community is one of nine coastal settlements or outports that fringe the shores of Fogo Island, about 10 miles off the coast of northeastern Newfoundland. The total 1991 population of Fogo Island was 4,257.

RESULTS RELATED TO RURAL AGING: Themes emerging from the data included: social organization; social status of old people; retirement and the old age pension; the rule of independent residence; the integrity of the nuclear family; the network of family and friends; and, transactions of dependency. Household self-sufficiency was identified as a goal of Grey Rock's residents that continued into old age. Some individuals experienced a loss of status in old age, especially men who had been skippers of fishing crews, but remained involved in the social life of the community. Retirement was positively valued as it provided relative financial security with the receipt of government assistance programs. In general, older adults were not isolated as they continued to live in an extended-kin neighborhood. Individuals who were dependent upon others for assistance such as transportation and miscellaneous errands usually compensated them in cash, even if their own children provided the services. Interdependence was evident, with older adults giving to the community as much as they received from it. A 65th birthday was viewed as an occasion of joy, not anxiety about the unknowns of retirement. "A sixty-fifth birthday is almost as good as a wake" (p. 82).

CONCLUSIONS: The author argues that the availability of government transfer payments made the economic status of older adults relatively high and sustained a cultural heritage that emphasizes household independence into old age. At the same time, the importance of cultural rules and patterns was evident.

Miedema, B., & Tatemichi, S. (2003). Gender, marital status, social networks and health: Their impact on loneliness in the very old. *Geriatrics Today, 6*(2), 95-99.

OBJECTIVES: To examine medical and social variables related to loneliness among relatively healthy adults aged 80 years in the predominantly rural province of New Brunswick.

METHODS: Data were from the 1998 wave of the Fredericton 80+ Study. A non-probability sample of all persons born in 1918 in the River Valley Health area, the geographical study area, was invited to participate. A total of 149 individuals (42%) agreed to participate in a social interview conducted by trained interviewers and in a medical interview conducted by retired nurses. All completed the social interview while 138 completed the medical interview.

DEFINITION OF RURAL: No definition of rural was provided. The authors indicate that "the percentage of rural population in New Brunswick ranges from 46% to 80%, depending on the definition of "rural" that is applied." (pp. 95-96). The study area had approximately a 50 - 50 split between rural and urban populations.

RESULTS RELATED TO RURAL AGING: Feeling lonely sometimes or regularly was reported by 30% of the participants. There were no statistically significant rural-urban differences in the likelihood of feeling alone, satisfaction with contact with children, or satisfaction with sibling contact. Weekly/daily contact with friends and with siblings was more likely for rural respondents than their urban counterparts.

CONCLUSIONS: Place of residence does not appear to be strongly related to feelings of loneliness. The authors acknowledge the self-selection bias of their study and indicate that their findings pertain to participants who are in good self-reported health.

Racher, F. E. (1996). *The challenge of coping: Frail rural elderly couples identify resources required to maintain their independence.* **Master's thesis, University of Manitoba, Winnipeg, MB. Retrieved from:**
http://proquest.umi.com/pqdweb?index=1&did=740463191&SrchMode=1&sid=12&Fmt=13&VInst=PROD&VType=PQD&RQT=309&VName=PQD&TS=1172606184&clientId=12301

OBJECTIVES: To explore the resources that frail elderly couples in rural communities perceive as necessary to maintain their living arrangements in southwestern communities in the province of Manitoba.

METHODS: This qualitative study involved a purposeful sample of 19 frail elderly couples where one or both were experiencing physical/cognitive deterioration and both were residing in their own home. Potential couples were identified through the Continuing Care and Support Services to Seniors programs in selected communities. Couples were interviewed initially together and then separately. The focus was on health care resources, other types of resources, supportive persons that assisted in their efforts to remain living independently in the community, and the spouses' roles and relationships in functioning and adapting to their living situations as couples. Ages ranged from 72 to 95.

DEFINITION OF RURAL: Rural was defined as communities with populations of < 5,000. All the communities in the study had 1995 populations ranging in size from 1,500 to 2,500 people (Boissevain – 1,604; Carberry – 1,649; Killarney – 2,311; Russell – 1,826; Souris – 1,673).

RESULTS RELATED TO RURAL AGING: The importance of family and friends as resources was evident among the couples. A continuum of spousal relationships was identified, from mutually supportive to very fragile, imbalanced relationships. Couples were generally satisfied with the services available. Several resources used by the couples, ranging from community services to health care services to family and friends, were identified. A model was developed to describe the factors which contributed to the independence of these couples.

CONCLUSIONS: The author argues that this study contributes to the understanding of resources and supportive services beneficial to frail rural elderly couples. The relevance to policy and to the field of study is discussed.

See also Racher, F. E. (2002) and Racher, F. E. (2003). Further information regarding the methodology is available in Racher, F. E., Kaufert, J. M., & Havens, B. (2000). Conjoint research interviews with frail, elderly couples: Methodological implications. Journal of Family Nursing, 6(4), 367-379.

Racher, F. E. (2002). Synergism of frail rural elderly couples: Influencing interdependent independence. *Journal of Gerontological Nursing, 28*(6), 32-39.

OBJECTIVES: To identify programs, services, and relationships perceived by the frail rural elderly couples as beneficial to their ability to continue to live independently in the community in the province of Manitoba.

METHODS: This phenomenological study involved a purposive sample of 19 frail rural elderly couples who were interviewed as dyads. Spouses were aged 75+, living in their own homes in selected communities or on farms near these communities, and experiencing challenges in living independently. They were identified by coordinators of the Support Services to Seniors and Continuing Care programs designed to assist older adults. Semi-structured interviews focused on the resources that contributed to the couples' ability to continue to live in the community. Communication between the partners, and roles and relationships were observed and discussed. Interviews were taped and transcribed. The partners ranged in age from 72 to 96 and had been married a mean of 52 years.

DEFINITION OF RURAL: Communities in southwestern Manitoba with populations of 1,500 to 2,500 were chosen for the study. The proportion of residents aged 65+ ranged from 21% to 31%.

RESULTS RELATED TO RURAL AGING: The findings showed that mutually supportive dyads generated a synergism or energy that acted as a vital resource to couples. The characteristics of the couple, their use of resources, the synergism and adaptability of the couple, and their ability to communicate were identified as important to the couple's success in living independently. A continuum of spousal relationships was developed, from mutually supportive to very fragile, unbalanced relationships. A trajectory of couple communication was presented, with a downward pattern from a situation where the more frail spouse has some early decrease in memory to one where s/he has lost the ability to contribute to a conversation.

CONCLUSIONS: The author suggests that support to the couple as a unit, to the couple relationship, and to address the couple's needs may be strategic foci for nurses in their delivery of care, and their involvement in planning programs and developing policy. Study limitations were discussed and calls for a longitudinal approach to increase understanding of situations and use of resources through time were made.

See also Racher, F. (1996) and Racher, F. E. (2003). Further information regarding the methodology is available in Racher, F. E., Kaufert, J. M., & Havens, B. (2000). Conjoint research interviews with frail, elderly couples: Methodological implications. Journal of Family Nursing, 6(4), 367-379.

Seniors' Education Centre. (March 1993). *Final report on creating prairie cronies, Older Women's Network Project.* **Regina, SK: Seniors' Education Centre, University Extension, University of Regina.**

OBJECTIVES: To research and address the specific needs of older women living in rural Saskatchewan.

METHODS: This community development project was undertaken in Saskatchewan from March 1991 to March 1993. It had several objectives, including: promoting networking among and providing support for existing groups working to meet the health, education, and community development needs of older women in Saskatchewan; supporting partners and their existing networks; making use of existing health promotion and educational resources, and developing new ones; ensuring the input and involvement of older adults throughout all stages of the project; and developing an ongoing process of evaluation. A project working group was established to plan, implement, and evaluate the project.

DEFINITION OF RURAL: No definition of rural was provided. The locations of the specific workshops were included in the report.

RESULTS RELATED TO RURAL AGING: During the project, 764 women participated in 28 educational workshops and regional gatherings designed to strengthen community networks that contribute to the well-being of older women. Topics included: naming the needs, gifts and challenges of growing older, giving and taking care, older women and poverty, widowhood, wise use of medication, and living with chronic illness and/or disability. Videos on older women and poverty and on the celebrations and challenges of growing older as a woman in society also were developed.

CONCLUSIONS: The experience of this network was perceived to be very positive. The group recommended that work be done on continuing to build, develop, and nurture the older women's network, and that gender-specific applied research and health promotion projects for older adults be encouraged.

INJURIES

Falls

Gumpel, M. (2004). *Northern Health Authority Veterans and Seniors Falls Prevention Initiative: Final report and evaluation.* Prince George, BC: Northern Health Authority. Retrieved from:
http://www.city.pg.bc.ca/pages/news/nha_falls_prevention.pdf

OBJECTIVES: To develop and implement strategies to reduce falls and the risk of falling among older adults, in outside and public spaces, in communities in the Northern Health Authority in the province of British Columbia.

METHODS: This 2002 pilot project, one of the five conducted in British Columbia under the federal Veterans and Seniors Fall Prevention Initiative, involved the monitoring of changes in fall status over a 10-month period by 85 volunteer participants aged 65+ who had a history of at least one fall in the previous 12 months and who were living independently in the community. Monthly follow-ups were completed.

DEFINITION OF RURAL: The five communities were Burns Lake, Fraser Lake, Vandenhoof, Prince George, McBride, and Valemount.

RESULTS RELATED TO RURAL AGING: Most of the original falls took place outside; 72% were reported to have occurred between 10 a.m. and 4:59 p.m. In the 10-month follow-up, 72 falls were recorded, with 24 one-time fallers and 16 multiple fallers. A higher proportion of falls during the follow-up took place indoors than outdoors. The greatest fears/concerns for falling were icy conditions in the community; slopes, curbs, and general condition of sidewalks; and public stairs. Several suggestions for change were reported.

CONCLUSIONS: The participants indicated that they felt monthly contact played a significant role in reducing falls. The authors call for consideration of their initiative as a starting point to reduce falls among older adults.

Payne, M. W. C., Perkin, T. R., & Payne, W. L. (2003). Incidence of falls by rural elders compared with their urban counterparts. *Canadian Journal of Rural Medicine, 8*(1), 25-32.

OBJECTIVES: To investigate how the incidence of falling by rural people aged 66+ differed from those in an urban community in the province of Ontario.

METHODS: This study relied on a volunteer sample at two independent medical practices in Blenheim and London, both in southwestern Ontario. During Summer 2000, the first 121 consecutive patients aged 66+ who visited their family physicians for reasons other than a fall were asked to volunteer. Nursing home residents and individuals who would not be able to complete a questionnaire due to cognitive impairment were excluded. A questionnaire was used to gather information on demographics, self-rated health, most recent eye examinations, use of walking aids, alcohol consumption, current medications, falls-specific situations for those reporting falls, specific exercise routines or daily activities, and two measures of fall-efficacy (the Modified Falls Efficiency Scale [MFES] and the Activities-specific Balance Confidence Scale [ABC]). The Timed 'Up & Go' (TUG) test was completed. The final sample consisted of 115 respondents. The rural-urban distinction was based on a self-reported current place of residence in an urban or rural community; 40 indicated that they resided in a 'rural' area and 75 from an 'urban' area. There were 9 rural respondents who were recruited from the urban practice and 26 urban respondents who were patients at the rural sites. Mean ages were 75.5 and 76.0 for the rural and urban samples, respectively. Females were slightly more prevalent in the urban sample (55%) than the rural (43%) sample.

DEFINITION OF RURAL: Blenheim is a rural community of approximately 4,500 residents while London has a population of approximately 350,000. The two communities are about 90 minutes apart by car.

RESULTS RELATED TO RURAL AGING: Falls were reported by 29% (n = 22) of the urban group and 30% (n = 12) of the rural group. The mean MFES scores were 8.86 and 8.94 for the urban and rural groups, respectively, while the mean ABC scores were 77.4 and 81.7, respectively. For the urban group, a high TUG score and a lower ABC score were associated with an increased risk of falling. For the rural group, no factors were significant. The small sample size may account of the lack of association in the rural subsample. Falling outside was reported by 46% of the urban and 58% of the rural respondents. Urban residents (55%) were more likely than their rural counterparts (33%) to experience a minor injury; few (5% urban, 8% rural) reported a major injury. Only 1 urban and 1 rural respondent went to the emergency department.

CONCLUSIONS: Falls by older adults in rural areas were as prevalent as falls by their urban counterparts. Future research is needed to examine whether there are different risk factors according to place of residence and to explore the consequences of falls. The challenge of defining rural and urban is discussed.

Yiannakoulias, N., Rowe, B. H., Svenson, L. W., Schopflocher, D. P., Kelly, K., & Voaklander, D. C. (2003). Zones of prevention: The geography of fall injuries in the elderly. *Social Science & Medicine, 57*(11), 2065-2073.

OBECTIVES: To investigate the geography of fall injuries among older adults in the Capital Health Region in the province of Alberta.

METHODS: Data were from three administrative health data systems constructed and maintained by Alberta Health and Wellness (Ambulatory Care Classification System, Alberta Long-Term Care Classification, and Alberta Health Insurance Registration). Cases were identified as community-living residents aged 66+ who visited an emergency department for a fall (defined by ICD-9-CM external cause of injury E codes) at least once during the 1997/98 fiscal year. A geographic information system (GIS) was used to describe the pattern of these falls. Empirical Bayes estimates were used to obtain a geographic measure of fall incidence over the study area and a cluster detection statistic was used to measure the presence of a significant spatial cluster in the region.

DEFINITION OF RURAL: The Capital Health Region is a regional health authority in Alberta which encompasses the city of Edmonton and several smaller outlying communities. The 1997 population was 827,337; 83,051 were aged 65+.

RESULTS RELATED TO RURAL AGING: There were 2,278 fall cases among individuals aged 66+ for a crude rate of 2.74 injurious falls per 100 older adults. Edmonton had the highest incidence of risk while rural areas and smaller communities had more moderate fall incidence. Within Edmonton, there appeared to be a gradient of risk with the highest incidence estimates located in Central Edmonton and lower incidence estimates in the outlying areas of the city.

CONCLUSIONS: The authors conclude that the high incidence of fall injuries among older adults is clustered over discernible regions, and thus geographically-specific prevention programs should be feasible. They call for consideration of the features of rural, suburban, and urban lifestyles that may explain relative differences in risk.

Farm Injuries

Brison, R. J., & Pickett, C. W. L. (1991). Nonfatal farm injuries in eastern Ontario: A retrospective survey. *Accident Analysis and Prevention, 23*(6), 585-594.

OBJECTIVES: To study the incidence of, and potential risk factors for, farm-related injuries on dairy and beef farms in the eastern part of the province of Ontario.

METHODS: This one-year retrospective survey was conducted between July 1989 and January 1990. The official farm registry from the 1986 Canada Census of Agriculture was used to select a random sample of dairy and beef farms that had annual farm sales in excess of $10,000. Only 113 farmers of the initial 391 participated (31%). In-person interviews focused on the demographic characteristics of the farm owner, workers, and family; characteristics of the farm operation; and self-rated farm-related injuries. A person was considered injured if s/he made use of the Ontario health care system to treat an injury or if s/he was unable to do a normal, daily working activity due to the injury.

DEFINITION OF RURAL: All farms were in the 60 kilometre catchment area of the Kingston Health Sciences Complex that had two teaching hospitals providing emergency health services for most of this farm population. Only active beef and dairy operations were studied.

RESULTS RELATED TO RURAL AGING: A total of 49 injuries occurred to 43 individuals on 36 farms in the year prior to the interview. The crude rate of injury was 9.6 per 100 person years. A significantly higher rate of injury was found for farm owners aged 70+ (16.7 per 100 person years). Age-specific information was not provided on the common patterns of injury or the likelihood of seeking treatment in a hospital-based emergency department.

CONCLUSIONS: The authors suggest that the higher rates for older adults may reflect reductions in the physical ability to perform specific farm tasks. They call for a surveillance system for farming injuries in eastern Ontario that might reliably be based on data from emergency departments.

See also Brison, R. J., & Pickett, C. W. L. (1992).

Brison, R. J., & Pickett, C. W. L. (1992). Non-fatal farm injuries on 117 eastern Ontario beef and dairy farms: A one-year study. *American Journal of Industrial Medicine, 21*(5), 623-636.

OBJECTIVES: To study the incidence of, and potential risk factors for, farm-related injuries on beef and dairy farms in the eastern part of the province of Ontario.

METHODS: This one-year prospective study involved 117 dairy and beef farms in the catchment area of the Kingston Health Sciences Complex. The official farm registry for the 1986 Canada Census of Agriculture was used as the source of farms; an initial random sample of approximately 400 farms was selected. Information on demographic characteristics of the farm owners, workers, and families, the characteristics of the farm operations, and behaviors potentially affecting injury risk was obtained through in-person interviews with one representative per farm. Monthly telephone contact was maintained for one year in order to document all farm-related injuries. An injury was defined as any event which resulted in either use of Ontario's health care system or an inability to do one's normal daily working activity. Overall and specific injury rates were calculated.

DEFINITION OF RURAL: All farms had rural postal codes in the region served by the two Kingston hospitals in the Kingston Health Sciences Complex.

RESULTS RELATED TO RURAL AGING: The overall injury rate was 7.0 persons injured per 100 person-years, with a rate of 13.5 in the 60+ age group. Age was a significant risk factor for work-related injuries, with increasing age associated with an increased likelihood of injury. As age and years of farm experience were highly correlated, only the latter was used in the multivariate analyses. No other age-specific analyses were provided.

CONCLUSIONS: The authors suggest that the relationship between farm experience and farm injuries may reflect differences in attitude towards risk taking behaviours between age groups. They call for further research on a province-wide basis.

See also Brison, R. J., & Pickett, C. W. L. (1991).

Brison, R. J., & Pickett, W. (1995). Fatal farm injuries in Ontario, 1984 through 1992. *Canadian Journal of Public Health, 86*(4), 246-248.

OBJECTIVES: To describe patterns of fatal farm injuries from 1984 to 1992 in the province of Ontario.

METHODS: Records from three death registries (Ontario Farm Safety Association, Registrar General of Ontario, Office of the Chief Coroner of Ontario) were used to identify all fatal farm injuries in Ontario for the 9-year period ending December 31, 1992. The coverage was greater by using all three sources rather than only one source. Each death was classified by person, place, time, and injury.

DEFINITION OF RURAL: No definition was provided; no information on farm size or type was given.

RESULTS RELATED TO RURAL AGING: A total of 368 fatal farm injuries were identified over the 9-year period; 73 deaths (20%) were in the 65+ age group. Among the 65+ group, males (95%) and owner-operators (75%) were the most likely to have died. The most likely mechanism of death was a farm tractor (52%), followed by a fall (11%). The location of the injury was most likely in the farm field (52%). The rate of fatal farm injuries per 10,000 farms per year was 1.1 for the 65+ age group.

CONCLUSIONS: The authors argue that the priority for preventive interventions related to farm machinery and associated hazards remains high as farm tractors continue to be the leading agent of fatal injuries.

See also Canadian Agricultural Injury Surveillance Program. (1998); Hartling, L., Pickett, W., & Brison, R. J. (1997); Hartling, L., Pickett, W., Dorland, J., & Brison, R. J. (1997); Pickett, W., & Brison, R. J. (1995); Pickett, W., Brison, R. J., & Hartling, L. (1996); Pickett, W., Brison, R., Niezgoda, H., & Chipman, M. L. (1995); and Pickett, W., Chipman, M. L., Brison, R. J., & Holness, D. L. (1996).

Canadian Agricultural Injury Surveillance Program. (1997). *Fatal farm injuries in Canada, 1991-1995.* **Kingston, ON: Canadian Agricultural Injury Surveillance Program. Prepared by R. Brison, W. Pickett, & L. Hartling.**

OBJECTIVES: To describe the magnitude of the farm fatality problem in Canada from 1991 to 1995 and to identify patterns associated with these facilities.

METHODS: Data were from the farm fatality registry developed by the Canadian Agricultural Injury Surveillance Program (CAISP). The resident farm populations within each province in 1991 were from the 1991 Canada Census of Agriculture. Work-related farm fatalities were deaths that occurred during the course of farm work. Other farm fatalities included deaths that, while occurring on a farm or caused by some aspect of the farm environment, were either not directly related to farm-work or not collected in a consistent manner across the country (e.g., drownings in farm ponds).

DEFINITION OF RURAL: A farm was defined as any farm, ranch, or other agricultural holding that produced at least one of the following agricultural products intended for sale: crops, livestock, poultry, animal products, greenhouse or nursery products, mushrooms, sod, honey, or maple syrup products.

RESULTS RELATED TO RURAL AGING: A total of 502 work-related farm fatalities were reported for the period 1991 to 1995. This included 89 in the 60 - 69 age group, 71 in the 70 - 79 age group, and 23 in the 80+ group. Excesses in the percentages of deaths compared to those expected from the farm population distribution started at age 50 - 59 and rose with age. For example, the 70 - 79 age group accounted for 3.2% of the farm population but 14.1% of the deaths. The rates per 100,000/year ranged from 23.2 for the 60 - 69 age group, to 50.8 for the 70 - 79 age group, to 65.1 in the 80+ group. In all age groups, deaths were much more likely among males. The leading mechanism causing death among the 60+ group was rollovers (n = 47). The highest rate of fatal farm injuries/100,000 in the 60+ group per year was in Atlantic Canada (54.2), followed closely by Quebec (49.8). The rates for the remaining provinces ranged from 26.6 in Alberta to 32.3 in Ontario.

CONCLUSIONS: The authors present nine recommendations. Given that males aged 60+ were at the highest risk for work-related farm fatalities, they argue for the development of effective safety initiatives aimed at older farm operators.

See also Canadian Agricultural Injury Surveillance Program (1999); Canadian Agricultural Injury Surveillance Program (2001); Canadian Agricultural Injury Surveillance Program (2003); Hartling, L., Pickett, W., Guernsey, J. R., Alberg, N., Redekop, T. D., & Brison, R. J. (1998); Pickett, W., Hartling, L., Brison, R. J., & Guernsey, J. R. (1999); Pickett, W., Hartling, L., Dimich-Ward, H., Guernsey, J. R., Hagel, L., Voaklander, D. C., & Brison, R. J. (2001); and Voaklander, D. C., Hartling, L., Pickett, W., Dimich-Ward, H., & Brison, R. J. (1999).

Canadian Agricultural Injury Surveillance Program. (1998). *Fatal farm injuries in Ontario, 1984-1996.* **Kingston, ON: Canadian Agricultural Injury Surveillance Program. Prepared by R. Brison, W. Pickett, L. Hartling, & M. Garner.**

OBJECTIVES: To describe fatal farm injuries from 1984 to 1996 and to identify patterns associated with these fatalities in the province of Ontario.

METHODS: Records from three death registries (Ontario Farm Safety Association, Registrar General of Ontario, Office of the Chief Coroner of Ontario) were used to identify all fatal farm injuries in Ontario between 1984 and 1996. Data abstraction and entry were completed for each eligible fatality. Cases were categorized into work-related fatalities and fatalities that were not necessarily work-related but were caused by a hazard of the farm environment.

DEFINITION OF RURAL: No definition was provided; no information on farm size or type was given.

RESULTS RELATED TO RURAL AGING: A total of 428 work-related farm fatalities were reported in Ontario between 1984 and 1996. In the 60 - 69 age group, there were 59 fatalities for males and 4 for females. In the 70+ group, the corresponding numbers were 69 and 0, respectively. Males aged 70+ accounted for the greatest numbers of fatalities of any age-gender group. Among the 65+ age group, 56% of the fatalities were caused by a tractor (higher than in the < 15 and 16 - 64 age groups), followed by 27% by non-machinery causes, and 18% by machinery other than tractors. Tractor rollovers, runovers of operators, and falls accounted for 54% of the fatal injuries. In total, there were 61 not work-related farm fatalities, including 5 for males aged 60 - 69, and 1 each for females aged 60 – 69, males aged 70+, and females aged 70+.

CONCLUSIONS: The authors conclude that the 50+ age group is one of the high risk groups. They argue for farm safety programs to continue to be guided by objective research.

See also Brison, R. J., & Pickett, W. (1995); Hartling, L., Pickett, W., & Brison, R. J. (1997); Hartling, L., Pickett, W., Dorland, J., & Brison, R. J. (1997); Pickett, W., & Brison, R. J. (1995); Pickett, W., Brison, R. J., & Hartling, L. (1996); Pickett, W., Brison, R., Niezgoda, H., & Chipman, M. L. (1995); and Pickett, W., Chipman, M. L., Brison, R. J., & Holness, D. L. (1996).

Canadian Agricultural Injury Surveillance Program. (1999). *Hospitalized farm injuries in Canada: 1990-96. A report from the Canadian Coalition for Agricultural Safety and Rural Health.* **Kingston, ON: Canadian Agricultural Surveillance Program. Prepared by R. Brison, W. Pickett, L. Hartling, & T. Matys.**

OBJECTIVES: To describe hospitalized farm injuries from 1990 to 1996 in Canada and to identify patterns associated with these injuries.

METHODS: Data were from the Canadian Agricultural Injury Surveillance Program (CAISP) database. Information was obtained from eight provincial Departments of Health, with cases considered for inclusion based on the primary external cause of injury (ICD9-E codes). Supplemental data were available from some provinces. Both farm machinery and non-machinery injuries were examined.

DEFINITION OF RURAL: No definition was provided; no information on farm size or type was given. Population counts were from the Canada Census of Agriculture that excluded hired workers, visitors to farms, and some farmers who did not live on their farm.

RESULTS RELATED TO RURAL AGING: There were 4,670 identified hospitalizations due to farm machinery injuries from 1990 to 1996. This included 681 (15%) in the 60 - 69 age group, 368 (8%) in the 70 - 79 age group, and 93 (2%) in the 80+ group although these groups represented 9%, 3%, and 1% of the farm population, respectively. Rates per 100,000/year increased with age (60 – 69: 126.9; 70 - 79: 188.1; 80+: 188.0). Males significantly outnumbered females. In the 60+ group, open wounds to the upper limb, spine and trunk fractures, lower limb fractures, and upper limb fractures were the most common. There were more hospitalizations due to non-machinery farm injuries (n = 7,418). Included were 1,679 in the 60+ age group (60 - 69: 940 [13%]; 70 – 79: 528 [7%]; 80+: 211 [3%]). Rates per 100,000/year again increased with age (60 - 69: 175.3; 70 – 79: 269.8; 80+: 426.7). Males continued to outnumber females but not to the extent evident for machinery-related injuries. Additional information for the provinces with supplemental data concluded the report.

CONCLUSIONS: Older farmers were identified as a high-risk group. The authors call for sociological research to identify why farm injury patterns vary according to sex and age, and to understand why older farmers are consistently at greater risk for farm injury.

See also Canadian Agricultural Injury Surveillance Program (1997); Canadian Agricultural Injury Surveillance Program (2001); Canadian Agricultural Injury Surveillance Program (2003); Hartling, L., Pickett, W., Guernsey, J. R., Alberg, N., Redekop, T. D., & Brison, R. J. (1998); Pickett, W., Hartling, L., Brison, R. J., & Guernsey, J. R. (1999); Pickett, W., Hartling, L., Dimich-Ward, H., Guernsey, J. R., Hagel, L., Voaklander, D. C., & Brison, R. J. (2001); and Voaklander, D. C., Hartling, L., Pickett, W., Dimich-Ward, H., & Brison, R. J. (1999).

Canadian Agricultural Injury Surveillance Program. (2001). *Gender analysis of fatal and hospitalized farm injuries in Canada, 1990-1996.* **Kingston, ON: Canadian Agricultural Injury Surveillance Program. Retrieved from:** http://meds.queensu.ca/~emresrch/caisp/gender.html

OBJECTIVES: To describe gender differences in fatal and hospitalized farm injuries in Canada from 1990 to 1996 and to identify patterns associated with these types of injuries.

METHODS: Data were from the Canadian Agricultural Injury Surveillance Program (CAISP) database. Cases were considered for inclusion based on the primary external cause of injury (ICD9-E codes). Supplemental data were available from some provinces. Both farm machinery and non-machinery injuries were examined.

DEFINITION OF RURAL: No definition was provided; no information on farm size or type was given. The 1993 Canadian farm population totalled 860,921; there were 44,355 males aged 60 – 69, 21,502 males aged 70+, 31,057 females aged 60 – 69, and 14,949 females aged 70+.

RESULTS RELATED TO RURAL AGING: There were 708 fatal farm injuries from 1990 to 1996 and 8,264 hospitalizations due to farm-related injuries from 1990 to 1994. For males, 18% of the fatal farm injuries were among the 60 – 69 age group and 21% were among the 70+ group. For females, the corresponding percentages were 2% and 10% respectively. In terms of hospitalized farm injuries among males, 14% were among the 60 – 69 age group and 10% among the 70+ group. For females, the corresponding percentages were 10% and 6%, respectively. Among the 60+ age group, fractures accounted for 52% of injuries that lead to hospitalizations for females and 40% for males.

CONCLUSIONS: The authors conclude that there are both common and distinct patterns of fatalities and hospitalizations due to farm injuries when comparing males and females. They call for further investigation of the cause for gender differences in farm injury.

See also Canadian Agricultural Injury Surveillance Program (1997); Canadian Agricultural Injury Surveillance Program (1999); Canadian Agricultural Injury Surveillance Program (2003); Hartling, L., Pickett, W., Guernsey, J. R., Alberg, N., Redekop, T. D., & Brison, R. J. (1998); Pickett, W., Hartling, L., Brison, R. J., & Guernsey, J. R. (1999); Pickett, W., Hartling, L., Dimich-Ward, H., Guernsey, J. R., Hagel, L., Voaklander, D. C., & Brison, R. J. (2001); and Voaklander, D. C., Hartling, L., Pickett, W., Dimich-Ward, H., & Brison, R. J. (1999).

Canadian Agricultural Injury Surveillance Program. (2003). *Agricultural injuries in Canada for 1990-2000.* **Kingston, ON: Canadian Agricultural Surveillance Program. Retrieved from:**
http://meds.queensu.ca/~emresrch/caisp/natrep.html

OBJECTIVES: To describe injury occurrence on farms and ranches in Canada from 1990 to 2000.

METHODS: Data were from the Canadian Agricultural Injury Surveillance Program (CAISP) database. Information on fatal injuries was obtained from a variety of agencies that varied by province. Data on hospitalized agricultural injuries were obtained from provincial Departments of Health, with cases considered for inclusion based on the primary external cause of injury (ICD-9 E codes).

DEFINITION OF RURAL: The farm population was based on Statistics Canada's (1996) definition of a farm as "any farm, ranch, or other agricultural holding that produces at least one of the following agricultural products intended for sale: crops, livestock, poultry, animal products, greenhouse or nursery products, mushrooms, sod, honey, or maple syrup products" (p. 6).

RESULTS RELATED TO RURAL AGING: Work-related farm fatalities from 1990 to 2000 numbered 398 in the 60+ age group (60 – 69: 176; 70 – 79: 154; 80+: 68). The estimated crude annual rate per 100,000/year increased with age (60 – 69: 21.7; 70 – 79: 45.5; 80+: 80.9). It was noted that the rates for the older age groups may be inflated due to limitations of the available denominator data. Males had much higher rates than females in all age groups. Machine rollovers accounted for 25% of the deaths. There were 1,811 cases of hospitalized agricultural machinery injuries for the 60+ age group, with few older females being hospitalized. Tractors were involved in 34% of these injuries while being entangled or caught in operating farm machinery (36%) was the leading cause of hospitalizations. A total of 1,757 cases of hospitalized agricultural non-machinery injuries were reported for the 60+ age group. The number for males exceeded that of females by approximately 4 to 1. The leading cause was animal-related traumas (35%).

CONCLUSIONS: Older males were identified as a high risk group. The authors call for effective prevention programs to be targeted to this and other groups at highest risk on farms and ranches.

Note: Results focusing on senior farmers specifically also were provided in a separate document entitled **Summary report: Agricultural injuries and deaths in senior farmers**, *available at* http://meds.queensu.ca/~emresrch/caisp/Seniors.pdf

See also Canadian Agricultural Injury Surveillance Program (1997); Canadian Agricultural Injury Surveillance Program (1999); Canadian Agricultural Injury Surveillance Program (2001); Hartling, L., Pickett, W., Guernsey, J. R., Alberg, N., Redekop, T. D., & Brison, R. J. (1998); Pickett, W., Hartling, L., Brison, R. J., & Guernsey, J. R. (1999); Pickett, W., Hartling, L., Dimich-Ward, H., Guernsey, J. R., Hagel, L., Voaklander, D. C., & Brison, R. J. (2001); and Voaklander, D. C., Hartling, L., Pickett, W., Dimich-Ward, H., & Brison, R. J. (1999).

Hader, J. M., & Seliske, P. (1993). *Injuries in Saskatchewan*. **Saskatoon, SK: Health Status Research Unit, Department of Community Health and Epidemiology, College of Medicine, University of Saskatchewan.**

OBJECTIVES: To explore patterns of injury from 1979 to 1988 in the province of Saskatchewan.

METHODS: The study drew on data from the Vital Statistics registries of death due to injuries, records from hospital emergency rooms and hospital inpatient records, physician records, and special tabulations such as Workers' Compensation Board injury reports. Injuries were analyzed by 18 external causes of injury groups (ICD-9 E codes), age (including 65 - 74 and 75+ age groups), sex, year, and four population groups (urban, northern Saskatchewan, rural Saskatchewan, and Registered Indians). The analysis was restricted to acute care hospitalization among Saskatchewan health care beneficiaries for the period 1979 to 1988 (n = 228,335).

DEFINITION OF RURAL: Urban was defined as cities with > 10,000 population. The population distribution was 47% rural, 46% urban, 5% Registered Indian, and 2% northern Saskatchewan.

RESULTS RELATED TO RURAL AGING: This report provided age-gender-population group rates per 100,000 population for all 18 external causes of injuries. Age-specific hospital separation rates per 100,000 were higher for rural versus urban older adults for motor vehicle injuries, pedestrian injuries, non-traffic injuries, falls, poisoning, fire injuries, and many occupational and environmental injuries. In general, violence and intentional injuries, and injuries due to adverse effects of drug use were higher in urban areas compared to rural areas for those aged 65+.

CONCLUSIONS: The authors argue that the results highlight the need for public health agencies and health professionals to give prevention of injury a higher priority. They call for multifaceted programs targeting high risk groups, including older adults, young men, and Registered Indians. Specific recommendations are provided.

Hagel, L. M., Dosman, J. A., Rennie, D. C., Ingram, M. W., & Senthilselvan, A. (2004). Effect of age on hospitalized machine-related farm injuries among the Saskatchewan farm population. *Journal of Agricultural Safety & Health, 10*(3), 155-162.

OBJECTIVES: To examine the relationship between age and various factors associated with farm machine-related injuries necessitating hospitalization in the province of Saskatchewan.

METHODS: This study involved a retrospective review of hospital discharge data from the administrative data set of Saskatchewan Health. The external cause of injury codes (ICD-9 E850–869 or E880-928) were used to identify cases of farm machinery injury that occurred in Saskatchewan from April 1, 1990 to March 31, 2000. Excluded were injuries that occurred in the farm home, recreational injuries, and second or subsequent admissions for the same injury. Information on activity at time of injury, mechanism of injury, agent of injury, multiple admissions for the same injury, and transfers to other health care facilities was abstracted.

DEFINITION OF RURAL: No definition of rural was provided; no information on farm size was available. Field crops were the main agricultural production in Saskatchewan, accounting for approximately 78% of total farm case receipts. This production was highly mechanized, with 26% of the total value of farm machines in Canada being located in Saskatchewan.

RESULTS RELATED TO RURAL AGING: Between 1990 and 2000, there were 1,493 hospitalizations attributed to farm machinery-related injuries, including 69 hospitalizations for the 60 - 69 age group, 157 for the 70 - 79 age group, and 44 for the 80+ age group. The average annual rate for 100,000 farm population was 102.5. The age-specific rates increased with age (60 – 69: 188.6; 70 – 79: 274.7; 80+: 353.4). Among the 60+ age group, males were 3.64 times more likely than females to have a machine-related event. The nature of the injury was most likely to be an open wound of the limbs or a fracture of the lower limbs. Entanglement in the machine, a fall from a machine, and being pinned by a machine were common injuries while the type of machine was most likely to be a tractor, harvest equipment, or an auger.

CONCLUSIONS: Age is an important factor in farm machinery-related injuries. The authors speculate that the higher rate of falls among the older farmers may be related to increased limitations of the musculoskeletal and neurological systems. They call for studies that describe the quantity and nature of farm machinery exposure in the farming population and examine the relationship between exposure and age.

Hagel, L., & Rennie, D. (2000). *Fatal and hospitalized farm injuries in Saskatchewan 1990-1996: A report from the Saskatchewan Farm Injury Surveillance Program.* **Saskatoon, SK: Centre for Agricultural Medicine, University of Saskatchewan and Canadian Agricultural Surveillance Program.**

OBJECTIVES: To describe farm injuries that required hospitalization or resulted in a death between 1990 and 1996, in the province of Saskatchewan.

METHODS: Data were from the Saskatchewan Farm Surveillance project. Sources of farm fatality data were the Occupation Health and Safety Division, Saskatchewan Labour, and the Provincial Coroner's Office of Saskatchewan Justice. Information on hospitalized farm injuries was obtained from administrative hospital discharge data from Saskatchewan Health (ICD-9 E codes). Enhanced data were obtained from health districts or affiliated hospitals. Fatalities were classified as work-related and not work-related.

DEFINITION OF RURAL: No definition of rural was provided. The 60+ age group represented 15% of the 1993 farm population.

RESULTS RELATED TO RURAL AGING: In total, there were 147 fatal and 2,293 hospitalized cases from 1990 to 1996. Over one-third of the fatalities were in the 60+ age group (60 – 69: 18%; 70 – 79: 12%; 80+: 8%). Among the 60+, there were 44 work-related and 11 not work-related fatalities. The most common work-related farm fatality involved being run over by a machine (30%). In terms of hospitalizations, 28% were accounted for by the 60+ age group (60 – 69: 16%; 70 – 79: 9%; 80+: 2%). Machinery-related injuries such as being entangled in a machine or falling from a machine represented 51% of injuries. Lower limb fractures (18%), neck and trunk fractures (13%), and upper limb open wounds (12%) were the most common primary diagnoses.

CONCLUSIONS: This report provides basic information on the circumstances surrounding farm injuries that resulted in death or hospitalization. The authors provide recommendations for farm injury prevention and call for further research on farm injuries.

Hartling, L., Pickett, W., & Brison, R. J. (1997). Non-tractor, agricultural machinery injuries in Ontario. *Canadian Journal of Public Health, 88*(1), 32-35.

OBJECTIVES: To estimate rates of fatal and hospitalized injuries related to the operation of farm machinery from 1985 to 1993 and to describe the nature of these injuries, in the province of Ontario.

METHODS: Records from three death registries (Ontario Farm Safety Association, Registrar General of Ontario, Office of the Chief Coroner of Ontario) were used to identify all fatal farm injuries in Ontario for the 9-year period ending December 31, 1993. Hospital discharge data and supplemental data provided by hospital medical records departments were used to identify hospitalized injuries. Only injuries related to a machine or vehicle used in agricultural production other than farm tractors, power-take-off devices, and motor vehicles (i.e., baler, combine, harvester, hay elevator, auger) were studied.

DEFINITION OF RURAL: No definition was provided; no information on farm size or type was given. The farm population included "all persons who are members of a farm operator's household, living on a farm in a rural or urban area" (Statistics Canada, 1992) (p. 35).

RESULTS RELATED TO RURAL AGING: Among male farmers, those aged 60+ accounted for 9 of 48 fatalities (19%) and 173 of 932 hospitalizations (19%). Among female farmers, those aged 60+ had no fatalities and only 17 of 136 hospitalizations (12%). Overall, males aged 60+ had the highest rates of both fatalities and hospitalizations.

CONCLUSIONS: Males aged 60+ were at the highest risk for injury in the farm population. The authors speculate that older farmers may be at increased risk because of physical limitations and slowed reaction times. They call for further research to determine whether older farmers are at increased risk due to ownership and use of older equipment, and for targeted agricultural safety programs.

See also Brison, R. J., & Pickett, W. (1995); Canadian Agricultural Injury Surveillance Program. (1998); Hartling, L., Pickett, W., Dorland, J., & Brison, R. J. (1997); Pickett, W., & Brison, R. J. (1995); Pickett, W., Brison, R. J., & Hartling, L. (1996); Pickett, W., Brison, R., Niezgoda, H., & Chipman, M. L. (1995); and Pickett, W., Chipman, M. L., Brison, R. J., & Holness, D. L. (1996).

Hartling, L., Pickett, W., Dorland, J., & Brison, R. J. (1997). Hospital costs associated with agricultural machinery injuries in Ontario. *American Journal of Industrial Medicine, 32,* 502-509.

OBJECTIVES: To pilot an approach to costing hospitalized farm injuries, and to describe ambulance and inpatient costs associated with these injuries from 1985 to 1993 in the province of Ontario.

METHODS: Hospital discharge records (hospital separations) for farm machinery injuries in Ontario were identified by ICD9-CM E-codes for 1985 to 1993. Supplemental data were obtained via chart abstraction of inpatient records by hospital medical records departments. Ambulance costs were estimated by the Ontario Ministry of Health. For each case, the hospital costs were calculated by multiplying the case-specific resource intensity weight by the average inpatient cost per weighted case. A total of 1,741 agricultural machinery injuries were identified as having occurred in Ontario from 1985 to 1993 and leading to an admission to an Ontario hospital. Of these, 1,610 were included in the analysis.

DEFINITION OF RURAL: No definition was provided; no information on farm size or type was given.

RESULTS RELATED TO RURAL AGING: The 65+ age group accounted for 13% of the injuries and had a median hospital stay of 7 days. The costs (1993 Canadian dollars) of the hospitalizations related to agricultural machinery injuries ranged from $768 to $62,643 for all ages, and $875 to $59,828 for the 65+ group. No age-specific information was provided for the mechanism of injury and the machine involved, or for the diagnostic category.

CONCLUSIONS: Although these figures represent a fraction of the total costs associated with farm injuries, the results provide a basis from which to justify and target preventive initiatives. The authors suggest that this approach to costing also may apply to other health issues. Implications for prevention are offered, including the prevention of injuries to older farmers through assignment of tasks that take into account the growing physical limitations and slowed reaction times associated with aging.

See also Brison, R. J., & Pickett, W. (1995); Canadian Agricultural Injury Surveillance Program. (1998); Hartling, L., Pickett, W., & Brison, R. J. (1997); Pickett, W., & Brison, R. J. (1995); Pickett, W., Brison, R. J., & Hartling, L. (1996); Pickett, W., Brison, R., Niezgoda, H., & Chipman, M. L. (1995); and Pickett, W., Chipman, M. L., Brison, R. J., & Holness, D. L. (1996).

Hartling, L., Pickett, W., Guernsey, J. R., Alberg, N., Redekop, T. D., & Brison, R. J. (1998). Injuries associated with the farm harvest in Canada. *Canadian Medical Association Journal, 158*(11), 1493-1496.

OBJECTIVES: To analyze agricultural injuries occurring during harvest season in Canada, and to provide an overview of harvest-related injuries resulting in death or admission to hospital as well as problems treated in the outpatient setting.

METHODS: Data were from three registries that form part of the Canadian Agricultural Injury Surveillance Program (CAISP), specifically the Canadian registry of fatal farm injuries (1991 -1995), Ontario registry of injuries caused by farm machinery and resulting in admission to hospital (1985 - 1994), and the Manitoba Department of Labour database for a sample of physician clinics in Manitoba (1994 - 1996). Harvest-related injuries were defined as farm injuries involving the most common agents of acute traumatic injury associated with harvest (i.e., tractors, power take-offs, balers, combines and harvesters, grain augers, conveyers and elevators, and farm wagons). Dates of injuries were July to November inclusive.

DEFINITION OF RURAL: No definition was provided; no information on farm size or type was given.

RESULTS RELATED TO RURAL AGING: A total of 172 fatal harvest-related injuries occurred between 1991 and 1995. The 65+ age group accounted for 30% of these fatalities, with a tractor rollover being the most likely machine related injury. Ontario had 804 harvest-related injuries that resulted in hospital admissions between 1985 and 1994. The 65+ group accounted for 13% of these admissions, and tractor runovers were the most frequent type of injury. Manitoba had 219 outpatient cases between 1994 and 1996; only 6% were in the 65+ age group.

CONCLUSIONS: As the nature of farm work necessitates the conduct of a wide range of tasks over long periods during the harvest season, the high risks for work-related injuries between July and October are not surprising. The authors call for physicians to recognize that farming is one of the most hazardous occupations in Canada, and the important role of rural physicians in the treatment and prevention of farm injuries.

See also Canadian Agricultural Injury Surveillance Program (1997); Canadian Agricultural Injury Surveillance Program (1999); Canadian Agricultural Injury Surveillance Program (2001); Canadian Agricultural Injury Surveillance Program (2003); Pickett, W., Hartling, L., Brison, R. J., & Guernsey, J. R. (1999); Pickett, W., Hartling, L., Dimich-Ward, H., Guernsey, J. R., Hagel, L., Voaklander, D. C., & Brison, R. J. (2001); and Voaklander, D. C., Hartling, L., Pickett, W., Dimich-Ward, H., & Brison, R. J. (1999).

Pickett, W., & Brison, R. J. (1995). Tractor-related injuries in Ontario. *Canadian Journal of Public Health, 86*(4), 243-246.

OBJECTIVES: To examine patterns of tractor-related injuries from 1985 to 1990 in the province of Ontario.

METHODS: Records from three death registries (Ontario Farm Safety Association, Registrar General of Ontario, Office of the Chief Coroner of Ontario) were used to identify all fatal farm injuries in Ontario for the 5-year period ending March 31, 1990. Injuries requiring hospitalization were identified from hospital discharge summaries obtained from the Hospital Medical Records Institute and described using information from medical records kept at 98% of the 162 Ontario hospitals where at least one agricultural machinery injury was treated during the study period. Only injuries related to the use of farm tractors and power-take-off devices installed on farm tractors and used to drive other farm implements were studied.

DEFINITION OF RURAL: No definition was provided; no information on farm size or type was given. The 1986 Canada Census of Agriculture was used to determine the total farm population defined as individuals living and working on farms with agricultural sales of more than $2,500 per year.

RESULTS RELATED TO RURAL AGING: A total of 71 fatalities and 392 hospitalizations for tractor-related injuries were identified. Among males, those aged 60+ accounted for 22 of the 61 fatalities (36%) and 75 of the 354 hospitalizations (21%). Among females, the 60+ age group had 2 of 10 fatalities (20%) and 3 of 38 hospitalizations (8%). Males aged 60+ had the highest rates per 100,000/year for fatalities (23.5) and for hospitalizations (72.6).

CONCLUSIONS: Males aged 60+ were at highest risk for injury in the farm population. The authors speculate that older farmers may be more at risk because they tend to make more use of older tractors which may have fewer safety features.

See also Brison, R. J., & Pickett, W. (1995); Canadian Agricultural Injury Surveillance Program. (1998); Hartling, L., Pickett, W., & Brison, R. J. (1997); Hartling, L., Pickett, W., Dorland, J., & Brison, R. J. (1997); Pickett, W., Brison, R. J., & Hartling, L. (1996); Pickett, W., Brison, R., Niezgoda, H., & Chipman, M. L. (1995); and Pickett, W., Chipman, M. L., Brison, R. J., & Holness, D. L. (1996).

Pickett, W., Brison, R. J., & Hartling, L. (1996). *Hospitalized farm injuries in Ontario: 1985-1993.* **Kingston, ON: Centre for Injury Prevention and Research, Queen's University.**

OBJECTIVES: To estimate the rates of agricultural machinery injury requiring hospital admission from 1985 to 1994 for the province of Ontario.

METHODS: Data were obtained from the Information and Systems Branch of the Ontario Ministry of Health for all persons admitted to an Ontario hospital who had sustained an agricultural machinery injury between April 1, 1985 and March 31, 1993, or had suffered a non-machinery injury on a farm over a 4-year period ending March 31, 1994. External cause of injury was determined by ICD-9-E codes. Additional data were abstracted from hospital charts. Analyses were calculated based on calendar year from 1985 to 1993.

DEFINITION OF RURAL: No definition was provided; no information on farm size or type was given.

RESULTS RELATED TO RURAL AGING: In total, there were 1,741 hospitalized farm machinery injuries from 1985 to 1993. Males aged 60 - 69 accounted for 209 of these injuries and males aged 70+ represented 132 injuries. The corresponding numbers for females were 17 and 5, respectively. Rates of farm machinery injury were highest for males aged 60+. Farm tractors were the most common farm machinery involved in the injuries. Fractures accounted for 50% of the 226 injuries for farmers aged 65+, with upper/lower extremities and the trunk being the leading sites of injury.

CONCLUSIONS: Older male farmers were a group at high risk for farm injuries. The authors argue for a continued priority for farm safety programs among male farmers of all ages, but in particular those aged 15 - 30 and 65+.

See also Brison, R. J., & Pickett, W. (1995); Canadian Agricultural Injury Surveillance Program. (1998); Hartling, L., Pickett, W., & Brison, R. J. (1997); Hartling, L., Pickett, W., Dorland, J., & Brison, R. J. (1997); Pickett, W., & Brison, R. J. (1995); Pickett, W., Brison, R., Niezgoda, H., & Chipman, M. L. (1995); and Pickett, W., Chipman, M. L., Brison, R. J., & Holness, D. L. (1996).

Pickett, W., Brison, R. J., Niezgoda, H., & Chipman, M. L. (1995). Nonfatal farm injuries in Ontario: A population-based survey. *Accident Analysis and Prevention, 27*(4), 425-433.

OBJECTIVES: To identify rates and patterns of non-fatal agricultural injuries in the province of Ontario.

METHODS: A population-based mail survey of 2,000 farms in eastern Ontario was conducted in Fall 1991. Information was requested on demographics, average number of hours worked on the farm during the study period, characteristics of their farm operations, and a detailed 1-year farm injury history. A farm injury was defined as any accidental injury that was serious enough to limit normal activities for at least 4 hours and that occurred during activities related to the operation of a farm or that involved any hazard of a farm environment. It also included farm-related injuries that occurred at an off-farm location (e.g., injuries that occurred on a neighbouring farm property) and injuries that involved motor vehicles that were being used for farm work. The final sample was comprised of 1,364 farms with 4,110 individuals living and/or working on these farms.

DEFINITION OF RURAL: A farm was defined as an active producer of agricultural commodities that appeared on the current mailing list of *Farm and Country*, an industry trade journal mailed to most Ontario farm operations.

RESULTS RELATED TO RURAL AGING: The crude rate of farm injury was 5.8 per 100 persons per year. For the 61 - 70 age group, the rates were 7.1 and 2.2 for males and females, respectively. For the 71+ group, the corresponding rates were 7.6 and 6.7, respectively. The leading mechanisms of injury for the 65+ age group were injuries related to the use of farm machinery, accidental falls, and injuries that occurred while working with farm animals. Males aged 65+ were more likely to report their family physician as the source of treatment while females were most likely to be hospitalized.

CONCLUSIONS: This population-based survey identifies common patterns of non-fatal farm injury among a large sample of Ontario farmers. The authors conclude that young adult male farmers have the highest rates of injury and warrant targeting by injury control programs. The age- and gender-specific findings in the upper and lower age ranges must be interpreted with caution due to the low rates of injuries (e.g., there were only 18 injuries among males aged 65+ and 4 among their female counterparts).

See also Brison, R. J., & Pickett, W. (1995); Canadian Agricultural Injury Surveillance Program. (1998); Hartling, L., Pickett, W., & Brison, R. J. (1997); Hartling, L., Pickett, W., Dorland, J., & Brison, R. J. (1997); Pickett, W., & Brison, R. J. (1995); Pickett, W., Brison, R. J., & Hartling, L. (1996); and Pickett, W., Chipman, M. L., Brison, R. J., & Holness, D. L. (1996).

Pickett, W., Chipman, M. L., Brison, R. J., & Holness, D. L. (1996). Medications as risk factors for farm injury. *Accident Analysis & Prevention, 28*(4), 453-462.

OBJECTIVES: To examine whether cases of farm injury were more likely than controls to have been regularly exposed to certain types of medication (narcotic and non-narcotic analgesics, heart or circulatory drugs, stomach remedies or laxatives, tranquilizers or sleeping pills, and antidepressants) in the province of Ontario.

METHODS: A case-control study was conducted between Fall 1990 and Fall 1991. Potential cases and controls were identified from an earlier study and were sent a mailed questionnaire that gathered information on self-reported exposure to medications and other potential risk factors for farm injury. Cases were defined as farm persons for whom at least 1 farm injury was reported for the 12 months prior to the initial survey. The controls had no reports of farm injuries in this time period and were matched to cases on the basis of the relationship to a farm owner, and then selected using a 4:1 ratio. The sample used in the analyses included 135 cases and 540 controls. Respondents who regularly used certain types of medication were separated into two groups: those who used the medications in isolation, and those who used the medications in combination with other medications.

DEFINITION OF RURAL: A farm was defined as an active producer of agricultural commodities on a mailing list of a trade paper sent to Ontario farm operators during Fall 1991. A farm person was defined as any person, aged 16+, who lived and/or worked on an Ontario farm on a full-time basis.

RESULTS RELATED TO RURAL AGING: Use of many classes of medication was low, including narcotic analgesics, antidepressants, and tranquilizers/sleeping pills. Strong and statistically significant increases in risk for injury were observed in association with the regular use of stomach remedies or laxatives by males in both the < 45 and 45+ age groups, and regular use of heart or circulatory medications by men aged 45+. These associations remained after adjustment for age, co-morbidity, tillable farm acreage, education, income, alcohol consumption, and tobacco use.

CONCLUSIONS: The authors provide several explanations for the associations between medication use and risk for injury. They argue that the identification of these associations can be a stimulus for further work on the relationship between medications and farm injuries.

See also Brison, R. J., & Pickett, W. (1995); Canadian Agricultural Injury Surveillance Program. (1998); Hartling, L., Pickett, W., & Brison, R. J. (1997); Hartling, L., Pickett, W., Dorland, J., & Brison, R. J. (1997); Pickett, W., & Brison, R. J. (1995); Pickett, W., Brison, R. J., & Hartling, L. (1996); and Pickett, W., Brison, R., Niezgoda, H., & Chipman, M. L. (1995).

Pickett, W., Hartling, L., Brison, R. J., & Guernsey, J. R. (1999). Fatal work-related farm injuries in Canada, 1991-1995. Canadian Agricultural Injury Surveillance Program. *Canadian Medical Association Journal, 160*(13), 1843-1848.

OBJECTIVES: To describe the occurrence of fatal work-related farm injuries in Canada between 1991 and 1995, and to compare these rates with those in other Canadian industries.

METHODS: Data for this descriptive, epidemiological analysis were from the Canadian Agricultural Injury Surveillance Program (CAISP) for 1991 to 1995. Deaths were fatal unintentional injuries that occurred during work-related activities associated with the operation of a farm, including deaths that occurred at off-farm work locations and those that involved motor vehicles used for farm work. Crude, age-standardized, age-specific, and provincial rates were studied as were overall death rates in other Canadian industries. Other factors examined were people involved, mechanism of injury, and place and time of injury.

DEFINITION OF RURAL: No definition was provided; no information on farm size or type was given.

RESULTS RELATED TO RURAL AGING: There were 503 deaths from work-related farm injuries identified during the study period; 89 deaths were in the 60 - 69 age group, 71 in the 70 - 79 age group, and 23 in the 80+ group. The male:female ratios were 88:1, 35:1, and 22:1 for the 60 - 69, 70 - 79, and 80+ age groups, respectively. The overall annual rate was 11.6 deaths per 100,000 farm population. Age-specific rates per 100,000 for the 60 - 69, 70 - 79, and 80+ age groups were 23.2, 50.8, and 65.1, respectively. The leading mechanism of fatal injury among the 60+ age group was a rollover of a farm vehicle, followed by a striking or crushing injury such as being hit by falling material or rollback of a large round hay bale, and a runover injury. Compared with other industries, agriculture appears to be the fourth most dangerous in Canada in terms of fatal injury behind mining, logging/forestry, and construction.

CONCLUSIONS: This analysis represents on one of the first uses of a national registry for the surveillance of fatal farm injuries. The finding that farmers aged 60+ had a rate of death 4 times that of the remaining farm population lead the authors to recommend the development and implementation of effective safety initiatives aimed at older farm operators.

See also Canadian Agricultural Injury Surveillance Program (1997); Canadian Agricultural Injury Surveillance Program (1999); Canadian Agricultural Injury Surveillance Program (2001); Canadian Agricultural Injury Surveillance Program (2003); Hartling, L., Pickett, W., Guernsey, J. R., Alberg, N., Redekop, T. D., & Brison, R. J. (1998); Pickett, W., Hartling, L., Dimich-Ward, H., Guernsey, J. R., Hagel, L., Voaklander, D. C., & Brison, R. J. (2001); and Voaklander, D. C., Hartling, L., Pickett, W., Dimich-Ward, H., & Brison, R. J. (1999).

Pickett, W., Hartling, L., Dimich-Ward, H., Guernsey, J. R., Hagel, L., Voaklander, D. C., & Brison, R. J. (2001). Surveillance of hospitalized farm injuries in Canada. *Injury Prevention, 7*(2), 123-128.

OBJECTIVES: To provide an overview of hospital admissions for the treatment of farm injuries in Canada.

METHODS: This descriptive analysis draws on data from the Canadian Agricultural Injury Surveillance Program (CAISP) for the period April 1991 to March 1995. Hospital discharges/separations for farm machinery injuries were identified by ICD9-CM E-codes where location was a farm. Cases were verified by medical records personnel and supplemental data describing injury circumstances were obtained. Cases were available for all but two provinces (Nova Scotia and Newfoundland/Labrador), or 98% of the farm population.

DEFINITION OF RURAL: No definition was provided; no information on farm size or type was given.

RESULTS RELATED TO RURAL AGING: A total of 8,263 hospitalized farm injuries were verified. Adults aged 60+ were over-represented in these injuries. The 60 - 69 age group accounted for 9% of the farm population but 14% of the hospitalizations for machinery injuries and 13% of the hospitalized non-machinery injuries. The corresponding percentages for the 70+ age group were 4%, 10%, and 8%, respectively. In the 60+ age group, the leading external causes of agricultural machinery injury included entanglements (27%), falls from a machine (20%), being pinned/struck by machinery (13%), and runovers (12%). Non-machinery causes included falls from heights (34%), animal-related trauma (34%), and being struck by/against objects (13%). Leading diagnoses for the 60+ age group included limb fractures/open wounds, intracranial injuries, skull fractures, and spinal/truncal fractures. The average length of hospital stay for the 60+ age group was 4 days, with a range from 2 to 10.

CONCLUSIONS: These descriptive data suggest that older farmers often experience injuries that are more severe than those experienced by their younger counterparts. The authors caution that the numbers of non-machinery injuries are underestimates. They argue that the data from CAISP can be used to inform prevention initiatives, and to indicate priorities for etiological and experimental research in the Canadian agricultural setting.

See also Canadian Agricultural Injury Surveillance Program (1997); Canadian Agricultural Injury Surveillance Program (1999); Canadian Agricultural Injury Surveillance Program (2001); Canadian Agricultural Injury Surveillance Program (2003); Hartling, L., Pickett, W., Guernsey, J. R., Alberg, N., Redekop, T. D., & Brison, R. J. (1998); Pickett, W., Hartling, L., Brison, R. J., & Guernsey, J. R. (1999); and Voaklander, D. C., Hartling, L., Pickett, W., Dimich-Ward, H., & Brison, R. J. (1999).

Thompson, J. M., & von Hollen, B. (1996). Causes of horse-related injuries in a rural western community. *Canadian Family Physician, 42*, 1103-1109.

OBJECTIVES: To determine the causes of horse-related injuries in a rural western community in the province of Alberta.

METHODS: This descriptive study involved the prospective identification of persons with horse-related injuries, and retrospective telephone interviews with patients or witnesses. From March 1989 to July 1991, all patients presenting to either of two family medicine clinics or to the Sundre General Hospital emergency department were identified by the physicians. Telephone interviews and chart reviews were used to gather information on the injury as recalled by patients or witnesses, and characteristics of the persons, horses, and injuries.

DEFINITION OF RURAL: Sundre is a rural community in the foothills of the Rocky Mountains in central Alberta, where the western style of riding predominated. During the study period, two private clinics were staffed by five family physicians. A small rural hospital with an emergency department was staffed by these same physicians. The physicians' catchment area was approximately 6,000 square kilometres, with a population of approximately 5,000 residents. There was seasonal variation in the population size due to a large visiting tourist population and a transient work force.

RESULTS RELATED TO RURAL AGING: The physicians reported 150 injuries during the study period; 102 were classified as caused primarily by horses. The most common horse behaviour that caused injuries was 'spooking'. Ages ranged from 2 to 86, but less than 10% of the injured males were in the 60+ age category and an even lower percentage of the injured females were aged 60+ (information provided in a Figure).

CONCLUSIONS: Horse-related injuries often are caused by characteristic horse behaviours. The authors call for further research to determine the incidence and prevalence of horse-related injuries and the associated risk factors.

Voaklander, D. C., Hartling, L., Pickett, W., Dimich-Ward, H., & Brison, R. J. (1999). Work-related mortality among older farmers in Canada. *Canadian Family Physician, 45,* 2903-2910.

OBJECTIVES: To describe the frequency and circumstances of work-related, fatal injuries among older farmers in Canada from 1991 to 1995.

METHODS: Data for this descriptive, epidemiological analysis were from the Canadian Agricultural Injury Surveillance Program (CAISP) for 1991 to 1995. Older farmers were aged 60+ and members of the farm population as defined by the 1991 Canada Census of Agriculture. Deaths were fatal, unintentional injuries that occurred during work-related activities associated with the operation of a farm, including deaths that occurred at off-farm work locations and those that involved motor vehicles used for farm work. Age-adjusted mortality rates were calculated using the Canadian farm population as a standard. Other factors examined included people involved, mechanism of injury, and place and time of injury.

DEFINITION OF RURAL: No definition of rural was provided; no information on the farm size or type was available. Members of the farm population included all members of a farm operator's household living on a farm in a rural or urban area (Canada Census of Agriculture, 1991).

RESULTS RELATED TO RURAL AGING: From 1991 to 1995, 183 older farmers died from work-related injuries in Canada. Almost all (98%) were males. The overall mortality rate for farmers aged 60+ was 32.8 per 100,000 population per year. Age-specific rates were 23.2, 50.8, and 65.1 for the 60 - 69, 70 - 79, and 80+ age groups, respectively. Fatality rates were higher in Quebec and the Atlantic Provinces. Men (98%) accounted for almost all of the deaths while 83% of the deaths were farm owner-operators (where the relationship of the person to the farm owner was reported). Leading mechanisms of fatal injury included tractor rollovers, being struck or crushed by objects, and being run over by machinery. Many older farmers appeared to be working alone at the time of injury.

CONCLUSIONS: The authors argue that the circumstances identified as leading to fatalities are not new and their continued prominence is a cause for concern. They call for innovative ways to reduce work-related injuries in this population and suggest that family physicians may be one of the few sources of safety information for this population.

See also Canadian Agricultural Injury Surveillance Program (1997); Canadian Agricultural Injury Surveillance Program (1999); Canadian Agricultural Injury Surveillance Program (2001); Canadian Agricultural Injury Surveillance Program (2003); Hartling, L., Pickett, W., Guernsey, J. R., Alberg, N., Redekop, T. D., & Brison, R. J. (1998); Pickett, W., Hartling, L., Brison, R. J., & Guernsey, J. R. (1999); and Pickett, W., Hartling, L., Dimich-Ward, H., Guernsey, J. R., Hagel, L., Voaklander, D. C., & Brison, R. J. (2001).

Young, S. K. (1995). Agriculture-related injuries in the Parkland region of Manitoba. *Canadian Family Physician, 41,* **1190-1197.**

OBJECTIVES: To review a series of farm injuries in the Parkland region of the province of Manitoba.

METHODS: This descriptive, retrospective case study involved a review of charts at the Dauphin General Hospital in Dauphin, Manitoba, and a review of the local medical examiner's records. Hospital cases were individuals who had been admitted to the hospital between January 1981 and December 1991 after being injured by agricultural machines, farm animals, herbicides or other chemicals, or fertilizers (n = 72). A review of the medical examiner's records identified cases of injuries resulting in death without a hospital admission (n = 4). Information on sex, age, time and date of injury, cause, type of injury, and body part involved were extracted for each case. Of the 76 cases, 87% were male and the mean age was 40.8 years.

DEFINITION OF RURAL: The Parkland region is comprised of the town of Dauphin and surrounding farms and communities. The total population at the time of the study was 57,000. Dauphin General Hospital had two general surgeons on staff and served as a regional referral centre.

RESULTS RELATED TO RURAL AGING: Approximately 12% of the cases were between the ages of 60 and 69, while 4% were among the 70+ age group (information provided in a Figure). Age-specific information was not provided for time and date of the injury, cause, type of injury, or body part involved.

CONCLUSIONS: The authors argue that the type and pattern of injuries they observed resembles those documented in other studies. They call for physicians to encourage and support educational programs in their communities, and to review safety practices with patients.

COMMENTS: **Thompson, J.M. (1995). Preventing injuries in rural Canada.** *Canadian Family Physician, 41,* **1141-1144.** This author acknowledged that Young's effort makes an important contribution, while recognizing the small sample size and its focus on a single community. He highlighted 5 problems that hamper rural injury prevention research and provided examples of child and youth farm injury prevention programs in Canada. He argued that rural family physicians should be encouraged to do more of this type of research.

COMMENTS: **Goertzen, J. (1995). Farm-related injuries taken seriously.** *Canadian Family Physician, 41,* **1670.** This author commended the research by Young who was enrolled in the Parkland Family Practice Residency Program in Dauphin at the time of the original research. He argued that family physician teachers need to support and nurture the research carried out by family practice residents across the country.

Suicide

Agbayewa, M. O. (1993). Elderly suicide in British Columbia: An exploration of regional variation and related factors. *Canadian Journal of Public Health, 84*(4), 231-236.

OBJECTIVES: To review suicide rates of older adults and identify differences according to region and population size in the province of British Columbia.

METHODS: Coroner's suicide reports in British Columbia from 1985 to 1988 were reviewed. Data also were gathered from population charts. Age-specific suicide rates were calculated for each region, community size, and the province. Five age groups (10 - 19, 20 - 44, 45 - 64, 65 - 74, and 75+) were examined.

DEFINITION OF RURAL: Community size was categorized as populations of < 1,000; 1,000 – 9,999; 10,000 – 49,999; 50,000 – 99,999; and 100,000+.

RESULTS RELATED TO RURAL AGING: There were 1,040 suicides during the four-year period; 91 suicides were in the 65 - 74 age group and 59 were in the 75+ group. The suicide rate was 38.40 per 100,000 for the 65 - 74 age group and 39.09 for the 75+ group. Region and community size could be identified only for 79 and 52 suicides in the respective age groups. Elderly suicides were disproportionate in some, but not all, regions. Overall, the elderly suicide rates were the lowest in the centres of 100,000+ population and highest in the communities with < 1,000 population. However, among the females, there were no suicides in the communities of < 1,000 population, and the lowest rate was for the communities with a population between 10,000 and 49,999.

CONCLUSIONS: The authors urge caution in the interpretation of the findings due to the small number of suicides, the small population base in certain regions, and the inability to identify community of origin for 13% of the elderly suicides. It is argued that variations in the suicide rates may be due to differences in cultural, historical, social, and economic events across the regions. Local community differences may be explained in part by local coroner's practices, biases, background, and available resources.

Pickett, W., Davidson, J. R., & Brison, R. J. (1993). Suicides on Ontario farms. *Canadian Journal of Public Health, 84*(4), 226-230.

OBJECTIVES: To estimate the nature of suicides on farms from 1980 to 1989, to describe the nature of farm-related suicides, and to examine associations between economic indicators and farm suicide, in the province of Ontario.

METHODS: A list of death certificates for all deaths that occurred between January 1, 1980 and July 1, 1989, where suicide was recorded as the type of injury and farm appeared as the location was obtained from the Ontario Registrar General. Coroner's investigator reports also were obtained for these deaths; data included age, sex, farm status, geographic residence, location of injury, and method of suicide. A farm suicide was defined as "a completed suicide which had occurred on an Ontario farm, where the victim was identified in a Coroner's Investigation Report as a farmer, an immediate member of a farm family, or a farm employee" (p. 226). Ten economic indicators such as the number of farm bankruptcies, average net farm income, prime loan rate, and rate of inflation were used in the analyses of the association between economic conditions and farm suicides.

DEFINITION OF RURAL: No definition of rural was provided; no information on the farm size or type was available.

RESULTS RELATED TO RURAL AGING: There were 126 farm suicides in the 9.5-year study period; 21 were in the 60 - 69 age group and 16 were in the 70+ group. After adjusting for age and under-reporting, the farm suicide rate was estimated at 7.2 per 100,000 per year. The highest farm suicide rate was in the 70+ group, followed by the 60 - 69 age group. Regression analyses failed to find any associations between the economic indicators and farm suicide rates.

CONCLUSIONS: The results do not support the notion that farmers in Ontario generally have a high rate of suicide. However, there was an increase at age 60 and particularly after age 70. There was no evidence for increased farm suicide risk with increasing economic strain. The authors argue for preventive measures, including the removal of potential agents of suicide (e.g., firearms) and identification of, and support for, high-risk groups.

Pickett, W., King, W. D., Faelker, T., Lees, R. E. M., Morrison, H. I., & Bienefeld, M. (1999). Suicides among Canadian farm operators. *Chronic Diseases in Canada, 20*(3), 105-110.

OBJECTIVES: To describe rates of suicide among male farm operators in Canada and to compare these rates with those in the general male population.

METHODS: Data were from Statistics Canada's Canadian Farm Operator Cohort (CFOC) database. Records from the 1971 Census of Agriculture, the 1971 Central Farm Register, and the 1971 Census of the Population were linked for a cohort of 326,256 Canadian male farm operators. Information on deaths from 1971 to 1987 was provided through a link to the Canadian Mortality Database. Outcome measures were age-specific and age-standardized rates of completed suicide (ICD-9-CM E-codes 950-959). Rates for the general Canadian male population also were calculated, based on published data.

DEFINITION OF RURAL AGING: No definition of rural was provided; no information on the farm size or type was available.

RESULTS RELATED TO RURAL AGING: A total of 1,457 cases of suicide were identified from the CFOC for the years 1971 to 1987; 24% of suicides were in the 60 - 69 age group and 14% were in the 70+ group. Age-specific rates of suicide in the CFOC increased over time. The largest increases were in the 70+ group that included more farmers over time. Age-standardized rates of suicide for those aged 30 - 69 were 29.2 per 100,000 person-years [PY] in the CFOC, 24.0 per 100,000 PYs in the CFOC excluding Quebec (which had data linkage concerns), and 27.0 per 100,000 PYs among Canadian males in general. After adjusting for age, provincial farm suicide rates were generally lower than or equivalent to those observed in the comparison populations of Canadian males.

CONCLUSIONS: Suicide rates for Canadian farmers appear to be lower than rates for the general population. The authors speculate that high levels of social support traditionally available in Canadian farm communities may protect farm operators from abnormally high rates of suicide. In addition, there may be differential under-reporting of farm suicides by coroners and medical examiners.

Quan, H., & Arboleda-Flórez, J. (1999). Elderly suicide in Alberta: Difference by gender. *Canadian Journal of Psychiatry, 44*(8), 762-768.

OBJECTIVES: To determine gender differences in suicides by individuals aged 55+ in the province of Alberta, particularly with regards to demographic characteristics, place of suicide, suicide method, previous suicide behaviour, and precipitant stressors.

METHODS: Information was abstracted from the records of the Office of the Chief Medical Examiner of Alberta for all suicides of individuals aged 55+ from 1984 to 1995. Demographic characteristics, autopsy reports, toxicological reports, copies of hospital charts or emergency records, suicide notes, psychological profiles, and any other information relevant to the suicide case available in the files were recorded. Precipitant stressors were categorized as physical illness, mental illness (including depression), marital problems, loss of job, death of close person, financial difficulties, legal issues (committed crime), fear of nursing home admission, and other.

DEFINITION OF RURAL: Alberta was divided in urban areas (Calgary, Edmonton, Fort McMurray, Lethbridge, Medicine Hat, Red Deer, and St. Albert) and rural areas with a threshold of 30,000 residents, based on the 1991 population.

RESULTS RELATED TO RURAL AGING: There were 920 suicides by individuals aged 55+; this included 66 females aged 65 - 74, 33 females aged 75+, 209 males aged 65 - 74, and 141 males aged 75+. Rural males accounted for 47% of the male suicides while rural females constituted 28% of the female suicides. Further analyses revealed no differences in the characteristics of rural and urban females committing suicide. However, rural elderly males who committed suicide, compared to urban males, were more likely to be single, and to employ more lethal methods of suicide such as gunshot. They were less likely to use poisoning or vehicle exhaust. Legal problems were more likely to be a precipitator while financial difficulties were less likely for rural males.

CONCLUSIONS: The authors urge careful and critical interpretation of their results due to issues of under-reporting. However, the study suggests that there are gender differences in the method of suicide and precipitators, as well as rural-urban differences that require further attention.

MEDICATIONS/IMMUNIZATIONS

Medications: General

Grymonpre, R. E., & Steele, J. W. (1998). The Medication Information Line for the Elderly: An 8-year cumulative analysis. *The Annals of Pharmacotherapy, 32,* **743-748.**

OBJECTIVES: To present an 8-year (1985 - 1992) cumulative analysis of the 12,743 calls received by the Medication Information Line for the Elderly (MILE), a consumer-oriented drug information service in the province of Manitoba.

METHODS: Data on all calls received by MILE between January 1985 and December 1992 were documented using a standard format. Certain calls were selected by a pharmacist for follow-up based on the nature and predicted severity of the inquiry. MILE was located in the Faculty of Pharmacy of the University of Manitoba and staffed by experienced, practicing pharmacists. Calls were received from older adults and their care providers. Only a local Winnipeg telephone number was used until 1987 when a toll-free number was available for rural Manitoba residents.

DEFINITION OF RURAL: Rural referred to calls originating outside Winnipeg. Winnipeg is the major urban centre in Manitoba.

RESULTS RELATED TO RURAL AGING: A total of 12,743 calls were made to MILE during the study period. Calls were more likely to have been made by females (73%). Fifty-eight percent of the calls were made by persons aged 65+. Only 6% of calls were from outside Winnipeg. The annual proportion of calls from rural Manitoba was consistently between 5% and 6%. Between 1987 and 1992, callers were asked about having a regular pharmacist. Older consumers in Winnipeg were more likely than their rural counterparts to indicate that they had a regular pharmacist. No other rural-urban differences were discussed.

CONCLUSIONS: The authors call for increased study of the underutilization of the service by the rural community. They speculate that individuals who called long distance to the busy, toll-free university switchboard may not have gotten through to MILE and that older rural consumers may have a closer relationship with their health care provider and rely on this individual for medication information.

Hagen, B. F., Armstrong-Esther, C., Quail, P., Williams, R. J., Norton, P., Le Navenec, C.-L., Ikuta, R., Osis, M., Congdon, V., & Zieb, R. (2005). Neuroleptic and benzodiazepine use in long-term care in urban and rural Alberta: Characteristics and results of an education intervention to ensure appropriate use. *International Psychogeriatrics, 17*(4), 631-652.

OBJECTIVES: To examine the use of psychotropic drugs in 24 rural and urban long-term care (LTC) facilities, and to compare the effects of an education intervention for LTC staff and family members on the use of psychotropic drugs in intervention versus control facilities. The facilities were located in the southern area of the province of Alberta.

METHODS: The study design was an interrupted time series with a non-equivalent no-treatment control group time series. Data on drug use were collected in LTC facilities (10 urban, 14 rural) for three 2-month time periods before and after the intervention. The 10 urban facilities had 1,666 beds and the 14 rural LTC facilities had 648 beds. Pharmacy records were used to collect data on drug, class of drug, dose, administration, and start/stop dates. Chart reviews provided demographics, prn (as-needed) drug use, and indications for drug use on 2,443 residents. An education intervention on psychotropic drug use in LTC was offered to intervention physicians, nursing staff, pharmacists, and family members in 5 urban and 7 rural facilities.

DEFINITION OF RURAL: The urban facilities were located in Calgary while the rural facilities were from the two surrounding rural health regions.

RESULTS RELATED TO RURAL AGING: Approximately one-third of residents received a psychotropic drug during the study, often for considerable lengths of time. More urban LTC residents received neuroleptics and benzodiazepines than their rural counterparts (26% vs. 16%, and 18% vs. 9%, respectively). There also were significant rural-urban differences in the prn use of neuroleptics: 30% of urban neuroleptic prescriptions were written and administered on a prn basis compared to 15% of the rural prescriptions. No significant differences emerged in the prn use of benzodiazepines. The education intervention did not result in any significant decline in the use of these drugs in intervention facilities.

CONCLUSIONS: The results suggest substantial use of psychotropic drugs in LTC, although rural LTC residents received approximately half the number of psychotropic drugs compared with urban residents. A resource-intensive intervention did not significantly decrease the use of psychotropics. The authors call for better monitoring of psychotropic drugs in LTC, particularly given that voluntary educational efforts alone may be ineffective agents of change.

Johnson, D., Jin, Y., Quan, H., & Cujec, B. (2003). Beta-blockers and angiotensin-converting enzyme inhibitors/receptor blockers prescriptions after hospital discharge for heart failure are associated with decreased mortality in Alberta, Canada. *Journal of the American College of Cardiology, 42*(8), 1438-1445.

OBJECTIVES: To evaluate use of beta-blockers and angiotensin-converting enzyme (ACE) inhibitors or receptor blockers (RBs) in congestive heart failure (CHF) among older adults in the province of Alberta.

METHODS: Administrative hospital discharge abstracts and drug data for the period October 1, 1994 to December 31, 1999 were analyzed for patients aged 65+. Data sources included the Canadian Institute for Health Information's Inpatient Discharge Abstract Database for Alberta (1992/93 - 1999/2000) and the Alberta Health Insurance Plan Registry File (1994/95 - 2000/01). Sociodemographic variables and transfers, as well as physician and hospital characteristics including hospital location were examined. All prescriptions for either beta-blockers or ACE inhibitors/RBs within a 3-month period before a hospital admission or after hospital discharge were considered. Heart failure outcomes were the length of stay and in-hospital mortality.

DEFINITION OF RURAL: Rural, regional, and metropolitan hospitals were compared, based on the service population size for each hospital and whether the hospital had angiography capability. The categorization was: rural hospitals with low volume (n = 77; < 200 cases); rural hospitals with a high volume (n = 25; 204 - 606 cases); regional hospitals located in one of the five non-metropolitan regional health care cities (n = 5; 238 - 646 cases); metropolitan hospitals located in the metropolitan health regions of Calgary and Edmonton without angiography capability (n = 6; 327 - 2,199 cases); and metropolitan hospitals located in the metropolitan health regions of Calgary and Edmonton with angiography capability (n = 3; 1,793 - 2,700 cases).

RESULTS RELATED TO RURAL AGING: There were 11,854 hospitalizations for newly diagnosed CHF. Compared to older patients receiving either beta-blockers or ACE inhibitors/RBs, or both, those not receiving either prescription were more likely to be admitted into a small rural hospital and less likely to be admitted into a metropolitan hospital with angiography capability. No rural-urban comparisons of health outcomes were provided. One-year crude mortality was higher in those not receiving either beta blockers or ACE inhibitors/RBs than in those receiving either drug or both. Adjusted one year mortality rates were lower for older adults who were prescribed either beta blockers, ACE inhibitors/RBs, or both.

CONCLUSIONS: The authors argue that this population-based study of incident CHF hospitalizations among older adults demonstrates an association between decreased mortality and the use of beta-blockers, ACE inhibitors/RBs, or a combination of both. They briefly discuss a paradox of need where those most likely to benefit from practice (low volume, small rural hospitals) are the least likely to receive them.

COMMENTS: **Thornton, P. L., & Ahmed, A. (2004). Angiotensin-converting enzyme inhibitors, Beta-blockers, and mortality in systolic heart failure.** *Journal of the American College of Cardiology, 43*(7), **1333.** The authors offered possible explanations for the relatively low rates of ACE inhibitors and beta-blockers in this population, and the apparent lack of survival benefits of their combined use. The comment and the reply from Johnson and Cujec do not include a discussion on hospital location.

Klinke, J. A., Johnson, J. A., Guirguis, L. M., Toth, E. L., Lee, T. K., Lewanczuk, R. Z., & Majumdar, S. R. (2004). Underuse of aspirin in type 2 diabetes mellitus: Prevalence and correlates of therapy in rural Canada. *Clinical Therapeutics, 26(3), 439-446.*

OBJECTIVES: To assess the rate of adherence to guidelines for aspirin use, and to describe the correlates of aspirin use in patients with Type 2 diabetes mellitus (DM) living in two northern rural regions in the province of Alberta.

METHODS: Data were collected between April and October 2000 from a cohort of patients at the time of their enrollment in a multidisciplinary outreach program designed to improve their quality of care. In-person interviews were completed with 394 patients who had been recruited by primary care physicians, nurses, DM educators, dieticians, and pharmacists. Self-reported use of antiplatelet therapy (aspirin or others) was recorded. Patients were classified into two groups. The antiplatet group regularly used at least one of the following: aspirin, clopidogrel, ticlopidine, or dipyridamole; the other group did not use these medications. The sample size for this analysis was 342 patients ranging in age from 28 to 86 (mean = 62.9); 56% were female.

DEFINITION OF RURAL: The study was undertaken in two rural regions of northern Alberta. The populations of the intervention and control regions were 20,000 and 25,000 residents, respectively.

RESULTS RELATED TO RURAL AGING: Despite guideline recommendations, only 78 patients (23%) were regularly taking aspirin alone, aspirin in combination with a thienopyridine, or a thienopyridine alone. The use of antiplatelet therapy increased with age, from 2% of patients aged < 50 years to 50% of the 80+ age group. The multivariate analysis revealed that older age, symptomatic coronary artery disease, and male sex were the only statistically significant factors associated with use of antiplatelet therapy.

CONCLUSIONS: The authors argue that aspirin is a safe, inexpensive, and readily available therapy that is effective for preventing cardiovascular disease, and that patients with Type 2 DM are particularly likely to benefit from such preventive therapy. Unlike other therapies for which undertreatment in older patients is common, the use of antiplatelets increased with age. From the authors' perspectives, aspirin should be included and better promoted as a factor in high-quality, evidence-based DM management.

Ko, D. T., Mamdani, M., & Alter, D. A. (2004). Lipid-lowering therapy with statins in high-risk elderly patients: The treatment-risk paradox. *Journal of the American Medical Association, 291*(15), 1864-1870.

OBJECTIVES: To examine the association between physicians' treatment aggressiveness and baseline cardiovascular risk for patients aged 66+ in the province of Ontario.

METHODS: Data were from the Geriatric Ontario Longitudinal Database (GOLD) that was created by linking several major health care administrative databases in Ontario. GOLD included 1.44 million Ontario residents aged 66+ as of April 1, 1998. This analysis was limited to the 396,077 patients who had a history of cardiovascular disease or diabetes while undergoing medical treatment. Cardiovascular disease was defined as one or more of the following: cardiovascular hospitalization within 5 years, coronary intervention (cardiac catheterization, percutaneous coronary intervention, or coronary artery bypass graft surgery) within 5 years, or angina (defined as concurrent use of nitrates within the year of cohort inception). Baseline cardiovascular risk was derived using a risk-adjustment index in which the probability of death after 3 years of follow-up was modeled. The likelihood of statin prescription was determined, stratified by baseline cardiovascular risk, after adjusting for age, sex, socioeconomic status, and rural or urban residence. The mean age of the study sample was 75 years, 55% were females and 18% resided in rural areas.

DEFINITION OF RURAL: Postal codes were used to categorize the sample as rural versus urban; no additional information was provided.

RESULTS RELATED TO RURAL AGING: Only 75,617 patients (19%) were prescribed statins. Patients not prescribed statins were more likely to live in rural areas; to have diabetes, congestive heart failure or stroke; and to have lower socioeconomic status. The prescription of statins diminished progressively as baseline cardiovascular risk and future probability of death increased.

CONCLUSIONS: Results are congruent with other studies indicating that statin therapy is underutilized. The authors suggest that, since the benefits of a therapy are dependent on the baseline risk, the maximum benefits of statins may not be fully realized.

Landry, C., Larose, D., & Collerette, C. (1999). La surconsommation de psychotropes. (Overuse of psychotropic drugs in seniors). *The Canadian Nurse, 95*(5), 45-50.

OBJECTIVES: To determine the rates of use of all types of prescribed medications by older adults, and to investigate practice regarding the use of psychotropic drugs in the province of Quebec.

METHODS: In this 1995 study, 549 respondents were randomly selected from 22 municipalities located in the territory CLSC of Hates Laurentides (response rate 77%). The structured interview was focused on six categories of interest: sociodemographic characteristics, familial and social relationships and habits, self-perceived health, use of medications, general attitude towards the use of medications, and life satisfaction.

DEFINITION OF RURAL: Comparisons were made between the rates of consumption of psychotropic drugs among the residents of 4 larger municipalities (population > 2,000) and the residents of the 18 smaller municipalities.

RESULTS RELATED TO RURAL AGING: While 19% of the respondents reported taking no drugs at all, 24% had at least five prescriptions. Having fewer medications was associated with being well informed about the medications. While 27% said they never received information about their prescription, 17% indicated that the labels on their prescription bottles were useless as the print was too small, too pale, or because they could not read them. Almost one-half (43%) acknowledged that they occasionally forgot whether they had taken their medication. Sex, perceived health status, depression, and population density were significantly related to use of psychotropic drugs. Older adults living in rural areas were less likely to use psychotropic drugs.

CONCLUSIONS: Issues related to the need for a partnership of nurses with the community and for the recognition of the nurse's role in contributing to older adults' sustaining their autonomy through understanding, learning, and recognizing their own and their networks' potential are discussed.

McBride, J. E., Pater, J. L., Dorland, J. L., & Lam, Y.-M. (1997). **Extent and variation of omeprazole prescribing in an elderly population of Ontario.** *The Annals of Pharmacotherapy, 31*, 411-416.

OBJECTIVES: To determine the extent of omeprazole prescribing over a 1-year period, the variation in omeprazole prescribing according to age group, gender, and geographic region, and the extent of inappropriate prescribing of omeprazole, in the population aged 65+ in the province of Ontario.

METHODS: This study was a retrospective drug utilization review of prescription drug insurance claims in the Ontario Drug Benefit program claims database. Claims for all individuals aged 65+ who received a prescription for omeprazole from April 1, 1992 to March 31, 1993 were included. Omeprazole is a prescription drug used to treat ulcers; gastroesophageal reflux disease (GERD), a condition in which backward flow of acid from the stomach causes heartburn and injury of the food pipe (esophagus); and conditions where the stomach produces too much acid, such as Zollinger-Ellison syndrome. The pharmacy division code for the first prescription was used as a proxy for county of residence. Prescribing of omeprazole was defined as inappropriate if a first-line antiulcer drug (i.e., histamine 2-receptor antagonist) was not prescribed within 1 - 6 months of the first prescription claim for omeprazole.

DEFINITION OF RURAL: No definition of rural was provided; analyses focused on 48 counties. The number of older adults in each county ranged from 11,195 in the rural island county of Manitoulin to 291,095 in metropolitan Toronto.

RESULTS RELATED TO RURAL AGING: A total of 29,936 older adults in Ontario received omeprazole from April 1, 1992 to March 31, 1993 (2.53 recipients per 100 eligible population). The group most frequently prescribed omeprazole was females aged 65 - 74, followed by females aged 75+ and males aged 75+, and then males aged 65 - 74 years. Omeprazole prescribing varied widely among the 48 provincial counties (range of 1.66 to 4.52 recipients per 100 eligible population). There was no evidence of a clustering effect in omeprazole prescribing at the county level. Prescribing of omeprazole was considered to be inappropriate for 81% of recipients, with county variation from 71% to 93%.

CONCLUSIONS: This study identified regional variations in omeprazole prescribing. The authors speculate that this may be due to differences in the population characteristics, availability of healthcare resources, and variability in physician-prescribing habits. They call for future research on the determinants of variation in prescribing by geographic region. The limitations of computer-based drug utilization reviews are discussed.

Shah, B. R. , Mamdani, M., & Kopp, A. (2003). Drug use in older people with diabetes. In J. E. Hux, G. L. Booth, P. M. Slaughter & A. Laupacis (Eds.), *Diabetes in Ontario: An ICES Practice Atlas* (pp. 3.51-3.75). Toronto, ON: Institute for Clinical Evaluative Sciences (ICES).

OBJECTIVES: To examine prescription patterns for therapies proven to be beneficial for older people with diabetes mellitus (DM) in the province of Ontario.

METHODS: Data were from the Ontario Drug Benefit (OBD) Program database that contained drug prescription information for Ontario residents aged 65+. Individuals with DM were identified, differentiating Type 1 from Type 2 diabetes was not possible. All dispensed medications were included without regard to ingestion rates. Drugs examined included antihyperglycemic drugs, antihypertensive drugs, angiotensin converting enzyme inhibitors (ACEIs), and lipid-lowering drugs. A cross-sectional yearly time series analysis of prescriptions dispensed from 1994/95 to 2000/01 was conducted. Variations by county were examined, using small area variation analysis.

DEFINITION OF RURAL: County-level data were provided. Although reference was made to rural counties, no definition was provided.

RESULTS RELATED TO RURAL AGING: The distribution and treatment regimes for all Ontarians with DM and aged 65+ in 1999 were as follows: no anti-hyperglycemic medications (40%), single oral anti-hyperglycemic drugs (29%), multiple oral anti-hyperglycemic drugs (17%), insulin only (11%), and oral anti-hyperglycemic drugs plus insulin (3%). There was little variation between counties in the use of these medications in 1999. The highest rate of ACEIs use was in predominantly rural and northern counties in 1999.

CONCLUSIONS: The authors call for subsequent analyses to examine the impact of the 1998 Canadian Diabetes Association clinical practice guidelines on prescription rates and of education efforts to improve provider adherence.

Supina, A. L., Guirguis, L. M., Majumdar, S. R., Lewanczuk, R. Z., Lee, T. K., Toth, E. L., & Johnson, J. A. (2004). **Treatment gaps for hypertension management in rural Canadian patients with Type 2 diabetes mellitus.** *Clinical Therapeutics, 26*(4), 598-606.

OBJECTIVES: To describe the patterns of medication use for hypertension by rural northern patients with Type 2 diabetes mellitus (DM) in the province of Alberta.

METHODS: Information was collected from a cohort of patients aged 20+ with Type 2 DM living in two adjacent rural regions of northern Alberta. These patients were enrolling in a diabetes care quality-improvement program as part of the Diabetes Outreach Van Enhancement (DOVE) study.

DEFINITION OF RURAL: Two comparable and geographically adjacent rural regions in northern Alberta were studied. The intervention region had a population of 20,000; the control region's population was 25,000. Both were about a 6-hour drive away from the nearest secondary- or tertiary-care referral centre.

RESULTS RELATED TO RURAL AGING: After controlling for systolic blood pressure, male sex, older age, lower self-reported physical health, higher body mass index, and past/current smoking all were significantly associated with receiving antihypertensive treatment.

CONCLUSIONS: Aggressive management of hypertension in patients with Type 2 diabetes is one of the more important treatment strategies for preventing long-term complications in these patients. However, results of this investigation indicate that a number of factors, including increased age, are significantly associated with a lack of treatment for hypertension.

Medications: Prescribing/Use

Dhalla, I. A., Anderson, G. M., Mamdani, M. M., Bronskill, S. E., Sykora, K., & Rochon, P. A. (2002). Inappropriate prescribing before and after nursing home admission. *Journal of the American Geriatrics Society, 50*, 995-1000.

OBJECTIVES: To compare the prevalence of inappropriate prescribing of drugs before and after nursing home admission, and to determine patient and physician characteristics associated with inappropriate prescribing in the nursing home setting in the province of Ontario.

METHODS: Data were obtained from the Ontario Drug Benefit Plan database. Between April 1997 and March 1999, 19,111 adults aged 66+ were considered as newly admitted residents of nursing homes in Ontario. Mean age at the time of their first nursing home prescription was 82.6 years; 72% were female. A subset of the Beers (1991, 1997) criteria was used to characterize and compare the prevalence of inappropriate prescribing (as indicated by the prescription of 1 of 49 drugs deemed to be inappropriate by those criteria 1 year before and 1 year after nursing home admission). The drugs covered 15 therapeutic classes: benzodiazepines, other sedatives or hypnotics, nonsteroidal anti-inflammatory drugs (NSAIDs), narcotics, antihypertensives, platelet inhibitors, dementia treatments, antiarrhythmics, skeletal muscle relaxants, antimuscarinics, antidepressants, oral hypoglycemics, antispasmodics, antiemetics, and antihistamines. Patient characteristics included sex and age; physician characteristics were sex, age as of April 1998, specialty, location of practice, and whether there were multiple prescribers.

DEFINITION OF RURAL: Practices were classified as urban when located in an area with a minimum population concentration of 1,000 and a population density of at least 400 per square kilometre (Statistics Canada, 1996). The remaining locations were described as non-urban.

RESULTS RELATED TO RURAL AGING: The proportion of patients receiving a prescription for at least one inappropriate drug decreased from 25% before to 21% after nursing home admission, a difference that was statistically significant. The most commonly prescribed inappropriate drugs after nursing home admission were anticholinergic antidepressants (6%), long half-life benzodiazepines (6%), and oxybutynin [a muscle relaxant] (5%). Rural-urban differences were not presented. However, patients who had a non-urban physician were more likely to have inappropriate prescribing than their urban counterparts, taking other physician and patient characteristics into account.

CONCLUSIONS: Despite the decrease in inappropriate prescribing before and after admission to a nursing home, more than 1 in 5 residents received inappropriate drug therapies in the nursing home. The authors call for further studies and interventions to reduce the risk of adverse events. Given their findings that patients outside major metropolitan areas in Ontario were at increased risk of inappropriate prescribing, they argue that targeted measures such as education programs based within a region may reduce the prevalence of those prescriptions.

McKim, W. A., Stones, M. J., & Kozma, A. (1990). Factors predicting medicine use in institutionalized and non-institutionalized elderly. *Canadian Journal on Aging,* *9*(1), 23-34.

OBJECTIVES: To explore factors predicting medicine use in institutionalized and non-institutionalized elderly in the province of Newfoundland.

METHODS: Data were from a larger study that involved representative samples from each region and random sampling of locales within each region. A total of 380 elderly adults living in the community and in institutions were assessed with a battery of mental health, physical health, and drug use questionnaires in 1979, with re-assessment 12 to 18 months later. Respondents were asked to describe all the drugs they were currently taking and specifically were requested to indicate both prescription and over-the-counter drugs. In the analyses of non-institutionalized respondents, a location variable (urban vs. rural) was included.

DEFINITION OF RURAL: Rural settings were defined as locales with populations of < 3,000.

RESULTS RELATED TO RURAL AGING: There were no significant rural-urban differences in the number of medicines taken by the non-institutionalized older adults. The severity of illness and subjective assessment of health determined the number of medicines taken by non-institutionalized respondents. Greater disease severity and poorer subjective health were associated with increased medicine use. For the institutionalized older adults, disease severity was the only variable that predicted medicine use (e.g., greater disease severity, increased medicine use). Males consumed an average of 1.60 medicines and females averaged 2.15 medicines. Medicine use was highly stable over the 12 - 18 month study period.

CONCLUSIONS: The authors call for further study on physician prescribing practices.

Tamblyn, R. M., McLeod, P. J., Abrahamowicz, M., Monette, J., Gayton, D. C., Berkson, L., Dauphinee, W. D., Grad, R. M., Huang, A. R., Isaac, L. M., Schnarch, B. S., & Snell, L. S. (1994). Questionable prescribing for elderly patients in Quebec. *Canadian Medical Association Journal, 150*(11), 1801-1809.

OBJECTIVES: To estimate the prevalence of questionable and rational high-risk prescribing to older adults of three drug groups most commonly implicated in drug-related illness, in the province of Quebec.

METHODS: This retrospective prevalence study drew on all prescription and billing records from the relevant provincial databases of the Regie de l'assurance-maladie du Quebec for the period January 1 to December 31, 1990. The three drug groups were cardiovascular drugs, psychotropic drugs, and nonsteroidal anti-inflammatory drugs (NSAIDs). Data were from a regionally stratified random sample of 63,268 elderly medicare registrants who made at least one visit to a physician in 1990 and were not living in a health care institution for the entire year. Prescription information was examined for three types of high-risk prescribing: rational and questionable drug combinations, excessive treatment duration, and drugs relatively contraindicated for use in elderly people.

DEFINITION OF RURAL: Twelve health regions were included in the analysis. Health care regions were grouped as southeastern, southcentral, southwestern, and north. Reference was made to the remote region of Nord du Québec.

RESULTS RELATED TO RURAL AGING: Overall, 53% of these older patients experienced one or more events of high-risk prescribing, and 46% experienced at least one prescribing event that was questionable. The remote region had the lowest prevalence of high-risk prescribing in all drug categories. There were significant unexplained regional differences in the prevalence of high-risk prescribing, particularly of psychotropic drugs.

CONCLUSIONS: The prevalence of questionable high-risk prescribing, especially of psychotropic drugs, was substantial among elderly people. The authors speculated that the lowest prevalence of high-risk prescribing among patients in the remote region may have been because of reduced access to medical services and differences in the way that medical services and drugs are reimbursed and recorded.

COMMENTS: **Pereles, L. (1994). Appropriate prescribing for elderly people.** *Canadian Medical Association Journal, 151*(9), 1236. This author suggested that researchers need to shift their emphasis from the analysis of large databases to the more difficult issue of appropriateness of prescribing in elderly people. No comments were made with regards to regional differences.

COMMENTS: **Alibhai, S. M. H. (1994). Questionable prescribing for elderly patients.** *Canadian Medical Association Journal, 151*(11), 1555. This author argued that there are difficulties in the inherent assumptions in the indirect methods used by the researchers, and that these problems make it difficult to interpret the results. No comments were made with regards to regional differences. Tamblyn, McLeod, and Gayton responded to these criticisms but regional differences were not discussed.

Torrible, S. J., & Hogan, D. B. (1997). Medication use and rural seniors: Who really knows what they are taking? *Canadian Family Physician, 43*, 893-898.

OBJECTIVES: To determine whether listings of current medications obtained from the office file of patients' attending physicians and the pharmacy record of patients' dispensing pharmacists corresponded to the actual use of medications in a group of non-institutionalized older adults residing in rural communities in the province of Alberta.

METHODS: The study involved in-home interviews followed by retrospective office chart and pharmacy database reviews in two southern Alberta rural communities. Eight family physicians agreed to participate and to approach patients in their practice to take part. In total, 25 patients aged 75+ as of January 1, 1994, living in a private dwelling, and having personal responsibilities for taking and monitoring their medications (with possible assistance by a spouse or other informal caregiver) were recruited between May 1, 1994 and September 1, 1994. There were 20 females and 5 males, with a mean age of 82.5 years. All four dispensing pharmacies agreed to participate. Information was obtained on currently consumed prescription drugs and over-the-counter (OTC) drugs, stored or discontinued prescribed medications, knowledge of medications by family physicians and pharmacists, and the number of prescribers or dispensing pharmacists.

DEFINITION OF RURAL: One community had a population of approximately 1,600, with 8% of the population aged 75+. This community had two family physicians, one pharmacy, and the local health unit. The nearest hospital was approximately 25 kilometres away. The other community had a population of about 6,900, with 9% aged 75+. There were 12 family physicians, several visiting specialists, a hospital, three pharmacies, and the local health unit.

RESULTS RELATED TO RURAL AGING: All patients were taking at least one medication regularly. The mean number of prescribed medications was 5.6 (range 0 - 14) while the mean of OTC medications was 3.5. The patients had a mean of 2.0 stored or discontinued medications (range 0 - 8). Cardiovascular drugs were the most common prescribed medication while vitamins and minerals were the most common OTC drugs. Attending family physicians and primary dispensing pharmacists typically only knew some of their patients' entire regimen of medications, with knowledge of OTC medications particularly limited. Pharmacists tended to be unaware of medications filled at other pharmacies or of drug samples given to the patients. The attending physician often was not aware of medications prescribed by former physicians or specialists. Concerns with medications (duplication of medications, potential drug interactions, or misuse of drugs) were evident for 22 of the 25 patients.

CONCLUSIONS: Misinformation about medication consumption by older adults was common among health care providers. Recommendations include undertaking routine medication reviews (with emphasis on OTC use), asking specific questions about actual consumption, encouraging use of one prescriber and one pharmacist, discouraging storage of discontinued medications, and reducing use of medication samples. The authors acknowledge that their small sample size from one rural area limits the generalizability of their results.

Vaccinations/Immunizations

Andrew, M. K., McNeil, S., Merry, H., & Rockwood, K. (2004). Rates of influenza vaccination in older adults and factors associated with vaccine use: A secondary analysis of the Canadian Study of Health and Aging. *BMC Public Health, 4*, 36-43.

OBJECTIVES: To determine influenza vaccination rates among community-dwelling older adults in Canada and to identify factors predictive of influenza vaccination.

METHODS: Data were from the Canadian Study of Health and Aging (CSHA), a population-based national cohort study of 10,263 older adults ($\geq$ 65) conducted in 1991. These analyses were limited to data from 5,007 community-dwelling CSHA participants without dementia for whom self-reported influenza vaccination status was known.

DEFINITION OF RURAL: Rural-urban comparisons were made but no definition of rural was provided.

RESULTS RELATED TO RURAL AGING: Slightly more than one-half of the respondents (55%) reported having received an influenza vaccination within the previous 2 years. Urban dwellers (56%) were significantly more likely to have been immunized than rural residents (51%). However, rural-urban residence did not retain significance in a multivariate analysis, suggesting that this association may be due to confounding factors.

CONCLUSIONS: Even in a publicly administered health care setting, influenza vaccination did not reach an important proportion of the elderly population. The authors raise the questions of access to vaccinations and how to improve uptake.

Duclos, P., & Hatcher, J. (1993). Epidemiology of influenza vaccination in Canada. *Canadian Journal of Public Health, 84*(5), 311-315.

OBJECTIVES: To assess influenza vaccine coverage among Canadian adults and to document reasons for not receiving the vaccine.

METHODS: Data were from Statistics Canada's 1991 General Social Survey that included questions about the fall/winter 1990/91 immunization campaign. A total of 11,924 usable responses were obtained (response rate 80%) from Canadians aged 15+, with weights applied to be representative of the Canadian population. Predictor variables included: sex, age, province of residence, size of community of residence, recommendation by a nurse or physician to receive a flu shot, level of family income, highest level of education obtained, and presence of at least one risk factor for complications of flu. A logistic regression model was run separately in populations aged < 65 and in populations aged 65+.

DEFINITION OF RURAL: Census metropolitan areas (CMAs) and all other areas (e.g., non-CMA areas) were compared.

RESULTS RELATED TO RURAL AGING: An estimated 14% of the Canadian population and 45% of the 65+ population surveyed received a 'flu' shot during the 1990/91 immunization campaign. The major predictor for receiving influenza vaccine was a recommendation by a nurse or physician. Two major reasons listed by persons aged 65+ for not receiving the flu vaccine were the belief they hardly ever get the flu, and the fear of side effects. Living in a metropolitan area did not increase the likelihood of receiving the flu vaccine.

CONCLUSIONS: The authors suggest that the most effective approach to increasing the proportion of high-risk Canadians (those aged 65+) receiving a vaccination would be to target health care providers. They indicate that limited sample size in less populated provinces prevented the detailed examination of the impact of demographic factors and reasons for not being immunized for each province.

Macdonald, A. J., Roberecki, S. A., & Cosway, N. L. (1996). Influenza immunization surveillance in rural Manitoba. *Canadian Journal of Public Health, 87*(3), 163-165.

OBJECTIVES: To examine influenza vaccine distribution and the population immunized by various health care providers, in the rural Interlake region of the province of Manitoba.

METHODS: This survey was conducted with primary care physicians, public health nurses, and institutions during the Fall 1994 provincial immunization program. Survey forms to record the number of doses given and the risk groups vaccinated were distributed in September 1994 and returned by January 1995.

DEFINITION OF RURAL: The study area was described as the rural Interlake region; no additional details were provided.

RESULTS RELATED TO RURAL AGING: Overall, 78% of the 8,960 doses distributed to the Interlake providers were actually given. Individuals aged 65+ were the most likely target group, receiving 67% of the doses. Coverage of Interlake residents aged 65+ was determined by Interlake providers to be 48%. This may be an underestimate of the extent of immunization as residents may have been vaccinated outside the region, particularly in Winnipeg. Public health nurses reported providing more vaccine to the well elderly, physicians reported vaccinating more of the chronically ill, and reports from institutions indicated that both residents and health care workers were vaccinated.

CONCLUSIONS: The authors speculate that influenza immunization coverage of the residents aged 65+ in the Interlake region is likely in accord with the recommended Canadian Consensus Conference of Influenza objectives. Information about the immunizations obtained outside the region is needed to confirm this. The use of public health nurses, physicians, and institutions was perceived to broaden the population coverage.

Russell, M. L. (1997). Influenza and tetanus immunization. Are adults up-to-date in rural Alberta? *Canadian Family Physician, 43*, 50-55.

OBJECTIVES: To estimate the proportion of adults living within the boundaries of the Drumheller Health Unit in the province of Alberta who had received tetanus or tetanus-diphtheria vaccine in the previous 10 years and the proportion of individuals aged 65+ who had received influenza vaccine within the last year.

METHODS: The study involved a directory-seeded, random digit dial telephone survey in Summer 1993. Information was collected about health knowledge, attitudes, and practices. Eligible subjects were aged 16+ and lived within health district boundaries. Data were presented for 343 respondents; 21% were aged 65+.

DEFINITION OF RURAL: The Drumheller Health Unit, a rural health unit in central Alberta, serviced a population of 31,000. The largest community in the area had a population of approximately 7,000.

RESULTS RELATED TO RURAL AGING: Overall, 55% of respondents aged 16+ had received tetanus vaccine in the last 10 years. This ranged from 95% of the 16 - 24 age group to 21% of the 65+ group. Over one-half (58%) of the 65+ age group had received influenza vaccine in the previous 12 months compared to 11% for those aged < 65. Individuals aged 65+ (90%) generally knew that influenza vaccine was recommended for people their age. Less likely was an awareness that influenza vaccine also was recommended for people with chronic health conditions, regardless of age.

CONCLUSIONS: The author concludes that coverage with influenza and tetanus vaccines varied with age but was generally unsatisfactory. Caution is urged in the generalizabilty of the results from this study that focuses on one relatively small rural area.

Russell, M. L., & Maxwell, C. J. (2000). The prevalence and correlates of influenza vaccination among a home care population. *Canadian Journal of Public Health, 91*(6), 441-444.

OBJECTIVES: To estimate the prevalence and correlates of influenza vaccination in a home care population in a rural Regional Health Authority (RHA) in the province of Alberta.

METHODS: This cross-sectional investigation involved linking the population-based Regional immunization and the Regional home oxygen information systems to the Regional home care information system. In Alberta, individuals aged 65+ and all younger persons with chronic health conditions are eligible for publicly funded influenza vaccine delivered by public health nurses, home care nurses, and private physicians. Each provider must provide the RHA with nominal data on the vaccines. The sample comprised 649 persons who had been admitted or discharged from the Regional Home Care Program from October 1 to December 1, 1998. Of the 649, 555 (86%) were aged 65+. Among the 65+ sample, the mean age was 81.8 and 70% were female.

DEFINITION OF RURAL: The total population of this rural RHA was 50,000. There were five districts within the RHA. No other information was provided.

RESULTS RELATED TO RURAL AGING: Among the 65+ age group, 65% were currently vaccinated against influenza. Multivariate analysis for the 65+ age group revealed that having a current vaccination was associated with not receiving nursing services, district of residence, and program status.

CONCLUSIONS: The Alberta target rate for influenza vaccination coverage for individuals aged 65+ was 75% in 1998. There were no specific targets for home care clients who tend to be both frail and elderly. Even using the 75% target, the current influenza vaccination rates for these home care clients were suboptimal. The authors suggest that possible explanations include health care provider factors, system-level factors, and client factors. Of particular interest was the finding that individuals who were not receiving services from registered nurses were more likely than other home care clients to have a current vaccination.

METHODS/CONCEPTUAL ISSUES

Havens, B., Stloukal, L., Racher, F., Norris, D., Keefe, J., & Coppin, A. (2001). Finding and using rural aging data: An international perspective. *The Journal of Rural Health, 17*(4), 350-355.

OBJECTIVES: To report on a workshop in which participants identified sources of data on rural aging.

METHODS: The workshop involved a series of presentations on issues faced in identifying and using various data to study rural aging.

DEFINITION OF RURAL: No definition of rural was provided.

RESULTS RELATED TO RURAL AGING: Participants shared many innovative and creative means for collecting, finding, and adapting more general data sources, and analyzing and using these data to further our understanding of rural aging phenomena.

CONCLUSIONS: The authors provide a number of recommendations, including the development of standard definitions of rural populations that are not simply a residual category of the population that is not urban, identifying the differences among rural communities, and whenever appropriate, establishing database linkages between agricultural census and other population data sets. Several directions for future research were identified.

Martin Matthews, A. (1988). Variations in the conceptualization and measurement of rurality: Conflicting findings on the elderly widowed. *Journal of Rural Studies,* *4*(2), 141-150.

OBJECTIVES: To examine distinctions between rural and urban older adults, based on whether rurality is conceptualized in ecological or sociocultural terms, in the province of Ontario.

METHODS: Four measures of rurality were contrasted: (1) current residence; (2) duration of community residence; (3) place of residence at age 16; and (4) a self-definition as rural. The first two were considered as ecological whereas the latter two were considered sociocultural. These differences were discussed in reference to a sample of 151 elderly widowed men and women.

DEFINITION OF RURAL: The definitions were as follows: current rural if living in a town of ≤ 9,999 population, long-time rural if rural now and had been rural for more than 15 years, rural reared if lived in town of ≤ 9,999 population at age 16, and self-definition of rural.

RESULTS RELATED TO RURAL AGING: Of the 151 individuals, 86 were currently rural, 61 were long-time rural, 97 were rural raised, and 61 were rural self-defined. Only 61% of the currently rural defined themselves as rural while 19% of the currently urban defined themselves as rural.

CONCLUSIONS: The author concludes that rurality exists as both an objective reality and a subjective identification. Calls are made for greater precision and specificity in the measurement of rurality.

Martin Matthews, A., & Vanden Heuvel, A. (1986). Conceptual and methodological issues in research on aging in rural versus urban environments. *Canadian Journal on Aging, 5*(1), 49-60.

OBJECTIVES: To identify conceptual and methodological problems characteristic of rural-urban comparisons in studies of population aging in Canada and the United States, focusing on implications for future Canadian research.

METHODS: A review of results from previous rural aging studies was undertaken.

DEFINITION OF RURAL: The issues of the definition of rural were central to this article.

RESULTS RELATED TO RURAL AGING: Three specific conceptual and methodological issues were identified as being problematic: lack of consistency and clarity in the definitions of rurality used and in the application of those definitions; inconsistency in the way rural-urban comparisons were made (either as a dichotomy or as a continuum) and representative communities chosen; and failure to acknowledge the importance of duration of residential experience in these studies.

CONCLUSIONS: The authors call for increased awareness of and sensitivity to issues of definition, comparability, and duration in future studies of rural aging.

Note: A similar paper also is available in the Papers of Rural Aging. Martin-Matthews, A., & Vanden Heuvel, A. (1986). Methodological issues in research on aging in rural versus urban environments (Papers on Rural Aging, No. 1). Guelph, ON: University School of Rural Planning and Development and Gerontology Research Centre, University of Guelph.

Rockwood, K., Stolee, P., Robertson, D., & Shillington, E. R. (1989). Response bias in a health status survey of elderly people. *Age & Ageing, 18*(3), 177-182.

OBJECTIVES: To compare respondents and non-respondents from the community sample of the 1981 Saskatchewan Health Status Survey of the Elderly.

METHODS: A stratified two-stage area probability sample was drawn from the Master Registration File of the Saskatchewan Hospital Services Plan. The sample was clustered by community and stratified by age (65 - 74, 75 - 84, 85+). A total of 1,614 individuals were considered as eligible for the study. Interviews were completed with 1,267 respondents (response rate 79%). Response bias was assessed by comparing the demographic characteristics and use of health care services of the two groups.

DEFINITION OF RURAL: No definition of rural was provided. Distinctions were made between cities, small cities/towns, and villages/rural municipalities.

RESULTS RELATED TO RURAL AGING: In the 85+ age cohort, the sample had disproportionately more urban dwellers who were interviewed. The rural 85+ group was no more difficult to contact and the number of refusals proportionally was lowest in the villages and rural municipalities. The issue was one of limited numbers of individuals aged 85+ in these communities; replacements were not always possible unlike in the cities and towns where there was a larger pool from which to draw. Among respondents, there were no significant urban/rural variations in the proportion of the 85+ group living alone, requiring assistance, receiving visitors, or using mobility aids. The proportions dependent in activities of daily living were similar for larger cities (50%), small cities/towns (45%), and rural (49%) residents. Overall, respondents used fewer hospital and physician services than non-respondents. These trends were significant for those aged 75+, suggesting better health for respondents.

CONCLUSIONS: Despite limitations in the field that lead to the under-representation of rural old adults aged 85+, urban-rural differences in the key health variables were not evident. However, the authors conclude that the statistics from this survey were conservative estimates of the ill health of the elderly.

MORTALITY

Burge, F. I., Lawson, B., & Johnston, G. (2005). Where a cancer patient dies: The effect of rural residency. *Journal of Rural Health, 21*(3), 233-238.

OBJECTIVES: To examine the relationship between rural residency of advanced cancer patients and location of death, in the province of Nova Scotia.

METHODS: Data were from three linked population-based administrative health data files: the Nova Scotia Cancer Centre Oncology Patient Information System (OPIS), the Nova Scotia Medical Services Insurance Physician Services file (MSIPS), and the Nova Scotia Hospital Admissions/Separations (HAS) database. Subjects were Nova Scotia residents aged 18+ who died of cancer from 1992 to 1997. Measures included location of death (hospital or out-of-hospital death) and urban-rural residency. The urban-rural indicator was based on an enumeration area and was created from postal code information.

DEFINITION OF RURAL: The Statistics Canada definition of rural as "living outside of places with a population size of 1,000 or more, OR living outside of places with population densities of 400 or more per square kilometre" was used (p. 234).

RESULTS RELATED TO RURAL AGING: Of the 13,652 cancer deaths for all ages in Nova Scotia, 6,174 (45%) occurred in rural areas. Of these rural deaths, 1,471 (24%) occurred out-of-hospital. Out-of-hospital deaths in rural areas increased from 16% in 1992 to just over 27% in 1997, a trend similar to that for urban deaths. The 65+ age group accounted for 75% of the deaths from 1992 to 1997 (29% aged 65 - 74; 31% aged 75 - 85; 15% aged >85). Overall, rural residents were less likely to experience out-of-hospital deaths than those in urban locations although age did not emerge as a significant factor.

CONCLUSIONS: The authors argue that patients with cancer living in the rural setting who wish to die at home may face unique challenges. The limitations of the definition of rural are discussed.

Hasselback, P., & Neutel, C. I. (1990). Risk for commercial fishing deaths in Canadian Atlantic provinces. *British Journal of Industrial Medicine, 47*(7), 498-501.

OBJECTIVES: To determine the risk of mortality related to occupation for commercial fishermen in the provinces of Nova Scotia, New Brunswick, and Prince Edward Island.

METHODS: A cohort of 31,415 fishermen licensed by the federal Department of Fisheries during the period 1975 to 1983 was identified from the registry of licensed commercial fisheries. Mortality data were obtained from the Canada Mortality Data Base and the Marine Casualty Investigation Unit (MCI), and were confirmed by examination of death certificates. Death rates were calculated for the age groups of 15 - 34, 35 - 54, 55 - 74, and 75+.

DEFINITION OF RURAL: No definition of rural was provided.

RESULTS RELATED TO RURAL AGING: Eighty-four deaths likely to be related to fishing were recorded; 12 were in the 55 - 74 age group and 1 death was in the 75+ age group. The annual mortality was 45.8 per 100,000 fishermen. The mortality rates for the 55 - 74 age group and the 75+ age group were 30.2 and 34.8, respectively.

CONCLUSIONS: Incidence of mortality was determined using the number of identified cases and the potential years of exposure of the cohort. The authors speculate that their results likely underestimate commercial fishing deaths because of the veracity of the data for both the numerator and denominator. They conclude that fishing is one of the most hazardous occupations in terms of work-related mortality.

See also Neutel, C. I. (1990).

Morrison, H., Savitz, D., Semenciw, R., Hulka, B., Mao, Y., Morison, D., & Wigle, D. (1993). Farming and prostate cancer mortality. *American Journal of Epidemiology, 137*(3), 270-280.

OBJECTIVES: To identify specific exposures that put farmers at an increased risk of prostate cancer in the provinces of Manitoba, Saskatchewan, and Alberta.

METHODS: This study was based on a retrospectively assembled cohort of male farmers aged 45+ in Manitoba, Saskatchewan, and Alberta, identified through the 1971 Census of Agriculture, the 1971 Central Farm Register, and the 1971 Census of Population. Data were linked to the Canadian National Mortality Database for the period June 1971 to December 1987. The relationship between the risk of dying from prostate cancer and various farm practices as identified on the 1971 Census of Agriculture, including exposure to chickens, cattle, pesticides, and fuels was examined.

DEFINITION OF RURAL: No definition of rural was provided and information was not provided on farm size or type.

RESULTS RELATED TO RURAL AGING: A total of 1,148 prostate cancer deaths and 2,213,478 person-years were observed. The standardized mortality ratio for all causes was .71. The rate for prostrate cancer decreased with increasing age, from 1.44 for the 45 - 54 age group to .63 for the 85+ age group. A weak, but statistically significant, association was found between the number of acres sprayed with herbicides in 1970 and the risk of prostate cancer mortality. When the analysis was restricted to farmers believed to be subject to the least amount of misclassification, the risk associated with acres sprayed with herbicides increased. No other farm exposures were associated with any detectable pattern of risk. No age-specific analyses on these associations were presented.

CONCLUSIONS: Exposure to herbicides appears to result in an increased risk of dying from prostate cancer. The authors suggest that exposure histories may be less accurate among older farmers who likely have experienced limited farm exposures and whose death certificates are less likely to be accurate. They encourage further research to examine the effects of herbicides on prostate cancer.

COMMENTS: **Ireland, B., Acquaviella, J.F., & Olsen, G. (1994). Re: Farming and prostate cancer mortality. *American Journal of Epidemiology, 140*(11), 1057-1058.** These authors raised three issues: (1) underascertainment of decedents; (2) exclusions from the analysis of rate ratio by acres sprayed with herbicides; and (3) the lack of correlation between reported exposures by individual farmers at various time points and the related variation in rate ratio that suggest any one cross-sectional measure is a questionable indicator of relevant exposure.

REPLY FROM AUTHORS: **Morrison, H., Villeneuve, P., Semenciw, R., & Wigle, D. (1994). The authors reply. *American Journal of Epidemiology, 140*(11), 1058-1059.** Response to the three issues were as follows: (1) *underascertainment of decedents*: The authors argued that the effect of more operators of larger, more successful farms appearing in the 1981 Census should result in a reduced mortality risk for farmers who spray, not an increased risk; (2) *exclusions from the analysis of rate ratio by acres sprayed with herbicides*: The authors re-analyzed the data relevant to Ireland et al.'s suggestion. Including unexposed farmers who reported customs expenses made only trivial differences in the risk estimates; and (3) *lack of correlation between reported exposures by individual farmers at various time points and the related variation in rate ratio that suggest any one cross-sectional measure is a questionable indicator of relevant exposure*: The authors agreed that a single year estimate of exposure is not the preferred route.

Neutel, C. I. (1990). Mortality in fishermen: An unusual age distribution. *British Journal of Industrial Medicine, 47*(8), 528-532.

OBJECTIVES: To compare age-specific standardized mortality ratios (ASMRs) of commercial fishermen aged < 55 years and those aged 55+ in the provinces of Nova Scotia, New Brunswick, and Prince Edward Island.

METHODS: A cohort of 31,415 fishermen licensed by the federal Department of Fisheries and Oceans during the period 1975 to 1983 was identified from the registry of licensed commercial fisheries. Mortality data were obtained through a link to the Canadian Mortality Data Base. Over 2,000 of the fisherman were aged 70+.

DEFINITION OF RURAL: No definition of rural was provided.

RESULTS RELATED TO RURAL AGING: Fishermen aged < 55 had ASMRs between 1.4 and 1.7 for death from all causes and around 1.0 for death from non-accidental causes. The older fishermen (aged 55+) had ASMRs as low as 0.6 for all causes and non-accidental causes. The same pattern was shown for death from specific causes such as ischaemic heart disease, accidents, and cancer, as well as for different years of entry into the cohort. This pattern differed widely from that of most other occupations. The high mortality ratios at younger ages existed in crew members only when the cohort was divided into owners and crew members.

CONCLUSIONS: The authors argue that the low mortality among older fishermen was not surprising as this group is known to be active workers. Also, as more individuals drop out of the cohort because of poor health with increasing age, the survivors are those whose health is relatively better.

See also Hasselback, P., & Neutel, C. I. (1990).

Schechter, M. T., Spitzer, W. O., Hutcheon, M. E., Dales, R. E., Eastridge, L. M., Hobbs, C., Suissa, S., Tousignant, P., & Steinmetz, N. (1990). A study of mortality near sour gas refineries in southwest Alberta: An epidemic unrevealed. *Canadian Journal of Public Health, 81*(2), 107-113.

OBJECTIVES: To investigate mortality rates in a rural population living downwind from natural gas refineries in southwestern areas of the province of Alberta.

METHODS: A residential cohort study was carried out as part of a large field epidemiologic study undertaken during Summer 1985. The cohort was defined as all those individuals who resided in the area (referred to as the Index area) in 1970. Deaths from January 1, 1970 to December 31, 1984 were enumerated by resident reports and by manual record linkage with the death records of the Alberta Bureau of Vital Statistics. A total of 30,175 person-years of risk within Alberta were experienced by this cohort. Referent populations were from Census Division 2 excluding the metropolitan area of Lethbridge and from Census Division 6 excluding the metropolitan area of Calgary, both located in southern Alberta.

DEFINITION OF RURAL: The Index area is a rural area located southeast of the town of Pincher Creek and east of the Rocky Mountains. It consists primarily of ranchland surrounding small communities (Twin Butte, Glenwood, Mountain View, Hill Spring, and Willow Creek). Sour gas is refined in the Index area; the community was convinced that they were "in the midst of a long-standing 'epidemic' of death" (p. 113).

RESULTS RELATED TO RURAL AGING: Based on expected rates from two pre-specified demographically similar, non-metropolitan southern Alberta populations, the age- and sex-standardized mortality ratios were 0.88 and 0.84, respectively.

CONCLUSIONS: The overall mortality experience for the cohort near the sour gas refineries was similar to the rates for other areas in Alberta. The authors conclude that these data cannot address the question of etiology but they can help to allay community anxieties about an epidemic of death.

See also Schechter, M. T., Spitzer, W. O., Hutcheon, M. E., Dales, R. E., Eastridge, L. M., Steinmetz, N., Tousignant, P., & Hobbs, C. (1989).

QUALITY OF LIFE/LIFE SATISFACTION

Duggleby, W., & Wright, K. (2004). Elderly palliative care cancer patients' descriptions of hope-fostering strategies. *International Journal of Palliative Nursing, 10*(7), 352-359.

OBJECTIVES: To describe perceptions of hope-fostering strategies of elderly patients with advanced cancer receiving palliative home care in rural Canadian prairie communities.

METHODS: Using a qualitative thematic research design, data collection included a demographic form, face-to-face taped interviews, and chart reviews. Participants completed the Herth Hope Index (HHI) and the Edmonton Symptom Assessment Scale (ESAS) to describe levels of hope and symptom intensity, respectively. Interviews were transcribed verbatim and analysed concurrently with data collection. Saturation was reached with 10 palliative home care patients (5 males, 5 females). Participants ranged in age from 65 to 85, with an average age of 75.

DEFINITION OF RURAL: The study took place in "rural Canadian prairie communities" (p. 353). No definition of rural was provided.

RESULTS RELATED TO RURAL AGING: Participants described hope for 'not suffering more', 'living life to the fullest in the little time I have left', a peaceful death, life after death, and 'hope for a better life in the future' for their family. The themes of fostering hope that emerged were leaving a legacy, achieving short-term goals, 'turn your mind off', supportive family and friends, faith, symbols of hope, positive thoughts, honest information, and symptom control.

CONCLUSIONS: The authors argue that the findings contribute to further understanding of the ways older palliative care cancer patients foster hope and provide a foundation for the development of effective hope-fostering strategies in this population.

See also Duggleby, W., & Wright, K. (2005).

Duggleby, W., & Wright, K. (2005). Transforming hope: How elderly palliative patients live with hope. *Canadian Journal of Nursing Research, 37*(2), 71-84.

OBJECTIVES: To describe the processes by which palliative patients live with hope, in a rural Canadian health region.

METHODS: Using a grounded theory approach, 16 interviews were conducted with 10 home-care palliative patients in their homes. Participants who met the eligibility criteria were identified by the Palliative Care Coordinator in the health region. Data collection included a demographic form, face-to-face taped interviews, and chart review. Participants completed the Herth Hope Index (HHI) and the Edmonton Symptom Assessment Scale (ESAS) to describe levels of hope and symptom intensity, respectively. Interviews were transcribed verbatim and analyzed concurrently with data collection. Participants ranged in age from 65 to 85.

DEFINITION OF RURAL: The study was conducted in a "rural Canadian health region" (p. 73). No definition of rural was provided.

RESULTS RELATED TO RURAL AGING: Participants defined their hope as expectations such as not suffering more and having a peaceful death. They described their main concern as wanting to 'live with hope' and achieved this through the basic social process of transforming hope. Transforming hope involved acknowledging 'life the way it is', searching for meaning, and positive reappraisal.

CONCLUSIONS: The authors argue that their results provide a foundation for future research and the development of interventions to engender hope in older palliative patients.

See also Duggleby, W., & Wright, K. (2004).

Harvey, C. D. H., Bond, J. B., Jr., & Greenwood, L. J. (1991). **Satisfaction, happiness, and self-esteem of older rural parents.** *Canadian Journal of Community Mental Health, 10*(2), 31-46.

OBJECTIVES: To examine the effects of interaction with middle-aged offspring on the self-perceived well-being of 137 older rural parents in the province of Manitoba.

METHODS: This cross-sectional study was conducted with parents aged 56 - 87 residing in the rural census subdivisions west of the Red River in Manitoba. A random sample of 2,000 persons aged 35 - 65 was provided by the Manitoba Health Services Commission in 1986. Only participants who had a living parent were eligible for the study; 607 returned mailed questionnaires that included the identification of at least one parent. A random sample of these parents was then selected, with a resulting sample size of 137 parents. Interviews were conducted in either German or English during March 1987. The mean age of the parents was 77.4 for males (range 64 - 86) and 74.7 for females (range 56 - 90); 67% of the respondents were female. The sample was largely Mennonite as the region has had successive migrations of individuals with a Mennonite background. In this analysis, three measures of well-being were used: the Parent Satisfaction Scale, an item on overall happiness, and a Self-Esteem Scale.

DEFINITION OF RURAL: The 10 contiguous and clustered rural census subdivisions in south central Manitoba had a combined 1981 population of 45,554. Communities varied in size from under 1,000 to 8,000.

RESULTS RELATED TO RURAL AGING: Parental contact with children predicted life satisfaction but was unrelated to global happiness or self-esteem for both fathers and mothers. Less contact was associated with higher levels of satisfaction for both females and males. Among elderly fathers, frequency of contact and religiosity were significantly related with satisfaction while global happiness was associated with health, religiosity, the amount the child can 'count on' the parent, and the amount the parent can 'count on' the child. No factors were related to self-esteem. Among elderly mothers, health and frequency of contact were related to satisfaction while health, religiosity, the number of siblings, and the amount the child can 'count on' the parent emerged as significant for global happiness. Only education was related to higher self-esteem for mothers.

CONCLUSIONS: The effects of interaction with middle-aged offspring on self-perceived well-being were not consistent across the three measures of well-being. The researchers call for future research on kin contact and the well-being of elderly parents, with particular attention to differences between mothers and fathers, marital status, religion, and income levels.

MacRae, H. (1990). Older women and identity maintenance in later life. *Canadian Journal on Aging, 9*(3), 248-267.

OBJECTIVES: To explore the nature and basis of self-identity in later life and the way in which self-identity is maintained among older women in a town in the province of Nova Scotia.

METHODS: Data were from a larger study on social network involvement and identity management of elderly women. In-depth, semi-structured interviews were completed with 142 women aged 65 to 98 (mean age 76.8) residing in three different settings. Women living in their own homes or private apartments (n = 101) were recruited by knocking on the door of every fifth house on the street through the entire town. Women living in apartment dwelling (n = 31) were drawn at random from 2 local seniors' apartment complexes, while those living in nursing homes (n = 10) were randomly selected from a wing for the 'more well elderly'. The self-identify section included a modified version of Kuhn's (1954) TST (twenty-statement test) or the *Who am I?* test. Participant observation was used to gain insight into the social world of these women; the researcher lived in the town for the 6 months when data were collected.

DEFINITION OF RURAL: This Nova Scotia town had a population of approximately 6,500 people at the time of the study.

RESULTS RELATED TO RURAL AGING: Almost all the women (99%) claimed that they never wondered about who they were. Most (74%) did not view themselves as elderly although 52% reported that there were situations that could make them feel old, such as during a period of illness, disability, or general weariness. Three main categories of meanings emerged: those pertaining to statuses and roles (organizational membership and informal roles, housewife and homemaker, mother); those pertaining to personal attributes; and those pertaining to the older women's interpretation of their relationships to others.

CONCLUSIONS: The author argues that these findings contradict the identity crisis view of old age in a number of ways. By building identities around meaningful relationships to others and informal role involvements, lifelong self-meaning was sustained by these rural older women.

Thurston, W. E., Blundell-Gosselin, H. J., & Rose, S. (2003). Stress in male and female farmers: An ecological rather than an individual problem. *Canadian Journal of Rural Medicine, 8*(4), 247-254.

OBJECTIVES: To examine health concerns of male and female farmers in the south central region of the province of Alberta.

METHODS: Data were from a cross-sectional mail survey on stress, farm operations, farm health and safety concerns, and demographic characteristics. The sample was drawn from a listing of 3,834 self-identified farmers complied by the Farm Business Communications List Service Group. Completed questionnaires were returned by 347 farms. The sample consisted of 332 males and 231 females. The average age was 49.9 for the males and 45.8 for the females (combined range of 23 - 81).

DEFINITION OF RURAL: The study was conducted in four municipalities and three counties in south central Alberta; population figures were not provided. The agricultural production was primarily beef and grain.

RESULTS RELATED TO RURAL AGING: Emotional problems and stress were among the top three problems mentioned by male and female farmers. Multivariate analysis revealed that the predictors of stress for male and female farmers differed. Remembering past events or accidents, having only two family members working the farm, and having a larger farming operation predicted stress for women when age, health status, and worrying about the effects of farming on their health were in the model. For men, believing farming was more dangerous than other occupations and having no employees predicted stress when age, health status, and worrying about the effects of farming on their health were included in the model.

CONCLUSIONS: The authors argue that their results suggest that the association between age and stress is best understood by using a broad framework that includes economic and farm management issues, as well as home factors. They support calls for an ecological model of mental health promotion (a model that acknowledges that social, economic, physical, and environmental factors interact to influence health).

Wood, L. A., & Johnson, J. (1989). Life satisfaction among the rural elderly: What do the numbers mean? *Social Indicators Research, 21*(4), 379-408.

OBJECTIVES: To compare quantitative and qualitative data on satisfaction with housing, family, spouse, self-esteem, health, friends, and life as a whole among rural older adults in the province of Ontario.

METHODS: Data were from a small subset of respondents who initially completed a survey on life satisfaction. These 15 respondents were purposively selected to represent different levels of life satisfaction, marital statuses, types of rural environments, and gender. They were interviewed for an intensive qualitative study of loneliness, social activities, and social relationships.

DEFINITION OF RURAL: Place of residence was categorized as village (< 500 population), town (500 - 1,000), town (2,000 - 2,500), town (3,000 - 3,500), city (> 5,000), and open country.

RESULTS RELATED TO RURAL AGING: The life satisfaction values based on the quantitative data were fairly similar to overall life satisfaction judgments made by investigators on the basis of qualitative data from interviews and diaries. However, there were a number of nonsystematic discrepancies across both participants and domains such as health and happiness.

CONCLUSIONS: The authors conclude that it is essential to take a qualitative approach to the study of life satisfaction. They view the quantitative approach with its use of numbers and statistical analysis as having supplementary utility.

TRANSPORTATION/DRIVING

Belton, K. L., Jhangri, G. S., MacDonald, S. D., & Voaklander, D. C. (2005). Nighttime impaired driving in rural Alberta. *Journal of Agricultural Safety & Health, 11*(2), 135-140.

OBJECTIVES: To quantify the nature and extent of impaired driving on rural roads during nighttime, and to describe driver demographics and information about the trip's origin and destination among rural nighttime drivers in the province of Alberta.

METHODS: A nighttime roadside survey was conducted with drivers of vehicles randomly sampled at rural locations in Alberta between the hours of 10:00 PM and 4:00 AM between August 22 and September 1, 2001. Sampling involved a two-stage process by community and then by day/time combinations. Each site was surveyed for 90 minutes. Drivers who agreed to participate were asked a series of short questions focusing on driver demographics, driving characteristics, information about the trip, and the driver's drinking and driving factors. They also provided a breath sample to determine blood alcohol concentration. A total of 1,431 drivers participated.

DEFINITION OF RURAL: No definition of rural was provided.

RESULTS RELATED TO RURAL AGING: There were 65 drivers aged 60+, representing 5% of the sample. Only 4 (20%) tested positive for alcohol and none (0%) were legally impaired. These percentages were the lowest of all age groups.

CONCLUSIONS: The authors argue that this study is a first step towards quantifying the problem of drinking and driving on Alberta's rural roads at night and identifying the characteristics of drinking drivers.

Bess, I. (1999). Seniors behind the wheel. *Canadian Social Trends, 54*, **2-7.**

OBJECTIVES: To examine the issues related to the use of cars by older adults in rural and urban Canada.

METHODS: This descriptive article draws on data for the 65+ age group from several Statistics Canada surveys, including the 1996 General Social Survey (GSS), the 1996 National Private Vehicle Use Survey, the 1996 Family Expenditure Survey, and the 1996/97 National Population Health Survey (NPHS). Most data were from the National Private Vehicle Use Survey conducted between January and September 1996.

DEFINITION OF RURAL: Rural areas were defined as regions with populations < 1,000 (or < 400 persons per square kilometre). Small towns were urban areas with < 30,000 people while large towns or cities were divided into two categories (30,000 - 500,000; and 500,000+).

RESULTS RELATED TO RURAL AGING: Older adults living in rural areas (59%) and small towns (60%) were more likely to be drivers than those in urban centres with a population > 500,000 (46%). Rural older adults spent a higher proportion of their budget on their cars than their urban counterparts. Regardless of place of residence, males were more likely than females to be drivers, even in households where the wife held a driver's license. When women did drive, it was most often for short distances. The increased need to drive or have access to a ride was evident in rural areas as nearly 20% of rural older adults lived more than a 30-minute walk from the nearest grocery or convenience store compared to only 5% of the urban group.

CONCLUSIONS: Driving is important as it allows older adults to engage in social, cultural, and recreational activities, and to perform routine tasks. This reliance on a vehicle is particularly pronounced in rural areas.

FitzSimons, J., Reid, D., & Fraser, B. (1987). *Transportation issues among the rural elderly in Mitchell, Perth County, Ontario: A report to the Perth County Seniors Planning Council.* **Guelph, ON: University School of Rural Planning and Development, University of Guelph.**

OBJECTIVES: To determine the transportation needs of older adults in the town of Mitchell in the province of Ontario.

METHODS: Students in a graduate-level research methods course developed the questionnaire, conducted a survey, and analyzed the data under the direction of a faculty member. A random sample of individuals aged 66+ was selected from a list of this population; the final sample size was 99 (66% female). The questionnaire focused on demographic characteristics, health status, availability of an automobile, environmental constraints, social support systems, essential and non-essential activities, frequency of activities, transportation modes, and transportation difficulties. A Transportation Difficulty Index (TDI) was calculated, based on the number of activities and the degree of difficulty experienced getting to each activity.

DEFINITION OF RURAL: The town of Mitchell had a 1985 population of 2,947, with 19% aged 66+. It is located in an agricultural area of Perth County and is approximately 200 kilometres from Toronto and 65 kilometres from London. At the time of the study, a Mobility Bus for handicapped or elderly people was in operation on a donation basis for local trips and on a mileage basis for out-of-town trips. Its availability was limited and users were "generally encouraged to plan their activities for Tuesdays" (p. 17).

RESULTS RELATED TO RURAL AGING: Walking was a frequent mode of transportation. Seventy percent of the respondents had a valid driver's license and owned a car; 48% indicated that there were other household members who drove. Among drivers, 30% did not drive at night, 19% avoided driving in the rain, 38% did not drive in the snow, and 21% indicated that they did not drive in cold weather. While 88% were aware of the Mobility Bus, only 6% had made use of it. Reasons for non-use included no need for this service and its limited availability. Seventy-four percent experienced no transportation difficulties, 22% had some difficulties, and 4% reported severe problems. The four individuals with severe problems were all widowed females, living alone, and possessing neither a car nor a driver's license; all rated their health as poor and experienced difficulty with walking. No significant differences were found in the TDI for essential versus social/recreational activities nor for local versus out-of-town trips.

CONCLUSIONS: The authors speculate that the 4% with severe transportation difficulties is an underestimate. They call for further research on individuals who are the most transportation-disadvantaged, the ways in which transportation is provided in rural communities, and preferences for various forms of transportation.

Hodge, G., & McKay, L. (1992). *Small town seniors and their freedom to move: Improving transportation for seniors in British Columbia's small towns*. (No. 4687-9-88/029). Vancouver, BC: Gerontology Research Centre, Simon Fraser University.

OBJECTIVES: To describe the structure/operation of existing transportation services and facilities available to seniors in 10 small communities in the province of British Columbia, to obtain profiles of transportation needs and travel behaviours among these older adults, to assess the role of the local bus systems under British Columbia's Paratransit program in 5 of the 10 communities, and to develop tools for use by seniors' groups to assess and plan for effective transportation.

METHODS: In each community, a leading seniors' organization or seniors' advocate was invited to participate in a test of the needs assessment tools. One senior was asked to become the focal point for that community. Two self-administered survey tools were used: the Seniors' Survey that focused on characteristics of senior transportation consumers, existing travel patterns, problems getting around, and transportation preferences; and the Transportation Survey that determined the kind and level of existing transportation services such as level and frequency of service, service areas, fares, utilization levels, and staffing. A total of 1,013 Seniors' Surveys were completed, with a range of 76 to 122 per community.

DEFINITION OF RURAL: Communities with Paratransit, their 1986 population size, and the percent aged 65+ were as follows: Duncan (4,035) (25%), Kimberley (6,735) (16%), Princeton (2,910) (12%), Quesnel (8,344) (8%), and Summerland (7,755) (25%). Communities without Paratransit were: Fernie (5,185) (9%), Keremeos (840) (32%), Ladysmith (4,390) (18%), Parksville (5,825) (25%), and Salt Spring Island (6,164) (23%).

RESULTS RELATED TO RURAL AGING: Characteristics of potential users of collective transportation services in small towns were summarized as follows: age in mid-70s, probably lives alone, has lived in community 20 to 30 years, presently lives in a single family house, rates health as good but not excellent, income in the $12,000 - $15,000 range, and probably doesn't drive. These small town residents aged 65+ had some transportation difficulties; 43% did not drive regularly and 37% lived in households where no one drove. Increasing age was associated with an increased percent of those not driving regularly (33% aged 65 - 74, 57% aged 75+). The most common source of difficulty was having to ask for a ride (25%). In communities with Paratransit, 61% of these respondents were familiar with their local bus and 22% considered themselves regular users, although only 37% of this group used the bus at least once a week. The best features were identified as convenience, courtesy, reliability, and door-to-door service while the worst features were no weekend or evening service, needing advanced booking, and waiting times. Fixed route or dial-a-bus options were the most favoured. The Transportation Survey revealed that the annual operating costs of the five existing Paratransit services were $53,746.

CONCLUSIONS: No single mode of transportation can serve the needs of all seniors. The authors identify a number of lessons/cautions and observations that may be helpful to other communities dealing with transportation issues.

Kelly, D., & Swiderski, A. (1988). *Program for the transportation of the mobility disadvantaged in rural Manitoba: A study of user needs and benefits.* **Winnipeg, MB: Manitoba Highways and Transportation.**

OBJECTIVES: To determine the extent to which handivan services meet the transportation needs of the mobility disadvantaged in rural Manitoba, and to determine the benefits to the community of establishing mobility disadvantaged transportation services in relation to the cost to the community and to the province of providing this service. The Program for Transportation of the Mobility Disadvantaged in Rural Manitoba provided assistance to rural communities to establish handivan programs to meet their unique needs.

METHODS: Questionnaires were sent to 458 users of handivans in 7 of the 33 communities participating in the transportation program and to 398 potential users who were eligible but not currently using the service (identified by a contact person in a seniors drop-in centre). Final sample sizes were 213 users and 193 potential users. Continuing Care Coordinators and administrators/drivers of handivans and mayors of the communities also were surveyed.

DEFINITION OF RURAL: The seven communities were Brokenhead (Beausejour), Boissevain, Gimili, Neepawa, Souris, Winkler, and Winnipegosis.

RESULTS RELATED TO RURAL AGING: The average handivan user was a female aged > 65, with some form of impairment (e.g., physical, visual), and living alone in either a single family home or elderly persons' housing. Users had an average total family income of $10,757. The potential user was equally likely to be male or female, slightly older on average than the user, more likely to live with one other person, and more likely to live in a single family home. The average family income for this group was $15,915. In 1987, the cost to the provincial government of the handivan program in the seven communities was $75,600, which represented approximately 37% of the costs. User fees (33%) and funds raised from the municipalities, donations, and interest (31%) were other sources of funding. Identified benefits included delaying admissions to long-term care facilities, extra consumer spending in the community, and possible improvements in road safety with the use of the bus. For the users themselves, benefits were described as a greater feeling of independence, an ability to travel whenever the user wished, an ability to attend social and recreational activities, and an ability to use available medical services.

CONCLUSIONS: The authors concluded that the benefits associated with the provision of handivan service to these communities outweighed the costs.

Lefrancois, R., & D'Amours, M. (1997). Exposure and risk factors among elderly drivers: A case-control study. *Accident Analysis & Prevention, 29*(3), 267-275.

OBJECTIVES: To study the risk factors associated with exposure, aging, and other characteristics of elderly drivers in the province of Quebec.

METHODS: This case-control study was conducted among residents of medium-sized small towns and rural areas in Quebec. French-speaking drivers aged 68+, holding a class-five driver's license, and living in the study area were selected from the database of the provincial Automobile Insurance Board (SAAQ). Cases was chosen on the basis of performance on the following in the preceding 3 years: (1) had been involved in 3+ accidents without any violations; (2) had been found guilty of at least 3 traffic-code violations but had not been involved in any accidents during the same period; and (3) had been involved in 2+ accidents and had at least 1 violation, or had 2+ violations and had been involved in at least 1 accident. Cases were matched to a control group (blank file for the last 3 years) on a stratification basis (age, gender, and region) in a 2:1 control to case ratio. Respondents were asked to complete a mailed questionnaire on the risk factors. The sample size consisted of 157 cases and 400 controls. Of the 157 cases, 11 cases met the criteria for crashes only, 37 for violations only, and 109 for crashes and violations. Average ages were 74.3 for cases and 74.0 for controls; 86% of cases and 84% of controls were males.

DEFINITION OF RURAL: Three categories of place of residence were examined: medium-sized municipalities, suburbs, and small municipalities; rural areas near a major highway network; and rural areas far from a major highway. No population figures were provided; no definition of the distance considered as 'near' or 'far' from a highway were discussed.

RESULTS RELATED TO RURAL AGING: Overall, the results suggested that risk was proportional to the frequency of daily vehicle use or the total kilometres driven per year. The risk was significantly higher for the 78+ age group. City or suburban residents were more at risk than those in rural areas away from major highways.

CONCLUSIONS: The hypothesis that older drivers who rarely drive have a greater risk than more frequent drivers was not supported by these data. However, exposure was measured after the crashes/violations had occurred and it is not possible to establish a definitive cause-and-effect link between exposure and performance. The authors suggest that dense traffic zones in urban areas and high-speed highway zones are problematic for older drivers, and that drivers aged 78+ are more likely to have difficulties compared to their younger counterparts.

See also Lefrançois, R., & D'Amours, M. (1997).

Lefrançois, R., & D'Amours, M. (1997). La performance des automobilistes âgés dans les situations de conduite difficile. (The performance of elderly drivers in difficult driving situations). *Canadian Journal on Aging, 16*(2), 320-335.

OBJECTIVES: To examine the exposure risk of drivers aged 68+ in different difficult driving situations such as inclement weather and traffic density in the province of Quebec.

METHODS: In this case-control study, French-speaking drivers aged 68+, holding a class-five driver's license and living in the study area for at least the last five years were selected from the provincial Automobile Insurance Board's (SAAQ) databases. Cases were chosen on the basis of driving performance (3+ accidents or traffic violations over a 3-year period) and paired on a 2:1 basis according to age, sex, and area (urban/rural) with a random-selected control group (clean driving record). Respondents were asked to complete a mailed risk factor questionnaire (n = 157 cases, n = 400 controls). Average ages were 74.3 for cases and 74.0 for controls; 86% of cases and 84% of controls were males. Rural participants represented 25% of cases and 31% of controls. Place of residence was used as a proxy for area of driving. Five driving situations were examined: driving in the winter; driving in the dark; driving in bad weather such as snow, rain, and fog; driving on the highways; and driving among heavy traffic in cities.

DEFINITION OF RURAL: Three categories of place of residence were examined: medium-sized municipalities, suburbs, and small municipalities; rural areas near a major highway; and rural areas at a distance from a major highway. No population figures were provided for the 'medium-sized' and 'small' municipalities; no definition of 'near' or 'far' distance from a highway were discussed.

RESULTS RELATED TO RURAL AGING: Increasing age was associated with giving up driving in risky situations. Regardless of age, the number of drivers who stopped driving in difficult conditions was proportionally higher in the control group. In general, men exposed themselves to risk by driving in difficult conditions proportionally more than women. Predisposition to risk appeared to increase with exposure level. Rural drivers were more predisposed to risk in all examined driving situations, with the exceptions of driving in the winter (after adjustments by age and sex). For rural older drivers, driving in bad weather and driving in the dark were particularly problematic. Rural older drivers who lived at a distance from highways were more of a risk when driving in bad weather and driving in heavy urban traffic compared to rural older drivers who lived in the proximity of highways. Self-perceived health status was not a significant risk factor for driving performance. Wearing visual aids was a risk factor for respondents who often drove in the dark and in bad weather, while wearing hearing aids was a significant risk factor when driving in heavy traffic or on the highways.

CONCLUSIONS: The results suggest that risk increases in relation to the level of exposure. In all age groups, there were proportionately more controls than cases who renounced driving in difficult conditions. Differences between relative levels of risk depending on where driving occurs were also evident.

See also Lefrancois, R., & D'Amours, M. (1997).

Thouez, J.-P., Joly, M.-F., Rannou, A., Bussière, Y., & Bourbeau, R. (1991). Geographical variations of motor-vehicle injuries in Quebec, 1983-1988. *Social Science & Medicine,* 33(4), 415-421.

OBJECTIVES: To describe the geography of motor vehicle accidents in the province of Quebec from 1983 to 1988, and to evaluate the risk factors associated with zones of high risk with regard to accidents for the 97 Municipalities Regionales de Comte (MRC).

METHODS: Data were from the Regie de l'Assurance Automobile du Quebec (RAAQ). The geographical distribution was examined through the use of statistics and maps. A standardized morbidity rate (SMR) was calculated for severe and non-severe injuries. An injury was classified as severe when there was a hospitalization (≥ 1 day in hospital). The demographic characteristics (age, sex) of the driver and passengers and the place of the accident (region, density) were used in a logit model to evaluate risk factors associated with high risk zones.

DEFINITION OF RURAL: An MRC was defined as urban when more than half of its population resided in the urban region. The population size of an urban region must be > 1,000 and the density must be > 400 inhabitants per square kilometre.

RESULTS RELATED TO RURAL AGING: Among the 65+ age group, non-severe motor-vehicle accidents were less frequent for both rural males and rural females than their urban counterparts. However, severe accidents were more frequent for both males and females in the rural context. In the logit model, women aged 65+ in urban areas emerged as a group at relatively low risk for accidents resulting in severe injuries. Both males aged 65+ and females aged 65+ were low-risk groups for accidents with non-severe injuries.

CONCLUSIONS: The authors state that the geography of motor-vehicle accidents is a relatively undeveloped area in the geography of health. They argue that the rural-urban differences may reflect differences in geographical accessibility to health care.

Vézina, A., & Pelletier, D. (1997). Les personnes âgées à mobilité réduite vivant à domicile : Modalités de réponse aux besoins et niveau de satisfaction perçu. (Older adults with reduced mobility living at home: modalities of responses to the needs and perceived satisfaction level). *Canadian Journal on Aging, 16*(2), 297-319.

OBJECTIVES: To explore access to transportation and its impact on the living conditions of older persons with reduced mobility in the province of Quebec.

METHODS: A classification provided by the Quebec Ministry of Transportation was used to distinguish between three levels of mobility: low, medium, and severely reduced. Study participants were 67 older adults dwelling in urban (Brossard-Greenfield Park), semi-urban (Sorel-Tracy), and rural (Hemingford) areas of the Monteregie region. Structured interviews with open- and closed-ended questions were conducted in the participants' homes, and lasted on average 1.5 hours.

DEFINITION OF RURAL: The urban context (Brossard-Greenfield Park) was defined as an important metropolitan area; semi-rural context (Sorel-Tracy) embraced regional centres of certain importance; and rural context (Hemingford) most often comprised a village surrounded by an agricultural area.

RESULTS RELATED TO RURAL AGING: Transportation tended to be supplied by family and friends, although individuals who lived alone tended to walk more to get to places and those who lived with partners tended to be taken by relatives and friends. For older adults with medium and severe mobility limitations, recreational activities were reported to be absent and their level of satisfaction was low. The strategies used to get out of the house varied according to place of residence, with the exception of getting to medical care where transportation was provided predominantly by community organizations in all three contexts. The principal transportation mode in urban and semi-urban context was a car driven by a friend or a relative, while in a rural context, it was on foot. The majority of rural respondents lived in a village and were proximate to certain services. Compared to their semi-urban and rural counterparts, urban respondents were more likely to express the most dissatisfaction with meals, dealing with local administration, leisure, and socializing.

CONCLUSIONS: Older rural residents with reduced mobility and living in rural contexts such as villages may be advantaged compared to their urban counterparts with regard to alternate means of transportation. Socio-physical conditions such as rapidity of traffic and crowdedness present barriers and a reduced sense of security for urban residents, with those barriers and perceptions mitigated somewhat in a rural setting. The authors argue that a diversity of transportation options is needed for adults with reduced mobility in all settings.

BOOKS

Books - Authored

Keating, N. C. (1991). *Aging in rural Canada.* **Toronto, ON: Butterworths.**

Keating reviews and analyzes the literature on rural aging in Canada, exploring the experiences of individual older adults as well as the elderly population as a whole. The book is divided into six chapters. Chapter 1 is a demographic overview and a discussion of the differing definitions of rural. In Chapter 2, patterns of work, retirement, and leisure are examined. The topic for Chapter 3 is environmental factors including housing, facilities such as electricity and water, access to services, and transportation. Families, social support, and interactions are the focus of Chapter 4. Issues of health status, attitudes towards health, and the role of health promotion in rural areas are explored in Chapter 5. Chapter 6 concludes the book with a discussion of the directions for rural research, policy, and practice. A bibliography is provided. Canadian data are used whenever possible and comparisons to other western countries are provided.

Books - Edited

Andrews, G., & Phillips, D. R. (Eds.). (2005). *Ageing and place: Perspectives, policy and practice.* **London: Routledge Studies in Human Geography.**

Issues of age and place are explored in this book. Chapter 10, *Ageing in rural communities: Vulnerable people in vulnerable places* was co-authored by Joseph and Cloutier-Fisher.

Basran, G. S., & Hay, D. A. (Eds.). (1988). *The political economy of agriculture in Western Canada.* **Toronto, ON: Garamond Press.**

This book consists of 18 chapters and is divided into 5 sections (The State of Agriculture in Western Canada; State, Class, and Agricultural Policies; Farm Health and Safety; Farm Women; Rural Communities and Services). Two chapters include a discussion relevant to rural aging in Canada. Chapter 1, entitled *The Western Canadian farm sector: Transitions and trends,* was written by Hay and Basran. Chapter 10, entitled *Respiratory disease in Saskatchewan: Some regional and social variations,* was prepared by Dickinson, Denis, and Li.

Beesley, K. B. (Ed.). (1991). *Rural and urban fringe studies in Canada* **(Geographical Monographs No. 21). North York, ON: York University-Atkinson College.**

The volume includes some of the rural and urban fringe research activity undertaken in Canada. Chapter 2, *Population change, economic activity and amenity landscapes at the outer edge of the urban fringe,* by Dahms and Hallman includes a short section on older adults.

Bollman, R. D. (Ed.). (1992). *Rural and small town Canada.* **Toronto, ON: Thompson Educational Publishers.**

Business linkages, rural labour markets, rural well-being, and the question of 'does rural matter?' are examined in this book. Chapter 15, *Population, income and migration characteristics for urban/rural areas and farm/non-farm families in Saskatchewan,* by Meyer includes a discussion relevant to rural aging.

Bull, N. C. (Ed.). (1993). *Aging in rural America.* **Newbury, CA: Sage Publications.**

Part I of this book highlights the characteristics of rural elderly; Part II examines resource development. In Part III, the physical and mental health status of rural older adults is discussed while Part IV addresses social supports. One chapter includes a discussion relevant to rural aging in Canada: *Health promotion and disadvantaged elderly: Rural-urban differences* by Penning and Chappell.

Cossey, K. M. (Ed.). (1989). *Rural environments and the elderly: Impact, contributions and needs fulfillment.* **Sackville, NB: Rural and Small Town Research and Studies Programme, Department of Geography, Mount Allison University.**

This monograph consists of papers that were presented at a 1988 conference. Each paper addresses the challenges of planning for an increasing aging population in rural and small town communities in Canada. Two papers address aging-related issues: *Issues and perspectives on services planning for the rural elderly: The One-Stop Access model,*

Huron County, Ontario (Wolfe, Fraser, & Fuller); and *Planned retirement communities in the rural-urban fringe: An elderly housing alternative* (Kuntz).

Dosman, J. A., & Cockcroft, D. W. (Eds.). (1989). *Principles of health and safety in agriculture*. Boca Raton, FL: CRC Press.

This book contains one chapter of relevance: *Respiratory health in farmers: Symptoms and pulmonary function* by Dosman and colleagues.

Epp, R., & Whitson, D. (Eds.). (2001). *Writing off the rural west: Globalization, governments and the transformation of rural communities* (1st ed.). Edmonton, AB: University of Alberta Press.

This book is divided into three parts: Part I: Globalization, government, and agriculture, Part II - Resource towns and recreation, and Part III - Defending real rural communities. Part III includes a chapter entitled *A good place to grow old? Rural communities and support to seniors* by Keating, Keefe, and Dobbs.

Gesler, W. M., & Ricketts, T. C. (Eds.). (1992). *Health in rural North America: The geography of health care services and delivery*. New Brunswick, NJ: Rutgers University Press.

This book focuses on high-risk populations as well as service provision and policy issues in rural North America. The chapter entitled *Issues in the provision of in-home health services to the rural elderly* by Joseph provides a Canadian perspective.

Gutman, G. M. (Ed.). (1992). *Shelter and care of persons with dementia*. Vancouver, BC: Gerontology Research Centre, Simon Fraser University.

This book consists of 14 papers on the shelter and care of persons with dementia in Canada. Part I focuses on specialized care in institutional settings and Part II addresses behavioral interventions and environmental design issues. Part III examines institution-community cooperation and collaboration; Part IV explores facilitation of shelter and care at home. The situations of rural older adults are considered in two papers: *Le Chez Nous Accommodation with a difference for cognitively impaired persons in rural Manitoba* by Lahaie and Theroux; and *Organization and co-ordination of services to individuals with dementia living in rural settings* by Sarchuk and Wiebe.

Holosko, M. J., & Feit, M. D. (Eds.). (2004). *Social work practice with the elderly* (3rd Ed.). Toronto, ON: Canadian Scholars' Press Inc.

This book provides an overview of trends and issues in social work practice with older adults. It includes three sections: Direct Practice Elements, Selected Practice Settings, and Future Considerations. Chapter 12 entitled *Social work practice with rural elderly* by MacKenzie is the sole chapter with a focus on rural older adults.

Hux, J. E., Booth, G. L., Slaughter, P. M., & Laupacis, A. (Eds). (2003). *Diabetes in Ontario: An ICES Practice Atlas*. Toronto, ON: Institute for Clinical Evaluative Studies.

This book consists of 14 chapters and provides information regarding diabetes in Ontario. Chapter 3, entitled *Drug use in older people with diabetes,* by Shah, Mamdani, and Kopp focuses specifically on older adults.

Lewis, S. J. (Ed.). (1989). *Aging and health: Linking research and public policy.* **Chelsea, MI: Lewis Publishers.**

The proceedings of the First International Symposium - Research and Public Policy on Aging and Health, held in Saskatoon, Canada, on February 8 - 10, 1988 are presented in this book. There are five parts: Health needs, programs, and policies; Money, politics, and public and private choices; Performing effective gerontological research; Applying gerontological research effectively; and Cementing research and policy connections. Chapter 10, entitled *One-Stop Access for seniors citizens: A model of integrated service delivery for rural areas,* by Fraser and Fuller is the only paper with a focus on rural aging.

Marshall, V. W. (Ed.). (1987). *Aging in Canada: Social perspectives* **(2nd ed.). Markham, ON: Fitzhenry and Whiteside.**

This book covers basic facts about age and aging, and reviews major theoretical approaches that characterize social gerontological research in Canada. Topics discussed include: aging among minority and ethnic groups, aging workers in the labor force, retirement and associated activities, family structure and social relationships, health and well-being in relation to age, health care, and the political, economic, and social implications of population aging in Canada. Two chapters provide information on rural aging: *Aging women in rural settings* by Cape, and *The relationship between formal and informal social support networks in rural and urban contexts* by Corin.

Marshall, V. W., & McPherson, B. D. (Eds.). (1994). *Aging: Canadian perspectives.* **Peterborough, ON: Broadview Press.**

This reader contains 10 papers on various aspects of aging in Canada and also appeared as a special issue of the *Journal of Canadian Studies,* with several relevant essays from other sources. The chapters focus on demographic aspects of aging and on the impact of population aging on major social institutions such as the community, work, leisure, and the family. One paper focuses on rural aging: *Growing old in aging communities* by Joseph and Martin Matthews.

Mawhiney, A. M., & Pitblado, J. (Eds.). (1999). *Boom town blues: Elliot Lake, collapse and revival in a single-industry community.* **Toronto, ON: Dundurn Press.**

This book focuses on the experiences of Elliot Lake, Ontario. Chapter 15, *Aging in a hurry: Changing population profile in Elliott Lake,* and Chapter 18, *Physician visits by older persons in Elliot Lake: Issues and challenges,* written by Pong, Salmoni, and Heard examine aging-related issues.

Minore, B., & Hartviksen, C. (Eds.). (1995). *Redressing the imbalance: Health human resources in rural and northern communities.* **Thunder Bay, ON: Northern Health Human Resources Research Unit, Lakehead University.**

This book brings together papers from a conference held in Thunder Bay, Ontario in October 1993. One paper is of relevance: *Adult home care services: A comparison of First Nations and non-First Nations communities in Ontario* by Browne and Shultis.

Montgomery, J. C., & Kitchenham, A. D. (Eds.). (2000). *Issues affecting rural communities (II): Proceedings of the Rural Communities and Identities in the Global Millennium International Conference.* Nanaimo, BC: Malaspina University College.

This book includes keynote addresses and paper presentations on issues affected rural communities. One chapter entitled *A healthy communities initiative in rural Alberta: Building rural capacity for health* by GermAnn, Smith, and Littlejohns is relevant for rural aging in Canada.

Novak, M. (Ed.). (1995). *Aging and society: A Canadian reader.* Toronto, ON: Nelson Canada.

This Canadian reader contains 47 research papers by Canadian gerontologists from 1988 to 1993. The chapters are grouped into 10 sections that examine myths and realities of aging in Canada; patterns of aging in various cultural groups in Canada; normal physical, psychological, and social changes related to aging; changes in health care and alternative approaches to health care delivery; Canadian retirement policy and practice; housing and lifestyle options for elders; approaches to education in later life; family life and relationships; social, legal, and ethical questions regarding death and dying; and alternative policies for an aging society. The only chapter that has a rural focus is entitled *Le Chez Nous accommodation with a difference for cognitively impaired persons in rural Manitoba* by Lahaie and Theroux. This article was first published in Gutman, G. M. (Ed.). (1992). *Shelter and care of persons with dementia.*

Pastalan, L. A. (Ed.). (1997). *Shelter and service issues for aging populations: International perspectives* (1st ed.). New York: Haworth Press.

This 12-chapter book, also an issue of the *Journal of Housing for the Elderly*, provides international perspectives on shelter and services for aging populations. Two chapters are relevant: *Housing the rural elderly: A place for Abbeyfield?* by Hallman and Joseph and *Rural-urban differences in seniors' neighbourhood preferences* by Zimmer and Chappell.

Rathbone-McCuan, E., & Havens, B. (Eds.). (1988). *North American elders: United States and Canadian perspectives* New York: Greenwood Press.

This book offers a Canada-US comparison of gerontological research and policy, with an emphasis on educational perspectives, practice and service delivery, and social policy. Included is a chapter entitled *Aging in rural Canada* by Martin-Matthews.

Strange, H., & Teitelbaum, M. (Eds.). (1987). *Aging and cultural diversity: New directions and annotated bibliography* (1st ed.). South Hadley, MA: Bergin and Garvey.

This book consists of 8 chapters and an annotated bibliography on cultural diversity within differing contexts of aging. McCay examines the situation of older adults in a rural Newfoundland fishing village in a chapter entitled *Old people and social relations in a Newfoundland "outport".*

AUTHOR INDEX

A

Abrahamowicz, M. 374
Adult Day Care Research Group.......... 195
Agbayewa, M. O. 359
Agwani, N. 176, 177
Ahmad, F. 299
Aho, M. 248
Alberg, N. 349
Alcock, D. 198
Alter, D. A. 367
Anderson, G. M. 372
Anderson, N. 130
Andrew, M. K. 376
Angel, A. 188
Angus, D. 198
Appavoo, D. 154, 158, 161
Arboleda-Flórez, J. 121, 362
Arbus, G. S. 135
Armstrong-Esther, C. 248, 364
Auton, G. 205

B

Ball, S. B. 67
Barnie, A. 178
Barr, S. I. 151
Barry, D. A. J. 134
Basran, G. S. 143
Bass, M. 300
Beanlands, H. E. 260
Beaudry, M. 110, 114
Beck, J. D. 172
Bédard, M. 305
Beeckmans, P. 29
Bekkering, M. 65
Béland, F. 320
Bell, J. 247
Belton, K. L. 397
Berkson, L. 374
Berthelot, J.-M. 231, 235
Bess, I. 398
Bhasin, P. 141
Bienefeld, M. 361
Bienvenue, R. M. 35
Birmingham, C. L. 190
Black, C. 189, 223, 261, 287
Blandford, A. A. 118, 294, 296
Blundell-Gosselin, H. J. 298, 395
Bocksnick, J. G. 91, 92
Bodig, M. G. 69
Bodnarchuk, J. 174
Bogdanovic, B. 212
Boily, C. 110, 114
Bollman, R. 80, 147
Bombin, M. 221
Bond, J. B., Jr. 17, 317, 321, 393
Bond, R. 174, 189
Bondy, S. J. 303
Bouchard, R. 110, 114
Bourbeau, R. 404
Bourque, P. E. 93
Brassard, P. 123
Break, H. 21
Brison, R. 336, 337, 338, 347, 348, 349, 350, 351, 352, 353, 354, 355, 357, 360
Brodeur, J. M. 171
Bronskill, S. E. 372
Brophy, J. T. 101
Brown, D. 301
Brown, K. H. 81
Browne, A. 199
Brownell, M. 174
Brozowski, K. 18
Bruce, S. 219
Bryant, C. 70
Brymer, C. 262
Buckley, N. J. 175
Burchill, C. A. 287
Burge, F. I. 385
Burke, S. O. 183
Bussey, L. A. 105
Bussière, Y. 404

C

Caetano, P. 302
Calam, B. 300, 301
Cameron, J. I. 299
Cammer, A. L. 250
Campbell, M. L. 152
Canadian Agricultural Injury Surveillance Program 339, 340, 341, 342, 343
Canadian Heart Health Surveys Research Group 188
Canadian Mortgage and Housing Corporation 22
Cape, E. 322
Carriere, K. C. 217, 287
Carver, D. 260
Chambers, L. W. 186
Chan, H. M. 159
Chappell, N. 34, 36, 82, 194, 296, 297
Chateau, D. 223
Chen, Y. 106, 107, 188
Chen, Z. 303
Chi, F. 221
Chiarelli, A. M. 303
Chipman, M. L. 352, 353

G

Gallagher, E. 198
Gauthier, E. 112
Gauvreau, D. 110, 112, 114
Gayton, D. C. 374
GermAnn, K. 40
Gettle, B. C. 84
Gfellner, B. 41, 74
Gilbertson, M. 101
Gillis, D. C. 129
Gittelsohn, J. 178
Gladstone, J. W. 238
Godon, D. 102
Goodby, C.-S. 163
Gorey, K. M. 101
Gorman, M. 256
Goss, M. J. 134
Grad, R. M. 374
Graham, B. L. 141
Graham, E. L. D. 295
Grant, P. R. 253
Greenslade, L. 98, 214
Greenwood, L. J. 393
Groupe de Recherche Interdisciplinaire
   en Santé 320
Grunau, M. 152
Grymonpre, R. E. 363
Gudaitis, E. 225
Guernsey, J. R. 349, 354, 355
Guimond, E. 235
Guirguis, L. M. 366, 371
Gumpel, M. 333
Gunderson, W. 268
Gutman, G. M. 25, 196

H

Hader, J. M. 344
Hagel, L. 345, 346, 355
Hagen, B. 248, 364
Hall, B. L. 91, 92
Hall, D. 18, 141
Hall, M. 324
Halladay, J. 152
Hallman, B. 24, 26, 73, 306
Halseth, G. 27, 269
Hamilton, M. 169
Hanley, A. J. G. 178
Hanlon, N. 27, 269, 288
Harbison, J. 19, 20
Harris, D. 265, 270
Harris, L. 221
Harris, S. B. 125, 178
Hartling, L. ...347, 348, 349, 351, 354, 355,
   357
Harvey, C. D. H. 317, 321, 393
Hasselback, P. 386
Hatcher, J. 377
Hatcher, L. 254
Havens, B. 35, 191, 324, 381
Hawranik, P. 203, 204, 307
Hay, D. A. 143
Hayward, L. 176, 177, 205
Healey, L. 164
Heard, S. 66, 259, 279
Hébert, R. 113, 246
Hellyer, D. 101
Hemingway, D. 271, 309
Hicks, T. 169
Hildebrand, E. A. 308, 317
Hill, G. 113
Hill, M. D. 139
Hobbs, C. 104, 389
Hodge, G. 25, 28, 29, 42, 63, 75, 400
Hogan, D. B. 375
Hollett, R. G. 30, 273
Holness, D. L. 353
Horne, J. 36
Houde, L. 114
Houle, L. G. 257
Huang, A. R. 374
Hubley, A. M. 309
Hulka, B. 387
Hunt, R. J. 172
Hutcheon, M. E. 104, 389
Hyman, I. 299

I

Iglesias, S. 222
Ikuta, R. 364
Ingram, M. W. 345
Intergovernmental Committee on Urban
   and Regional Research 29
Isaac, L. M. 374

J

Jaglal, S. 228
James, A. M. 289
James, G. G. 85, 86
James, R. C. 139
Janzen, B. L. 202
Jean, H. 114
Jhangri, G. S. 397
Jin, Y. 217, 218, 365
Jivan, T. 324
Johnson, D. 217, 218, 365
Johnson, J. 366, 371, 396
Johnson, R. 135, 136
Johnson, S. 136
Johnston, G. 385
Joly, M.-F. 404
Jones, L. 222
Joseph, A. E. 26, 30, 43, 44, 45, 46, 70,
   76, 206, 264, 272, 273, 290

K

L

M

R

S

Y

Z

GEOGRAPHIC INDEX

Note: Each Entry is listed only once, based on the province or region where the study occurred.

Alberta

40, 91, 92, 104, 120, 121, 133, 138, 139, 144, 145, 146, 149, 150, 167, 173, 187, 217, 218, 220, 227, 276, 278, 298, 335, 356, 362, 364, 365, 366, 371, 375, 379, 380, 389, 395, 397

Atlantic Canada

19, 20, 23, 37, 147, 314, 318, 319, 386, 388

British Columbia

27, 42, 63, 77, 109, 128, 130, 151, 156, 190, 196, 197, 269, 271, 275, 277, 300, 301, 309, 333, 359, 400

Canada

18, 22, 25, 29, 38, 46, 47, 48, 49, 53, 59, 61, 75, 78, 79, 80, 83, 87, 113, 122, 175, 176, 177, 186, 188, 192, 198, 202, 205, 210, 222, 225, 295, 306, 310, 311, 312, 313, 339, 341, 342, 343, 349, 354, 355, 357, 361, 376, 377, 383, 398, 407

Central Canada

70

Manitoba

17, 34, 35, 36, 39, 41, 71, 74, 82, 97, 98, 103, 115, 116, 117, 118, 152, 174, 180, 184, 189, 191, 194, 195, 203, 204, 211, 212, 213, 214, 219, 223, 224, 229, 230, 231, 233, 235, 237, 239, 242, 244, 255, 261, 280, 286, 287, 292, 293, 294, 302, 307, 308, 317, 321, 324, 330, 331, 358, 363, 378, 393, 401

New Brunswick

93, 95, 329

Newfoundland and Labrador

100, 111, 119, 164, 201, 216, 254, 258, 304, 328, 373

Northern Canada

131, 132, 157, 158, 159, 165, 166

Northwest Territories

127, 153, 154, 155, 160, 161, 163

Not Specified

179, 381

Nova Scotia

105, 207, 256, 260, 315, 326, 385, 394

Ontario

21, 24, 26, 28, 30, 31, 32, 33, 43, 44, 45, 52, 54, 55, 56, 57, 58, 62, 66, 67, 69, 72, 73, 76, 81, 90, 96, 101, 108, 125, 126, 134, 135, 136, 168, 169, 170, 172, 178, 181, 182, 183, 193, 199, 206, 208, 209, 215, 221, 226, 228, 236, 238, 245, 252, 257, 259, 262, 263, 264, 265, 266, 267, 270, 272, 273, 274, 279, 281, 282, 283, 284, 285, 288, 289, 290, 299, 303, 305, 316, 322, 327, 334, 336, 337, 338, 340, 347, 348, 350, 351, 352, 353, 360, 367, 369, 370, 372, 382, 396, 399

Quebec

99, 102, 110, 112, 114, 123, 124, 148, 162, 171, 200, 232, 243, 246, 320, 323, 368, 374, 402, 403, 404, 405

Saskatchewan

50, 51, 64, 68, 84, 85, 86, 88, 89, 94, 106, 107, 129, 137, 140, 141, 185, 234, 240, 241, 247, 249, 250, 251, 253, 268, 291, 325, 332, 344, 345, 346, 384

Western Canada

65, 143, 248, 296, 297, 387, 391, 392

APPENDIX A

INCLUSION/EXCLUSION SHEET

RURAL HEALTH AND AGING ANNOTATED BIBLIOGRAPHY

Reviewer (circle one only): LS   CV
ID#:
Author:
Title:
Journal:
Search Abstract # (RAC #):

HUMAN: ___ Human   ___ Not Human (E)

GEOGRAPHIC LOCATION OF SAMPLE:
___ Canada (specify:_____)   ___ Not Canada (E)

TYPE OF ARTICLE:
___ Research-based   ___ Program description/review   ___ Program evaluation
___ Review   ___ Opinion piece/popular magazine/general audience (E)
___ Case Study (E)   ___ Conference proceedings (E)   ___ Methodological (E)
___ Other (specify:_____) (I or E)

STUDY PARTICIPANTS:
_____ Population under 65 (E)
_____ General population including older adults, with no age-specific analysis (E)
_____ General population including older adults, with age-specific analysis (I)
_____ Older adults only (specify age range:_____) (I)
_____ Other (specify_____) (I or E)

RURAL/URBAN:
_____ Urban only (E)   _____ Urban & rural; no rural-urban analysis (E)
_____ Urban and rural; rural-urban analysis (I)   _____ Rural only; no intra-rural analysis (I)
_____ Rural only; intra-rural analysis (I)   _____ Other (specify_____): (I or E)

LANGUAGE OF ARTICLE:
___ English (I)   ___French (I)   ___Other (specify:_____)(E)

TOPICS ADDRESSED (Check all that apply):

Functional health status ☐	Cognitive functioning/dementia ☐	Pain ☐
Oral health ☐	Nutrition ☐	Sleep ☐
Health promotion ☐	Medications ☐	Self-rated health ☐
Psychological well-being ☐	Depression ☐	Loneliness ☐
Quality of life ☐	Attitudes ☐	Injuries/falls/accidents ☐
Mortality/life expectancy ☐	Home care ☐	Senior centers ☐
Adult day programs ☐	Transportation ☐	Other community services ☐
Preventative health services ☐	Pharmacy services ☐	Physician services ☐
Hospital visits ☐	Personal care/nursing homes ☐	Telehealth/telemedicine ☐
Caregivers ☐	Support for caregivers ☐	Health of caregivers ☐
Social support/social networks ☐	Service accessibility ☐	Service providers ☐

Other (specify _____)

INCLUDE:	___ Yes, based on abstract	___Yes, based on full paper
	___ No, based on abstract	___ No, based on full paper

Table A-1. Topic and Sub-topic Areas

Topic	Number of entries
ABUSE	**4**
COMMUNITY AMENITIES/SUPPORT	**39**
Housing/Neighbourhood Amenities	14
Supportive Communities	25
DEMOGRAPHICS/MIGRATION	**24**
National Demographics	5
Provincial, Regional, and Local Demographics	7
Migration and Mobility	12
ECONOMICS	**2**
EDUCATION/LEISURE	**18**
Education	8
Leisure/Recreation	10
EPIDEMIOLOGY	**41**
Cancer	4
Cardiovascular	5
Dementia/Cognition	10
Depression	3
Diabetes	10
Gastro-intestinal	2
Immunity	2
Neurological	3
Respiratory	2
FARM TRANSFERS/WORK	**8**
FUNCTIONAL/PHYSICAL HEALTH	**44**
Nutrition	16
Oral Health	7
Physical/Functional Status	21
HEALTH AND SOCIAL SERVICES	**100**
Day Programs	3
Home Care	19
Hospitalization/Emergency Room	12
Nursing Homes: Factors Associated with Institutionalization/Prevalence	7
Nursing Homes: Structure/Services	13
Nursing Homes: Staffing Issues/Education	5
Physician Services	8
Service Planning/Delivery Models	23
Service Use/Non-use	10
HEALTH PROMOTION/SCREENING	**10**
Health Promotion	4
Screening	6

Table A-1. Topic and Sub-topic Areas (cont'd)

Topic	Number of entries
INFORMAL CARE/SUPPORT	**28**
Caregiving	12
Perceptions/Beliefs about Caregiving	3
Social Support/Isolation	13
INJURIES	**30**
Falls	3
Farm Injuries	23
Suicide	4
MEDICATIONS/IMMUNIZATION	**18**
Medications: General	9
Medications: Prescribing/Use	4
Vaccinations/Immunizations	5
METHODS/CONCEPTUAL ISSUES	**4**
MORTALITY	**5**
QUALITY OF LIFE/LIFE SATISFACTION	**6**
TRANSPORTATION/DRIVING	**9**
MULTIPLE (AUTHORED BOOKS)*	**1**
TOTAL	**391**

* Excludes edited books although these are included in the book section of the bibliography.